Breakthrough

THE SAGA OF JONAS SALK

Richard Carter

Library of Congress Catalog Number: 65-26621

Published simultaneously in the United States and Canada
by Trident Press.

Distributed by Affiliated Publishers, a Division
of Pocket Books, Inc.

Printed in the United States of America

Second Printing

to

MY FAMILY

Young man, a great tragedy has befallen you—
you have lost your anonymity.

—EDWARD R. MURROW to JONAS SALK

Breakthrough

THE SAGA OF JONAS SALK

1

ON APRIL 12, 1955, THE WORLD LEARNED THAT A VACCINE developed by Jonas Edward Salk, M.D., could be relied upon to prevent paralytic poliomyelitis. This news consummated the most extraordinary undertaking in the history of science, a huge research project led by a Wall Street lawyer and financed by the American people through hundreds of millions of small donations. More than a scientific achievement, the vaccine was a folk victory, an occasion for pride and jubilation. A contagion of love swept the world. People observed moments of silence, rang bells, honked horns, blew factory whistles, fired salutes, kept their traffic lights red in brief periods of tribute, took the rest of the day off, closed their schools or convoked fervid assemblies therein, drank toasts, hugged children, attended church, smiled at strangers, forgave enemies.

Delighted journalists stoked the fires. It seemed that this Salk, a somewhat withdrawn and indistinct figure during the months of excitement that preceded the announcement of his success, was not really an ivory-tower type at all. Behind the studious reserve, it seemed, was a warm, even saintly human being. He had worked seven days a week, sometimes for twenty-four hours at a stretch, it was reported, lest the vaccine be delayed for one needless minute and one child be crippled for lack of it. Yet he had not allowed his humanitarian feelings to stampede him. He was too much the man of science to compromise the rigid discipline of his calling: No medical experiments had ever been carried out with more laborious care than his. Moreover, he had a sunny smile. He was only forty. He and his attractive wife had produced three lively boys. He liked good music and long walks. He was charmingly bashful about personal publicity. He had been raised on the verge of poverty and had accumulated no wealth of his own, but was not seeking to enrich himself with his discovery (as the vaccine was so often described). Indeed, he had not patented it, would get no royalties from its sale, and had insisted that all qualified manufacturing laboratories everywhere enjoy free and equal access to the formula.

The ardent people named schools, streets, hospitals, and new-born infants after him. They sent him checks, cash, money orders, stamps, scrolls, certificates, pressed flowers, snapshots, candy, baked goods, religious medals, rabbits' feet and other talismans, and uncounted thousands of letters and telegrams, both individual and round-robin, describing their heartfelt gratitude and admiration. They offered him free automobiles, agricultural equipment, clothing, vacations, lucrative jobs in government and industry, and several hundred opportunities to get rich quick. Their legislatures and parliaments passed resolutions, and their heads of state issued proclamations. Their universities tendered honorary degrees. He was nominated for the Nobel prize, which he did not get, and a Congressional medal, which he got, and membership in the National Academy of Sciences, which turned him down. He was mentioned for several dozen lesser awards of national or local or purely promotional character, most of which *he* turned down.

Not all of this happened on April 12, 1955, but much of it did. Salk awakened that morning as a moderately prominent research professor on the faculty of the University of Pittsburgh School of Medicine. He ended the day as the most beloved medical scientist on earth. Worshipful humanity had borne him far beyond mere fame and had enthroned him among the immortals, where he sat gasping in a paroxysm of embarrassed discomfort, wondering whether he would ever be able to extricate himself from this, the latest and most horrendous pickle of an eventful career.

Jonas Salk saw calamity in his triumph because he knew perfectly well that his colleagues in biological science were offended by the uproar and would hold him accountable for it. Nine years later the pain was still fresh: "The worst tragedy that could have befallen me was my success. I knew right away that I was through —cast out."

The need to be admired by professional colleagues is more noticeable among scientists than among other men. An author may repel his peers with sentences that do not parse, but if the public buys his books, the attitude of other authors will cause him only brief regret. Other creative types comparable to scientists, such as poets, painters, actors, and musicians, can also extract a measure of gratification from the praise of an inexpert laity. But the scientist is trapped. However pleasantly the occasional cheers of the multitude may resound in his ears, he depends for lasting professional and emotional security on the respect accorded him by other scientists. Charles Darwin was candid about it when he wrote that his love of science had "been much aided by the ambition to be esteemed by my fellow naturalists." Max Planck observed that the scientist's joy is "the certainty that every result he finds will be appreciated by specialists throughout the world."

This spiritual dependence on the opinion of the scientific community arises from the nature of scientific work and is but incidentally related to the hungers of vanity. After all, scientists alone are able to appreciate fully what a Darwin or Salk talks about. They alone can evaluate his work by subjecting it to confirmatory tests. They alone can give the word that opens or closes the door to larger opportunity. They alone can award the professional honors that signify accomplishment.

Salk was painfully aware that his colleagues did not agree with the laity that he was a new Pasteur or even that he had "discovered" anything. They would not fail to notice that the press was exaggerating the significance of his contribution to what had been a prolonged, cumulative effort by many distinguished workers. Had he not allowed the vaccine to be named after him? Was this not in itself a betrayal of those on whose work his own had depended—a usurpation of credit?

They had been annoyed for years by his unconcealed desire for professional independence and recognition. All of them had been propelled by the same ambition and many had satisfied it, but few had ever seemed as inexorable about it as Salk. They were uneasy about the self-assurance with which he tackled major problems, the speed with which he offered his solutions, the glibness with which he defended them, the stubbornness with which he refused to be deflected from whatever course he had mapped for himself, the nimbleness with which he altered course when ready. They did not know that he had only lately stopped quaking in their presence. They thought him cold as ice.

One of their most imperative traditions required them to protect their freedom of thought and inquiry against the political power and financial blandishments of nonscientists. But the age of the multimillion-dollar scientific crash program had arrived, and they had already begun to breach the tradition, measuring each other now in terms of the monetary grants they were able to obtain from nonscientists. Salk's prowess was confirmed and his unpopularity consolidated when he emerged, practically overnight, as the most lavishly supported biological scientist in history, having vaulted over the heads of older, better established, equally ambitious workers. His virus laboratory in Pittsburgh was, in the words of one critic, "the smoothest, biggest, damnedest thing you ever saw, like a big, damned industrial plant except it was in a medical school."

No discussion of Salk's spectacular detour from the professional pecking order was complete without cynical reference to his close friendship with Basil O'Connor, high-flying President of the National Foundation for Infantile Paralysis. As head of the organization through which the public fought polio, the celebrated lawyer was by far the most influential layman in American medical research. Scientists clucked their tongues at the flamboyant aggressiveness with which he promoted the polio menace, the ease with which he raised more money for his cause than was collected for cancer, heart disease, or mental illness. But his organization dispensed grants of unprecedented generosity; scientists who deplored O'Connor's methods fell all over themselves to court the Foundation's favor. O'Connor knew this and kept himself unreachable, scrupulously making no scientific move without the approval of his advisory committees of hard-boiled senior scientists; unreachable, the gossip suggested, until he met Salk and found in him a friend as close as a son.

Salk had already begun to lap his field before he attracted O'Connor's personal interest, but this was either unknown or ignored. Virologists unable to reconcile themselves to Salk's high-pressure performance decided that he had traded his scientific freedom to O'Connor in exchange for undeserved, unseemly stardom.

The events of April 12 seemed to confirm such gossip. Among the offenses committed that day against the totems and taboos of the scientific community was the raucous manner in which the big news was announced. Scientists who came (by invitation) to the University of Michigan at Ann Arbor to hear whether the vaccine had actually prevented paralytic polio found the place overrun with reporters and television camera crews. The atmosphere was as febrile as that of a political convention or a sex trial, more conducive to press agentry than to academic deliberation. And if this were not enough to illuminate the primrose path down which Salk allegedly was traveling, somebody noted that the day was the tenth anniversary of the death of Franklin D. Roosevelt, founder of the National Foundation for Infantile Paralysis. Basil O'Connor had been Roosevelt's law partner and crony. The choice of April 12 was seen, therefore, as a promotional vulgarity intended to fill the coffers of the National Foundation. Thus was supplied one more controversial note to the proceedings, one more affront to Salk's exasperated peers, one more embarrassment to Salk himself.

As a social thinker whose interest in the ways of mankind antedated his interest in medical science, Jonas Salk felt that the matters of form to which his detractors gave so much uncomplimentary attention were not quite the heart of the problem. The basic difficulty, he believed, was far more serious: His vaccine was actually a development of epochal importance. If it turned out to be as lastingly efficacious as he claimed it might be, one of the older and more comfortable tenets of orthodox virology would be annulled. History demonstrates, as Salk well knew, that he who undermines dogma undermines its champions and earns their wrath.

His original intention had not been to find fame as developer of a polio vaccine. As a basic scientist, he merely had sought to test the traditional notion that only natural infection or an infectious vaccine made of living disease organisms could offer durable protection against a viral disease. According to that hallowed theory, a vaccine compounded of killed, noninfectious viruses simply would not do. Salk suspected that this was nonsense. For one thing, it was unverified lore received from the past. For another, it conflicted with realities observed in the prevention of other kinds of infectious disease. For yet another, it had about it the stink of the shaman, the medicine man, the magician—as if the effectiveness of a vaccine depended not on chemistry but on some occult life force. In other words, Salk saw his challenge to orthodoxy as not only experimental but ideological.

It certainly was. The professional controversies that obstructed the development and testing of his unconventional killed-virus vaccine were waged with the intensity that man usually reserves for his holy wars. The brilliant, articulate Dr. Albert Sabin attacked Salk's work and defended orthodoxy on the front page of every important newspaper in the United States—not once but often. Despite these polemics, Sabin retained the respect of most virologists, demonstrating that there are, after all, circumstances wherein a scientist can obtain publicity without provoking hostility among his colleagues.

There were, of course, no scrimmages of that sort on April 12, the day of announcement and celebration. When the eminent Dr. Thomas Francis, Jr., declared that his studies had proved the vaccine safe and effective, Sabin and other antagonists of the Salk position participated in the general applause. And when Salk himself took the podium, they all rose from their chairs to award him the standing ovation demanded by a public occasion of that kind.

But if anyone actually intended an armistice, this sentiment was never conveyed to Jonas Salk. "I felt like a drowning man," he says. Before April 12 he had dared hope that the success of his vaccine would give him the beginning of a foothold on the professional esteem he needed so badly. He had hoped that the success, if it came, might at last direct close attention to some of his beautiful experiments, the revolutionary implications of which had for so long been overlooked, minimized, or misconstrued. Instead he felt more than ever an object of scientific scorn.

Worse difficulty lay ahead. So did greater triumph.

2

To understand the predicament of Jonas Salk at Ann Arbor, it is necessary to understand something about the disease that his vaccine was intended to eliminate. It is assumed that paralytic polio was fairly familiar to the ancients. Egyptian mummies have been found with one leg shorter than the other, and a monument of about 1500 B.C. depicts an Egyptian priest with a leg withered, as if from the disease. But there is no written record of epidemic until 1835, when the village of Worksop, England, had "four remarkable cases of suddenly induced paralysis, occurring in children. . . ."

At about the same time there seems to have been an outbreak on the island of St. Helena, and in 1841 there may have been one in Louisiana. A physician who visited the parish of West Feliciana saw one patient and was told of eight or ten others. He wrote that "the little sufferers were invariably under two years of age and the cause seemed to be the same in all, namely teething."

By midcentury some few physicians were learning to associate the paralysis with mysterious damage to the spinal cords of children. Jakob Heine, a German orthopedist, was the first to describe this in detail. He called the disease "spinal infantile paralysis," a name that stuck. "Poliomyelitis" also came into use, describing inflammation *(itis)* of the gray *(polios)* anterior matter of the spinal cord *(myelos)*. The inflammation apparently destroyed nerve cells, paralyzing the muscles that the cells had governed.

In the second half of the century, epidemics were reported in Oslo, Lyon, Stockholm, Boston, and, most devastating of all, in the Otter Creek valley of Vermont, where, among 132 stricken children, eighteen died. By then it had become known that the disease was not always spinal but was sometimes bulbar, centering in or about the medulla oblongata, or bulb, of the lower brain. Such cases were more often fatal than the spinal ones. But the cause was completely unknown, although an occasional cluster of cases in a single household seemed to suggest infection of some kind. Efforts to substantiate this were unavailing until 1908, when Karl Landsteiner and Erwin Popper reported from Vienna that they had produced polio in monkeys by inoculating the animals with tissue taken from the spine of a human killed by the disease. And in 1909 Simon Flexner and P. A. Lewis of the Rockefeller Institute carried the experiment further, passing a human infection from monkey to monkey. The infectious agent could not be seen under microscopes but was unmistakably a living parasitic organism, able to multiply in the cells of its victims. Because it was harmful and could pass through the finest available filters, it was classified among the filterable viruses.

By the end of another year it was demonstrated that monkeys that survived the disease often resisted reinfection. It was also shown that the blood of monkeys that recovered contained a substance that neutralized the virus when mixed with it in a test tube. These clues to the possibility of developing an immunizing vaccine were not as obvious in 1910 as they might seem now, but they were recognized by investigators like Landsteiner and Flexner. It occurred to them that attempts should be made to modify the virus so that it might produce this neutralizing, protective substance in the blood of monkeys without paralyzing them. The experiments were premature. Far too little was known about the poliovirus, the process of immunity, how to measure the potency of viral preparations, or, indeed, even how polio established itself in monkey or man. Efforts to immunize invariably produced confusing results. Moreover, this was the age of sanitation, when tuberculosis, typhoid, and similar diseases were being attacked with some success by attention to environmental squalor. Whatever attention was devoted to polio tended, therefore, to center on a search for environmental sources of infection, such as insects or domestic animals.

Many years were to pass before polio would be understood. Transmitted in fecal matter or in secretions of the nose and throat, the virus enters its victim by way of the mouth, establishes itself in the intestines, and travels therefrom to the spinal cord or brain. In societies that lack indoor plumbing and do not practice the personal hygiene usually associated with amenities of that kind, the disease is endemic. Most polio infections occur in infancy, a time of life when paralysis is rare. Having been infected, the infant remains immune for life. Epidemics are unheard of. The Scandinavian epidemics of the late nineteenth century and the American epidemics of the twentieth were signs that the hygienic standards of an advancing culture had protected certain individuals from infection until a stage in life when they were more susceptible to paralysis.

The incidence of polio rose steadily. The American public became fully and lastingly conscious of the problem in 1916 when 27,363 cases, including 7,179 deaths, were reported in those twenty of the forty-eight states whose public-health regulations required that such cases be reported. The worst epidemic occurred in New York City. Nine thousand twenty-three cases, of which 2,448 ended in death, touched off a public frenzy unlike any since the medieval plagues.

When threatened by contagion which kills or leaves its victim permanently disabled and against which medicine offers neither prevention nor cure, one's natural inclination is to flee. As soon as the extent of the epidemic became publicly known, thousands of New York families fled to outlying areas, frequently taking infection with them and spreading it. Others did not leave the city but fled into their homes, shut the windows, drew the blinds, and locked the doors. There was no certainty that any hospital would even give a victim a bed, so great was the fear of infection. On the other hand, after the municipal health commissioner, Dr. Haven Emerson, compelled hospitals to set aside facilities for polio care, police sometimes used force to get sick children away from their frightened families. Meanwhile outlying communities began treating New York City refugees as if they were lepers or vagrants, turning them back with guns.

Like any community deranged by fear, New York became unusually receptive to the ministrations of quacks. After a hot tip about the curative powers of fresh ox blood, numerous parents appeared at the East Side slaughterhouses with buckets. A former state legislator made a small fortune selling bags of cedar shavings, which he said would protect any child. He was finally fined $250 and sentenced to thirty days in jail. Among the cures offered, sometimes at a price, were a serum made of frog blood, a drink compounded of rum, brandy, and champagne, and mustard plasters, radium water, and wine of pepsin.

In September, Health Commissioner Emerson committed an act of enormous courage, considering that he was operating on limited experience; he said it was all right to reopen the schools. He was correct in his belief that paralytic polio was a seasonal affliction and that the epidemic would burn itself out. By October, the city was back to normal, except that every summer for the next forty years its people and the people of all other American communities were to be terrified by the possibility of new epidemics. The United States had become polio conscious. Terror multiplied and polio consciousness became more acute than ever when a figure much in the public eye was stricken.

Franklin D. Roosevelt had been the Democratic candidate for Vice-President in 1920 and had emerged from that unsuccessful campaign as the most lustrously promising young figure in his party. The following year he fell ill of paralytic polio and lost the use of his legs forever, but this in no way lessened his political ambitions. His nominating speech for Alfred E. Smith at the 1928 Democratic convention ("He is the Happy Warrior of the political battlefield. . . .") reestablished him more securely than ever as the man of his party's future. He could not walk but he was on his way.

The suggestion that he enter a law partnership with Basil O'Connor in 1924 had come from a friend who was one of O'Connor's clients, an oil man named John B. Shearer. Roosevelt was in the insurance business, and a law association—especially with a force like O'Connor—offered a suitably attractive addition to his political credentials. Roosevelt agreed. He and O'Connor managed nicely at the first lunch. When Roosevelt suggested that the firm be known as O'Connor and Roosevelt, his future partner grinned, "No, I think Roosevelt and O'Connor would be more euphonious."

Daniel Basil "Doc" O'Connor had been a skinny, frostbitten newsboy on the streets of Taunton, Massachusetts. His father had never earned more than eighteen dollars a week. But the son was voted "most likely to succeed" at Dartmouth College, through which he worked his way in three and a half largely sleepless years by fiddling in dance bands. He then earned his law degree at Harvard with money advanced by a lawyer impressed with his prowess as a debater. By 1924 he was a wiry fashion plate, cock of the Wall Street walk, a smart, wealthy thirty-two, but not too cocky or too wealthy to recognize the advantages that might accrue from a partnership with the prominent Roosevelt.

Some of their later negotiations took place in a broken-down resort hotel, the Meriwether Inn, at Warm Springs, Georgia. Roosevelt believed that swimming in the warm, buoyant water of the Warm Springs pool was helping him recover partial use of his legs. Eventually he and some friends bought the hotel, its dilapidated outbuildings, the pool, and 1,260 surrounding acres for $200,000, hoping to make it one of the world's great health centers, combining all the features of a posh resort with facilities for the treatment of polio.

"I thought he was crazy to want that big goddam four-story firetrap with the squirrels running in and out of the holes in the roof," says O'Connor. "I couldn't have been less interested in the project. But in 1926 he bought it and made a nonprofit foundation of it and in 1928 he ups and becomes Governor of New York and nonchalantly says to me, 'Take over Warm Springs, old fella: you're in.' I tell you, I had no desire to be 'in.' I was never a public do-gooder and had no aspirations of that kind. But I started enjoying it. Like Andrew Jackson at the battle of New Orleans, I found myself up to my rump in blood and liked it."

At first there was nothing but trouble. Roosevelt's enthusiasm about the swimming pool was publicized nationally, and this attracted an influx of the lame and wasted, many of whom, alas, were penniless. Their water-basketball games with Roosevelt were marvelous for morale, and even helped tone up their bodies, but their presence had a lamentable effect on business. Paying guests preferred not to have to look at what were known in those days as "cripples," refusing at one point to eat in the same dining room with them. They soon avoided Warm Springs altogether. By 1932, when Roosevelt was elected President, the Foundation was on the rocks. The 1929 stock market crash had dried up its few sources of philanthropic revenue, and the desk of Secretary-Treasurer O'Connor was piled high with unpaid bills.

But now that Roosevelt was in the White House, it seemed possible to stir up support for Warm Springs as a polio center. The means did not become evident until late in 1933, when Carl Byoir, a virtuoso among public-relations experts, suggested that people might like to pay their way into dances celebrating the President's birthday. The money so collected could go to Warm Springs. O'Connor and Roosevelt both welcomed the idea, although they were less than ecstatic about the client in whose behalf Byoir acted. Henry L. Doherty, a crusty old utilities tycoon and grinder of political axes, was not on anyone's list of those most likely to want to celebrate Roosevelt's birthday. His willingness to un-cork $25,000 to establish a National Committee for the Birthday Ball for the President, with himself at its head, looked suspiciously like the prelude to a request for favors. But nobody in the Warm Springs contingent could afford to examine the dentition of this gift horse.

While O'Connor fended off creditors, Byoir launched floods of publicity and Keith L. Morgan, a Warm Springs trustee and friend of Roosevelt, attended to administrative details of the fund drive. Postmasters, collectors of internal revenue, and other functioning Democrats organized most of the local balls. There were not many complaints about this. Not yet. Republicans, Democrats, corporate management, labor, farmers, and the un-employed were still equally relieved by the steps Roosevelt had taken to ward off economic collapse during his first months in office. Nobody yet reviled him as "that man in the White House."

The President's Birthday Balls of 1934 were not only occasions "to dance so that others may walk"—they were celebrations of the national hope and courage that Roosevelt personified at that time.

The biggest radio network in history was assembled to broadcast Roosevelt's thanks. Speaking "as the representative . . . of the hundreds of thousands of crippled children in our country," he predicted that "it remains . . . only to spread the gospel for the care and cure of crippled children in every part of this kindly land to enable us to make the same relative progress that we have already made in the field of tuberculosis. . . . It is with a humble and thankful heart that I accept this tribute through me to the stricken ones of our great national family. I thank you but lack the words to tell you how deeply I appreciate what you have done and I bid you good night on what is to me the happiest birthday I have ever known."

This first public appeal for funds to combat paralytic polio brought in $1,049,577.45 from almost 6,000 balls in 4,376 communities. After deducting expenses, Henry Doherty gave O'Connor a check for $1,016,443, which was presented to Roosevelt in a White House ceremony. It then went back to O'Connor.

The American most noticeably disgruntled by what had happened was Dr. Michael Hoke, chief surgeon at Warm Springs. He wrote O'Connor that the publicity had been more appropriate for "a box factory or a foundry" than a polio treatment center, and that the sponsors of the undertaking "fit in with a medical outfit about as accurately as a jackass would with a symphony orchestra." His patients had been interviewed on radio, and the impression had been circulated that paralysis sufferers should flock to Warm Springs, where there was no room for them, and be cured, which was impossible. Hoke also complained to Marguerite Le Hand, the President's secretary, of the "enormous number of letters that no sane person could answer from all sorts of poor derelicts all over the United States who couldn't be helped here."

Hoke was a pioneer of the medical displeasure that would alternately annoy, amaze, and bore Basil O'Connor for the rest of his career. Hoke's attitude derived, of course, from pure alarm about the excesses of press agents. In the years ahead other orthopedic surgeons would be outraged by O'Connor's "interference" in the care of polio patients for whom the National Foundation was paying the bills. This "interference," undertaken on sound medical advice, consisted of elevating the quality of the medical treatment that the Foundation purchased.

A more generalized professional antagonism toward the polio crusaders manifested itself among the conservative leaders of organized medicine. They and others of their political persuasion in and out of medicine decided, about 1935, that Roosevelt was a kind of Bolshevik, that his Warm Springs Foundation was spurious, and that it had been a gross error to elect him. Anything with the imprint of Roosevelt was now in season for newspaper editorialists and columnists. Questions were raised as to the propriety of the annual birthday dances. Syndicated columnists spread the libel that the Roosevelt family was profiting from Warm Springs. Eugene Talmadge, the Governor of Georgia, whose previous fame had depended, like his trousers, on the galluses he displayed in public, called the resort "a racket."

The 1935 ball brought in only $750,000. Less than $600,000 was realized in 1936. Keith Morgan recognized the "falling off of the President's universal popularity, particularly among the class of people accustomed to giving larger sums of money." Roosevelt and the Warm Springs treatment center were suffering from each other. If a fittingly vigorous polio movement was to be established, it would have to be as nonpartisan as possible. The existing polio movement was not.

In September 1937 Roosevelt took the advice. He announced the establishment of a new foundation ". . . to lead, direct, and unify the fight on every phase of this sickness. It will make every effort to ensure that every responsible research agency in this country is adequately financed to carry out investigations into the cause of infantile paralysis and the methods by which it may be prevented. It will endeavor to eliminate much of the needless aftereffect of this disease—wreckage caused by the failure to make early and accurate diagnosis. . . . The new foundation will carry on a broad-gauged educational campaign, prepared under expert medical supervision, and this will be placed within reach of the doctors and the hospitals of this country."

The New York Times welcomed the announcement as "a constructive answer . . . finely and humanely conceived . . . touches every root and fiber. . . . What Roosevelt proposes is a fairly large experiment in socialized medicine. . . ."

The National Foundation for Infantile Paralysis began operations in January 1938, in the law offices of its president, Basil O'Connor, at 120 Broadway, New York. Its board of trustees included George E. Allen, William Clayton, Marshall Field, Edsel Ford, James V. Forrestal, Jr., Averell Harriman, Robert E. McMath, Carroll B. Merriam, Jeremiah Milbank, Edward Stettinius, Jr., Thomas J. Watson, Robert W. Woodruff, and Clarence M. Woolley, to name the most prominent. O'Connor, having been, as he puts it, "drafted" into his connection with Warm Springs and having undergone and enjoyed the Jacksonian experience of finding himself up to his arse in blood, was entirely clear in his mind that the first fund-raising campaign of the new foundation had to be the biggest, most lucrative promotion of its kind ever seen. He got what he wanted.

"America, more than any other nation, is slogan conscious," wrote Roland H. Berg in his book *Polio and Its Problems.** "An advertising copywriter will trade his eyetooth for that . . . combination of syllables that will catch the elusive fancy of the public and stick in its memory. . . . Many successful businesses have only a memory-arresting phrase to thank for their phenomenal rise. Along with 'It's Toasted,' 'They Satisfy,' 'Breakfast of Champions,' and scores of others which come easily to mind, 'March of Dimes' also has its niche. . . ."

The phrase actually was improvised by Eddie Cantor at a National Foundation strategy meeting on the Metro-Goldwyn-Mayer lot in Hollywood. According to Berg, the show-wise Cantor suggested that all national radio programs be asked to donate a half minute of broadcast time for an appeal for small contributions from the audience. "We could ask the people to send their dimes directly to the President at the White House," said Cantor. "Think what

* J. B. Lippincott Company, Philadelphia, 1948

a thrill the people would get. . . . And we could call it the March
of Dimes!"

Once again the big night was January 30, the President's birthday. But the atmosphere was different. What had formerly been
an opportunity to compliment the President and incidentally help
polio patients was now a national alliance against the disease. The
Democratic careerists who had been promoting the annual birthday
balls in most communities now appeared in less partisan livery,
heading local chapters of the new National Foundation for Infantile
Paralysis. The unmistakably nonpolitical composition of the new
organization's board of directors also helped broaden the appeal.
For the first time one could strike a blow against polio without
seeming to endorse the Roosevelt Administration. During January
O'Connor's communications experts saturated the public consciousness with thoughts of polio. Physicians discussed the disease on
radio and in newspapers. Hundreds of thousands of dollars in
donated advertising appeared in every conceivable publication.

"Basil O'Connor," a professional fund raiser once observed
enviously, "had an unbeatable combination. He had the kid in the
wheelchair, the heart-throb without which you can't raise a *sou*
in this country. He had the sponsorship of Franklin D. Roosevelt.
He had the disease that everyone was afraid of." Two days after
the big radio appeal, it looked as if O'Connor, with all these assets,
had achieved the most stupendous fiasco in the history of mass
manipulation.

"You fellows have ruined the President," said a White House
functionary to Tom Wrigley, the National Foundation's publicist.
"All we've got is seventeen and a half dollars. The reporters are
asking how much has come in. We're telling them we haven't had
time to count it."

The next morning, before emergency measures could be invented, the White House called New York with a new complaint:
"This thing is out of hand. There are mail trucks and mail sacks
all over the place. We can't find our official mail in all the mess.
Nobody can do any work." Thirty thousand letters arrived that
day. Mailbags were piled on desks and spilled onto floors. During
the next two days 200,000 more letters arrived. Mailbags blocked
corridors. It took five months to sort through the offerings, which

included 2,680,000 dimes, many of them baked into cakes or wrapped in sticky tape. Total receipts from all sources in this first campaign of the National Foundation for Infantile Paralysis were $1,823,045. With each new campaign the proceeds increased. The 1955 receipts were just short of $67 million. The money was spent. O'Connor never lacked ways to dispose of money.

"Until we came along," reminisces O'Connor, "most hospitals wouldn't accept polio patients and hardly anyone knew how to care for them. There was a terrible shortage of trained minds and trained hands. It was our duty to correct this by offering fellowships and scholarships and postgraduate instruction, meanwhile keeping physicians and other professionals up-to-date on diagnosis, therapy, rehabilitation, and so on."

But this was only one side of the problem. Very little was being spent in actual research. From the proceeds of the first Birthday Ball in 1934, the trustees of the Warm Springs Foundation had set aside $100,000 "to stimulate and further the meritorious work being done in the field of infantile paralysis elsewhere." In August of that year, the Warm Springs gadfly, Dr. Michael Hoke, had pointed out to Franklin Roosevelt's friend Keith Morgan that the money was lying fallow. "I think the trustees should appoint somebody right away to determine what constitutes 'meritorious' effort in the study of poliomyelitis," wrote Hoke.

Others were of similar mind. Paul de Kruif, a former Rockefeller Institute bacteriologist who had turned author and become the world's foremost popularizer of science, recalls in his memoirs, *The Searching Wind,** that he asked the manager of Warm Springs, "Why do you use all that dough to dip cripples in warm water? That doesn't cure them any more than it cured . . . the President. Why don't you ask the President to devote a part of that big dough to research on polio *prevention?* Nobody knows a thing about that."

The President's Birthday Ball Commission for Infantile Paralysis, with Henry L. Doherty as figurehead and Paul de Kruif as operational thinker, came into being at the end of 1934. It got

* Harcourt, Brace & World, Inc., New York, 1962

$241,000 from the proceeds of the 1935 birthday celebrations, and de Kruif promptly set about trying to purchase miracles with the money. He had been a first-rate bacteriologist with a reputation for impetuosity, a trait more advantageous to his career as a journalist. If he knew that basic research was necessary before anyone could approach polio prevention with substantial hope of success, he did not let the knowledge discourage him. He was enthusiastically willing to support polio prevention efforts by persons totally unprepared for the work. Nobody on earth was prepared for such work. Little had been decided about the disease since the early experiments of Landsteiner and Flexner. What had been decided was mainly erroneous. For instance, the consensus among virologists in 1935 was that vaccines could not work against polio.

The desultory condition of polio research was attributable to its immense costliness, exasperating difficulties, and unclear results. The only laboratory animal susceptible to the virus was the monkey, a cranky, expensive creature, which, in those days (prior to the discovery of antibiotics), had a way of succumbing to other diseases before the researcher could measure its responses to polio. No laboratory combined sufficient curiosity with enough funds to buy and maintain all the monkeys needed for thorough study of the poliovirus and the disease it caused. As of 1935, when the Birthday Ball Commission began scattering money around, virologists tended to agree that the disease was caused by only one type of virus (an error), that the virus grew only in living nerve cells (an error), and that it entered the body through the nose (an error), traveling thence to the brain and spine by way of nervous tissue (an error). The presence in polio victims' blood of antibody, a substance capable of neutralizing the virus, was granted little significance. In other diseases antibody was a sign of immunity, representing bodily defense against infection; vaccines were a means of creating immunity by stimulating the system to manufacture antibody. But the principle did not seem to work in polio. For one thing, it was not known that the poliovirus entered the bloodstream. Indeed, it was assumed mistakenly that the virus did *not,* which led to the conclusion that there was little point in trying to put antibody

there. Furthermore, laboratory monkeys that recovered from polio
did not develop noticeable amounts of antibody in their blood
until long after recovery. Logically enough, the consensus held
that antibody in this disease was a by-product of illness, un-
important to immunity or recovery.

The real trouble, of course, was technical. Polio workers had
not yet developed reliable methods of measuring the concentration of virus or antibody in monkey tissue, in blood, or in an
experimental vaccine. It was therefore impossible to get more
than crudely quantitative results from experiments. These discour-
agements were compounded by contradictory experimental findings. Often a worker who thought he was dealing with the one
and only type of poliovirus was actually complicating his life by
working with two different types. His experiments would end
in confusion. It was no wonder that polio was accepted as a
unique phenomenon to which conventional means of attack simply did not apply.

If adherence to all prevalent fallacies about the disease had
been unanimous among scientists, lives would have been spared
in 1935. Unfortunately, two polio vaccines were injected into
human beings during that year. One, given to nine thousand
children under a $65,000 grant from the President's Birthday
Ball Commission, had been thrown together by a bumptious young
research worker named Maurice Brodie, who did not see why
polio was necessarily as unique as claimed. He ground up the
spinal cords of polio-infected monkeys, attempted to inactivate
the virus with formaldehyde, put the resultant solution in hypodermic needles, injected monkeys with it, and announced, after
studies which nobody was ever able to duplicate, that he had
immunized the animals. He then tried the vaccine on himself and
a few other volunteers and declared the results excellent.

Brodie's main strength in the scientific community was the
sponsorship of Dr. William H. Park, Director of the Bureau of
Laboratories of the New York City Department of Health. Dr.
Park had been one of the giants of American public health
medicine, credited with basic contributions to man's knowledge
of diphtheria, measles, dysentery, and influenza. He was now
becoming senile. In explaining the debacle of the Brodie vaccine,

a contrite but scarcely crestfallen de Kruif later wrote to Jeremiah Milbank, an influential member of the Birthday Ball Commission:

> It will be remembered by all that, at our first meeting on January 5, at Colonel Doherty's apartment [this was the only time the Commission actually convened during its three years of existence], I brought the news, given me that day by Dr. Park, that *one* dose of a vaccine, prepared by treating the spinal cord of monkeys infected with poliomyelitis with formaldehyde, for a certain number of hours, produced evidence of immunity in the blood of a majority of children thus injected. That immunity, according to Dr. Park, was of a degree equal to, or surpassing, that following a mild attack of the disease in nature.
>
> At this time I was well aware that the experimental work on this question had been done not by Dr. Park himself but by Dr. Brodie, his associate. I had read Dr. Brodie's scientific papers, and saw no serious discrepancies in them. I had the uttermost faith in the scientific reputation of Dr. Park, and when he said: "This is a fact, this works," it worked, so far as I was concerned.
>
> As you recall, when Dr. McCoy [George W. McCoy, Senior Surgeon of the United States Public Health Service], was suggested as Chairman of the Advisory Medical Committee, it was on the ground not only of his unique experience in these matters, but also of his skepticism, born from his long experience with vaccines and other preventives, which, though put forth with hopes, had failed. Very shortly after this, I had a long talk with Dr. Charles Armstrong, of McCoy's laboratory, who expressed skepticism to me, regarding Brodie's work, and who also, first of anybody with whom I talked, hinted that Dr. Park, because of his advanced age, was no longer able to follow all the details of Brodie's experiments. He was skeptical on the ground of contact he had had with Brodie. At the time I should have been warned to advise the Commission to go easy with the support of any widespread experiment with Brodie's vaccine on human beings, but such was my faith in Park, that I brushed aside Armstrong's warning, and pushed the idea of a large-scale experiment with all I had in me.

When the Advisory Medical Committee met in June, this
year, Dr. McCoy expressed skepticism of the outcome of
any large-scale vaccination with the Brodie vaccine. His
objections were on the following grounds: (1) Of all children in the age group of those susceptible to the disease, so
few are really susceptible that an enormous number would
have to be vaccinated in order to tell whether the proposed
remedy would have any preventive power. (2) He further
objected on the ground that any vaccine, composed as
Brodie's was, of tissue foreign to that of the human being
(namely, monkey tissue) might, when given to many thousands of children, result in a certain number of dangerous,
and even deadly, reactions. . . .

But carried on the wave of his original enthusiasm, Paul de
Kruif had steamed past all such objections. Brodie was hailed in
the *Literary Digest* as a potential successor to Pasteur. The vaccine
was pumped into children.

Meanwhile, Dr. Peter Olitsky and other scientists at the
Rockefeller Institute, who "knew" that an inactivated vaccine
could not work and doubted as well that any other known variety
of vaccine would work, took time out to prove Brodie a fraud.
They tried to duplicate his work and found it impossible. Monkeys
survived injection with the vaccine but keeled over when their
supposed immunity was challenged by inoculation with living
poliovirus. Brodie's claims were baseless. The conventional wisdom had been upheld; a killed-virus vaccine was safe but ineffective.

While all this was going on, a more lethal preparation was
being tested by its inventor, Dr. John A. Kolmer of Temple
University, Philadelphia. Deriding Brodie's claims, Kolmer offered
not a killed-virus vaccine but one composed of what he devoutly
believed were viruses chemically modified to give immunity but
no symptoms of illness. After the usual preliminary heroics of
remaining vertical after shooting the material into himself, Kolmer
gave it to twelve thousand children, of whom six died and three
more were left paralyzed.

Having put all his eggs into the Brodie-Park basket, de Kruif
was free from responsibility for the Kolmer tragedy. Unhappily

for the Birthday Ball Commission and the public image of polio science, however, the nation was not sure where Brodie left off and Kolmer began, or vice versa. The distinction became even more difficult when Dr. James P. Leake, of the United States Public Health Service, announced that one child had died and three more had been paralyzed after taking the Brodie vaccine. Whether their illnesses were polio is not clear. In any event, Leake and Dr. Thomas M. Rivers of the Rockefeller Institute attacked both vaccines with such authoritative conviction at meetings of the American Public Health Association that Kolmer publicly expressed a wish that the floor would open and swallow him. Brodie was less gracious but was outnumbered. He lost his job at the New York University School of Medicine, where Jonas Salk was then a student (Salk says they never met), and died a few years later, allegedly by his own hand. His failure, and Kolmer's, had one salutary effect. They demonstrated that it might be well to learn more about polio before injecting polio vaccines into people.

One of those who was to be instrumental in this search for more "know-how" was the late Thomas M. Rivers. As head of the hospital of the Rockefeller Institute, Rivers had trained, hectored, and whipsawed more young virologists than any other man on earth. He was dean of the field and reveled in his eminence. As chairman of committees that advised O'Connor about research grants, he was a potent factor in winning for the National Foundation the scientific respectability that it needed, considering the organization's lay character and the piebald record of its predecessor, the Birthday Ball Commission. Rivers was a thickset man with a round, ruddy face, incipient dewlaps, a strident voice compared by some to the moose's and by others to the bullfrog's, and an accent that would have revealed his Cracker origins if his social prejudices had not. He was a handful, but so was O'Connor, and they got along splendidly for years.

"That old man didn't know any more about science than my left shoe," Rivers once said of O'Connor. "But he was willing to learn. Willing? Hell's fire, you couldn't stop him from learning. He figured if he was going to be responsible for spending all that money he needed to know what he was spending it on. He became a goddam good virologist after a while, and don't let anybody tell you different. But he never overstepped the bounds. We'd fight sometimes, but he never tried to make a scientific decision. There was a point where we were getting all kinds of hell from those guys at the National Institutes of Health who didn't know anything about polio—and there we were trying to get going with a national trial of the Salk vaccine and the NIH was holding us up, but O'Connor sat as cool as can be and told our Advisory Committee to call off the trials if we thought it was the right thing to do. He wouldn't take a single step on the scientific side without our advice and consent. All he wanted was to know why, and you learned to have a goddam good reason why. He could make you feel like your head was stuck in an electric fan."

Rivers had been added to de Kruif's group of advisers during the difficulty over the Brodie-Park vaccine. As he delighted in saying, "They needed me because I was a roughneck. They were afraid to deny old Dr. Park any more funds, but I wasn't." After that there wasn't much else Rivers could do for the Birthday Ball group. De Kruif's $241,000 ran cut in 1937, and his various grantees turned for support to Jeremiah Milbank and Edward Harkness, members of the Birthday Ball Commission who were devoted to polio research and had philanthropic funds of their own to donate.

Basil O'Connor did not became a direct force in the affairs of science until he found himself President of the new National Foundation for Infantile Paralysis, responsible for mounting some kind of research program. In discussions with de Kruif, O'Connor discovered how slapdash polio research had been and how unproductive it might remain unless order were introduced. He knew almost nothing of science but his intelligence was offended by realization that the Brodie-Park incident could have been avoided. He called Tom Rivers and said, "I'm only a layman, of course, and I'm not trying to tell you what to do, but I think maybe we haven't been building our case from the ground up. Perhaps we've been trying to get a conviction with insufficient evidence. How about drawing up a list of research priorities, so that we can emphasize first things first and try to get somewhere for a change?"

Rivers was pleased. "I hardly knew O'Connor at that time and couldn't tell whether he'd still like the idea after he saw the list, but I figured we had nothing much to lose. I polled the Advisory Committee and came up with a pretty good list."

There were eleven items, of which an attempt to develop a vaccine was last. There would be no more reliance on miracles. First priority was given to the fundamental studies on which cure or prevention of polio would ultimately depend. The main items called for study of the human disease, rather than the essentially artificial ailment that research workers had been provoking in laboratory monkeys. How did the virus affect human tissues? How did it get into the human body, how did it depart, and how did it get from man to man? Exactly where did it establish itself in the body, and what course did it follow to the central nervous system? Was there a relationship between the individual constitution and individual susceptibility to paralysis? Also, what exactly was poliomyelitis? Was it being confused with other neuromuscular diseases? Was chemotherapy possible? Could the virus be established in laboratory animals smaller and less expensive than monkeys? Were there better methods to purify and concentrate the virus for experimental use? Item eleven, "Production of a good vaccine," was included because nobody wanted to discourage financial support by seeming to rule out the possibility of polio prevention. But the vaccine was last on the list because everyone considered polio prevention extremely remote.

O'Connor's willing acceptance of this strategy was a happy omen for Rivers and his fellow scientists. The lawyer obviously did not confuse science with sorcery. He actually seemed ready to spend years—decades—waiting for unspectacular laboratory techniques to produce results. The days of sensational improvisation were drawing to a close.

Polio research became secondary to other matters during World War II, but the Foundation continued to support what investigations it could, meanwhile conducting its annual fund campaigns, improving its medical assistance to polio patients, and educating

specialists and technicians. Severe epidemics in 1943 and 1944
helped keep the nation polio-conscious and National Foundation-
conscious. In 1945, contributions reached $18,883,000.

But war or no war, O'Connor was unhappy with the research
he was supporting. The eleven-point program had promised no
quick solutions; neither did he expect any. But he had now been
around scientists long enough to recognize that they were as
susceptible to inertia as other men. "Some of the most unscientific
people you've ever met are scientists," he says. "Most of them
are fine people, don't get me wrong, but they can be as chuckle-
headed as anyone." To him, there was no excuse for lack of
headway. His staff medical director, Dr. Don W. Gudakunst,
shared the feeling. Gudakunst wrote in a memorandum, "The
approach of the individual workers has been narrow. They have
been satisfied to work over and over again those fields of exploration that have been covered by their contemporaries and
other workers of the past." At conferences on the subject, scientists were accused of spending altogether too much time raking
through stool samples in quest of poliovirus and not enough time
seeking new avenues of inquiry. O'Connor's impatience mounted.
In 1944, he wrote to Gudakunst, "What, if anything, have the
grantees . . . discovered since January 3, 1938? If the answer is
'nothing,' let's say so; if it is 'something,' then let's set it forth
clearly and intelligently."

Gudakunst finally gave O'Connor a long, painful report which
included the following views:

> The problems . . . have been approached year after year
> by the same personnel using . . . techniques that apply to
> the study of bacterial diseases. These techniques have not
> been fruitful; yet they are continued without appreciable
> modification. . . . The vision of poliomyelitis research work-
> ers is sharply limited. For the most part they have narrow
> backgrounds . . . are self-satisfied . . . jealous of preroga-
> tive. They not only are unable to comprehend the view-
> points of men trained in the basic sciences of physics, chem-
> istry, and mathematics, but they resent their intrusion in
> the field of medicine. . . .

O'Connor thought the indictment was well drawn. He had sensed much the same thing. Exceptions were all too rare. For all his disclaimers of not wanting to tell scientists what to do, O'Connor had several tussles with Tom Rivers about the sad state of progress. Rivers, a stout defender of the scientist's right to freedom from lay interference, urged patience. But O'Connor was accountable to the public, and the public deserved results for its money. The eleven-point program was all very well, and Rivers' refusal to approve grant applications inappropriate to that program was a great help, but more muscle was indicated. Someone had to take polio research by the scruff of the neck and move it. The trick was to move it without allowing its practitioners to realize that they were being held by the scruff of the neck. And O'Connor had a reputation for being able to do just that. He got things done; when he flipped the switch, the lights went on—or else. As an intimate adviser to Franklin D. Roosevelt in the construction of the New Deal, and in his spectacular success on Wall Street, he had developed a reputation for shaking disparate elements into synchronization. A case in point was the American Red Cross. When he took over at Roosevelt's request during World War II, the relief organization was tradition-ridden and archaic. He lopped off deadwood, introduced democratic procedures, and expanded Red Cross programs. He ruffled numerous feathers in the process but O'Connor was always ruffling feathers. Did it work? That was the thing that mattered. And the only thing. Now he was about to launch a postwar polio push that would culminate in the Salk vaccine.

3

JONAS SALK WAS AN OBJECT OF CURIOSITY DURING HIS YEARS AT
the New York University School of Medicine. He did not want to
practice medicine.

The spare time that others gave to discussion of diagnostic and
therapeutic nuances was used by him to advance his knowledge of
basic biology and chemistry, preferably at the laboratory bench.
Yet he sucked up the required medical curriculum like a vacuum
cleaner, feeding it back to his instructors so tidily that he was
named to Alpha Omega Alpha, the Phi Beta Kappa of medical
education, while still in his third year.

Later some of his classmates had to be reminded of this achievement before they could be induced to concede that he had shown
authentic promise. Their principal recollections were that he had
been quiet, competent enough, pleasant enough, and dependent
more on dogged application than brilliance. His preference for
research was considered an eccentricity, the more so because
he impressed his fellows as a prosaic type who would become
a competent private physician but in whom one could not perceive the transcendent creativity of the basic scientist. Some
medical students were, of course, fated to end in the security of
laboratories because they were simply not well organized enough
to practice medicine. But Jonas Salk was hardly that type. In
any event, none of his classmates dwelled intently on him or his
eccentricities. He was among them, but not closely so, and his later
fame raised their eyebrows.

It raised no eyebrows in his own family. His mother, Dolly

[28]

Salk, was a forceful woman, and she had designed him for fame. She felt it her duty to make her presence felt in the world through her sons. Jonas, the first of three, was born on October 28, 1914. No baby was granted earlier or more concerted instruction in the pitfalls of self-indulgence and the benefits of duties well, albeit joylessly, performed. His first spoken words were, "Dirt, dirt," instead of the conventional, uninspired "No, no" or "Momma." He was a responsive child.

These early lessons in perfection took place in a tenement at 106th Street and Madison Avenue, in East Harlem. Then the family moved to an apartment in the Crotona section of the Bronx, a section several cuts above Harlem and leagues beyond the Lower East Side where the Salks had started out.

It was a neighborhood of small apartment buildings whose iron fire escapes hung reassuringly over the sidewalks, identifying the houses as lower middle class—neither firetrap nor fireproof. The air of the tiled lobbies, stairways, and corridors was sour with the decomposed vapors of bygone meals, the chickens, carps, flankens, and briskets, the cabbages, carrots, onions, and groats that fueled the blond-haired, blue-eyed, dark-haired, dark-eyed, hook-nosed, snub-nosed, tall, short, fat, lean, smart, dumb Jews who occupied the flats. Most of the elders spoke in the accents of Yiddish Europe, and their young emitted a sputtering singsong, later to be confiscated by speech instructors at the College of the City of New York or by experience in the striver's college of hard knocks.

Dolly Salk recognized the neighborhood as a stepping-off place. She also saw it as a crucible. Other children were being propelled toward success by their own competent energies, the hopes of their parents, and the dynamics of the times, but Dolly's son Jonas was subject to additional, exceptional stimuli. It was not sufficient that he be bright and dutiful and demonstrate it at every step. To Dolly Salk there was no such thing as sufficiency. Even excellence itself was insufficient. Her standards were marvelously flexible: As soon as Jonas measured up to them, he discovered that they had been raised, as in a pole-vaulting competition.

Among his contemporaries he was a personage of small importance, neither an inspiration nor a threat. A thin, small-boned child untalented at games and not so extraordinarily gifted in school as to win special intellectual acclaim from the bright children with whom he associated, he was tolerated and liked, but not sought after. At twelve he was accepted by Townsend Harris High School, where the College of the City of New York provided a free, accelerated secondary education to those among New York's tens of thousands of bright boys who were driven enough to want to complete a four-year course in three. Townsend Harris was colloquially regarded as hard to get into and easy to get kicked out of.

Even before adolescence, there had begun to form in Jonas' private mind an unspoken ambition which was to facilitate his rise in the world. It was a specific ambition, on the order of a plan, and resembled in no way the familiar, generalized, boyhood determination to get ahead someday. Indeed, getting ahead had very little to do with it at first. This ambition or plan served instead to warm and comfort him. It gave him endurance on innumerable occasions when he might otherwise have wept with rage and frustration. The plan was this: "Someday I shall grow up and do something in my own way, without anyone telling me how."

With his fiftieth birthday approaching, and much of his childhood forgotten, he could still evoke the joy and pain of that earliest ambition. "I knew I was competent," he recalls. "I knew I had proved it by achieving that which I was supposed to achieve, time and time again. The remainder of childhood was for me a period of patient waiting, and not much else."

If the intellectual competition around Crotona Park had been brisk, at Townsend High it was overwhelming. The student body consisted entirely of large talents, most of them equipped with built-in goads. The typical student was, in short, a grind—either because he had been brought up that way or because the school environment convinced him that he had better become one in the interests of self-preservation. Jonas, who had been living since birth in a personal Townsend Harris of his own, adapted without the slightest trouble. He is remembered by classmates as a nice, unremarkable boy.

It had not yet occurred to him to become a scientist. He assumed that he would become a lawyer. Naturally, there had been discussions at home about whether he should be a lawyer or a doctor, the only really acceptable choices. He preferred the law. As a veteran, secret ruminator on the unreasonableness of life and, through his interest in current events, a budding critic of the unreasonableness that afflicted the lives of others, he actually felt somewhat drawn to the law. Lawyers obstruct injustice.

His plans changed shortly after he entered City College at fifteen and discovered the beautiful, orderly, compulsory irreverence of science. The scientist, he realized during a moment of illumination in a chemistry course, not only bares the nature of things but is at his best when he goes about it in his own way, daring to expose shackling dogma to the challenge of trial. Best of all, the scientist's workshop is his own mind. If Jonas prepared it carefully, guarding it from distraction, demanding of it the tidiness that rewards, it would serve him well, allowing him to approach the unimpeachable perfection that was, thanks to Dolly Salk, the craving of his fiber.

Like other indwellers, Jonas learned to dole out to his environment only bits of himself, morsels that he selected according to his assessment of the person or undertaking at hand. One who knew and liked him reminisced about it years afterward: "He was awfully difficult to know well. Not that he wasn't agreeable and companionable, but he hoarded his being more than most people do, as if he had walled it up for safekeeping in a sanctuary surrounded by a labyrinth and moats. Yet he danced and dated and coped and you somehow got the sense that perhaps he was holding back not out of plain fear but because he was preoccupied with something."

Lest we forget, Jonas was living in a period of history when political and economic analysis took precedence over the psychological. Times were difficult. Millions of unemployed Americans were becoming receptive to suggestions that there might be more sensible ways to run a country. They and tens of millions who sympathized with them measured happiness in terms of food, shelter, clothing, and the opportunity to get more. The palliatives of the New Deal had eased political tensions to some extent, but the country was still in the woods, its controversies embittered by omens of deep change and threats of war. Adolf Hitler had stopped being a joke all of a sudden: American admirers of his simple cruelties were becoming as vociferous as others who favored the complicated prescriptions of Marx.

As a young man filled with empathetic tenderness toward those who suffered innocently under the heavy hand of unreason, Jonas Salk acquired in those days a man-oriented or humanistic outlook on life. It would underlie his approach to science. It would underlie his popularity and his greatness. In this connection it is interesting to observe that one of the few truths of his personality that he was unable to conceal from an inquisitive press during his years of polio-vaccine experimentation was his ungovernable love for children—all children. He needed to smile into their eyes until they smiled back into his. He coveted the privilege of picking them up and hugging and smelling them. He all but tasted them as if they were plums. Reporters noted more than once that he refused to inoculate any child who cried at the sight of the needle. He inoculated his own boys at night, when they were asleep and would not be frightened.

I leap twenty-five years ahead of the story not to tease the reader with a foretaste of later scenes but to make the point that Salk never outgrew or sought to outgrow the tender concern for humanity that had been so much a part of him during his early years. If his affinity for science was largely a result of his childhood conditioning, so was the kind of science that attracted him. He was most inspired, most absorbed, and most successful when at work on projects of immediate or at least imminent concern to man.

Jonas Salk saw medical school as more an opportunity than a challenge. Challenge, he knew, would arise later or would be sought out if it failed to arise. But now his job was to consume fact and develop skill. In his calmly obsessive quest of both, he directed his attention to members of the faculty and therefore made more profound impressions on several of them than he did on his classmates. At the end of his freshman year, the distinguished Dr. R. Keith Cannan suggested that he might like to take a year's leave of absence to study biochemistry under a fellowship. Salk grabbed at the chance and exploited it fully, learning the protein chemistry that later would account for some of the sophistication of his vaccine work. He returned to medical classes in the fall of 1936, and, before the year was over, made his debut as a creative laboratory worker.

"We were working with the Q-155 strain of indifferent streptococcus," he remembered almost thirty years later. "It ordinarily was grown in a broth culture from which it had to be removed with a centrifuge apparatus. This was a slow process, and we needed large quantities of the bacteria. I got the idea that if we froze the broth culture the water would freeze first and the bacteria would concentrate—just like the partial concentration of milk proteins in an ice-cream freezer. So I put a can of the culture inside a larger can and packed calcium chloride and ice between them, as if I were making ice cream, and waited for the bacteria to concentrate.

"It didn't work. But when I poured alcohol in, the bacteria precipitated right out. It was astonishing. And what was even more astonishing was that when I tried it again, the alcohol had no effect at all, and the bacteria remained imprisoned in the culture. After considerable thought and a great deal of retracing of steps I discovered what had happened. The time I got the desired effect some of the calcium chloride had apparently seeped from the freezing compartment into the bacterial broth, forming calcium phosphate. The alcohol had really nothing to do with it. To concentrate the bacteria all I now had to do was add calcium phosphate. It worked at will. I wrote a paper about the technique—my first published paper."

An even more significant achievement of that academic year found Salk in the role of scientific philosopher and left him quite consciously geared up for the historic assault he would mount one day against conventional theories of vaccination. He heard in a lecture that immunization against viral diseases required vaccines made of infectious, living viruses. But he heard in another lecture that the deadly bacterial toxin of diphtheria could be converted into a harmless, noninfectious toxoid by the addition of Formalin, a solution of formaldehyde. This toxoid offered reliable immunity against the disease.

As a connoisseur of paradoxes and a veteran expert on the vagaries of unreason, Salk found these lectures contradictory, therefore stimulating. If a harmless, noninfectious, killed preparation would work against a bacterial disease, why not against a viral disease? What was so special about the chemistry of a virus, or about its relationships with the human host? One day he would find out.

In the meantime he kept his own counsel. "Of course I didn't challenge the professor's statement about live-virus vaccines," he says, somewhat perplexed that anyone might think the situation called for challenge. "He was reviewing orthodox immunology for us, setting forth the articles of his faith, you might say. For all I knew, he was right, even though he sounded wrong. I gave the matter a lot of thought for years, began testing it at the first opportunity, and learned that my early suspicions had been well founded."

Dr. Currier McEwen, Dean of the School of Medicine, allowed interested students to attend weekly faculty symposiums in his department. "We had sandwiches and coffee and any student ambitious enough to join us on an elective, no-credit basis was entirely welcome. Jonas came every week for a full year," McEwen recalls. "As often as not, students who sought out the dean in that way were more interested in wangling favor than in adding to their already substantial work loads, but if Jonas had that in mind, I never noticed it. He had an extraordinary fund of information for an undergraduate medical student, but did not try to engulf us in it. His behavior was really quite exemplary and I, for one, was entirely pleased and not at all surprised when he later made his major contribution to immunology. During the senior year each student was allowed a two-month period of elective work. I knew that Jonas would give that time to basic research. I thought he might join us and test the kinds of ideas we had been discussing at lunch, but he had become intensely interested in bacteriology and went to work with Tommy Francis."

Dr. Thomas Francis, Jr., had just come to the medical school's chair of bacteriology. At the Rockefeller Institute he had assisted the great biological pioneer Oswald T. Avery in studies of the pneumococcus, one of the causes of pneumonia, and, after moving to the Rockefeller Foundation, had made a considerable reputation as discoverer of the Type B influenza virus. Jonas had hoped to spend his two-month elective period at the Rockefeller Institute, sniffing out possible associations between infection and the rheumatic diseases, but was turned down. He then went to see Francis.

Francis and Salk. It is inconceivable that either depended on the other for the ideas and skills that were to lead each to great fame. When they met in 1939 Francis was already a front-rank microbiologist and, as hindsight indicates, by 1939 Jonas Salk was already certain to make his mark in one or another field of science. But the special quality of each man's later prominence, and the special nature of the work from which the prominence derived, trace directly to the relationship that began when Salk adopted Francis as his mentor. In time the protégé would find his subordinate role stifling, would set forth on his own, and presently would develop a project of such significance to society and of such purported peril to science, industry, and government that Francis would have to be enlisted to evaluate its worth.

But in 1939 Salk was a twenty-four-year-old anxious to spend his elective period learning something useful about microbiology. Francis, a well-tailored man of medium height with a clipped mustache, cultivated speech, and wry perceptions, happened to be one of the few top-rank microbiologists in the country who really believed that killed-virus vaccines could be useful. At the time he was experimenting with the notion that ultraviolet irradiation might kill influenza viruses without impairing their ability to stimulate a degree of immunity comparable to that produced by the disease itself.

"I remember the Jonas of those days as a slender, well-groomed, dark-haired youngster with time to spare. I was happy to get him," recalled Francis recently. "He turned out to be extremely able, having taken a year with Cannan in biochemistry. There was something appealing about the pleasantly energetic way in which he kept impressing you with his desire to do research. He and I grew influenza virus in my place at the medical school and then he'd take it up to George Lavin at the Rockefeller Institute, where they'd irradiate it and test it. Jonas wasn't exactly the messenger boy but you might say he did the back-and-forth work between Twenty-fourth Street and Sixty-sixth."

Salk elaborates: "I spent the first month learning to take out the lungs of infected mice and extract the influenza virus from them. Up at the Institute I helped Lavin with the ultraviolet irradiation and learned how to test the results of that inactivation process. We also irradiated virus grown in a culture of minced chick embryos. It was excellent preparation for later studies and later ideas."

During his spare time he turned up at the New York School of Social Work so frequently that he was mistaken for a student. The attraction was Donna Lindsay, whom he had met at Woods Hole, Massachusetts, where she was vacationing and he was earning summer pay as a laboratory worker. A tall, strikingly attractive, formidably brilliant girl with a swift, sharp wit and a most evident distaste for social injustice and other forms of irrationality, she had been elected to Phi Beta Kappa while earning her degree in psychology at Smith College. She was now preparing for a career in social-welfare work. As the daughter of a socially prominent dentist, her background was considerably more elegant than Jonas', a discrepancy that caused comment in both families.

Later, after Jonas had become a living legend, one of the rumors about their relationship that pleased Donna the least was embodied in irate letters sent to her mother-in-law by ladies who did not know Donna was Jewish and thought it a shame that she had lured Jonas away from the faith of his fathers. Another annoyance was the persistent, quite baseless story that Jonas had been a humble taxi driver in New York, a man of meager prospects, until the day she swept into his cab like a fairy princess and Found Love. True, Dolly Salk had borrowed the money to enroll Jonas as a medical college freshman, but from that point on he made it on his own, by scholarships and whatever odd jobs he could manage without interfering with a rigorous academic schedule.

The courtship of Jonas and Donna coincided with and un-

doubtedly contributed to Jonas' emergence as an active force
in life after so many years as a spectator and analyzer. "There
was no shell in evidence when I met him," Donna smiles. "He
was a good dancer, an amusing and exciting conversationalist,
and as different from the stereotype of the one-track scientist as
anyone could possibly be."

They were married the day after his graduation from medical
school. They moved to their own apartment and Jonas Salk, M.D.,
resumed work with Tommy Francis and George Lavin on ultraviolet irradiation. Francis had got him a grant of $100 a month
from the Rockefeller Foundation, which helped. The project
continued until March 1940, when Jonas went to New York's
Mount Sinai Hospital for his internship.

"To be an intern at Mount Sinai in those days," says a
distinguished physician still associated with that hospital, "was
like playing ball for the New York Yankees. Internships were
filled on a competitive basis, and only the top men from the
nation's medical schools dared apply. Out of the 250 who sought
the opportunity, only a dozen were chosen, so it goes without
saying that we had not only the best in the country, but the
most aggressive. Most went on to some sort of distinction. It was
no place for a shrinking violet.

"It was a hell of a place, run like a feudal barony by old
George Blumenthal, chairman of the board, who couldn't understand why interns were not satisfied to work without pay
or residents demanded more than the prevailing fifteen dollars
a month. The old man thought we should be grateful for the
free theater tickets he gave us once in a while, and for the opportunities we had to date nurses. The idea that *interns* should
get fifteen a month was communistic anathema. And with the
European war going on and people tense about it, the atmosphere in the hospital just crackled.

"From 1940 through '42 the most stable young man in that
place was Jonas Salk. With all the tensions and pressures, the
need to learn the arts of medicine, the squabbles about hours
and pay and work rules, the excitement about war and politics,

and the need to put the patient's interests ahead of everything else, not many interns, residents, or members of the upper crust were able to remain calm at all times. Yet nobody ever saw Jonas ruffled. It's no injustice to anyone to say that he was the best intern in the hospital—as versatile and promising a physician as any of them and by far the most mature and most reliable. He worked under me for a while and it was like having another self. You told him to do something and it got done. It got done and so did a dozen things you hadn't thought of. Furthermore, he was elected president of the house staff by the forty or fifty interns and residents because he was the best damned talker in the bunch, had the most common sense and the most charm, and was able to keep the administration out of the staff's hair more often than not."

Salk's interest in the practice of medicine was no livelier then than it had been in medical school, and he continued to make time for himself in the laboratory whenever he could. But his perfectionism—especially in the presence of human suffering— demanded that he exceed all normal standards of medical performance. It seemed that nothing was beyond his capacity. He performed spectacular diagnostic feats; he had a warm, unfussy, genuinely sympathetic bedside manner, and his surgical talent was so impressive that at least one prominent surgeon invited him to join his practice. When he became house physician, responsible for the performance of newer interns, he won their devotion. One remembers: "He was a fine clinician and an incredibly patient, responsive mentor. It was a joy to work for him. When I hear some of the unpleasant things that have been said about him in recent years, I get sick. I can't believe them."

He stayed in touch with Tom Francis, of course, and, under Francis' auspices, was allowed to report his calcium phosphate discovery at the Society for Experimental Biology and Medicine. He had applied the technique to the purification of influenza virus, and believed the chemical actually increased the virus' power to immunize. One of the leaders of virology, Dr. Joseph E. Smadel, was present and found the concept displeasing, partly because influenza virus was now being grown in embryonic

chickens and no longer required elaborate purification. Smadel
was never to become a fan of Salk's but on certain occasions
would be a powerful ally. On that day, however, he chose to play
exterminator.

"I don't remember what he said, it shocked and upset me
so much," Salk says. "I was only an intern with a lot of ambition, and here this guy gets as nasty as if I had committed a
crime against science. I was crushed. I remember writing him
a letter, hoping to explain whatever it was he objected to in
my work. I'm not sure whether he replied. If he did, it did
not relieve my apprehensions."

The apprehensions were well founded. Largely as a result of
his exposure to Tom Francis, Salk's interests had begun to
converge on man's immunity to viral disease. The field was
untilled except by a relative handful of virologists, many of
whom were crankily defensive about their work and elaborately
inhospitable to newcomers. This was understandable. Virologists
suffered manifold frustration. The nature of viruses was mostly
unknown, and their secrets were but slowly yielded to scientists
who attempted to employ investigative techniques developed for
studies of larger organisms, such as bacteria. The virus of poliomyelitis, for example, survived only in living man or monkey;
unlike bacteria, it could not be grown in test tubes or laboratory
dishware. It could not be stained, seen, or measured. It could
not even be counted, except by approximation. Other disease
viruses presented similar difficulties. Altogether naturally, the
elusive qualities of the organisms commanded more attention
among laboratory workers than the diseases with which the
organisms were associated. The relations between the invading
virus and its human host—the systemic, cellular, or molecular
relations which spelled infection, illness, and immunity—were
frequently overlooked, even by virologists who spent time trying
to develop new vaccines on a trial-and-error basis. This presented
opportunity to young Salk. The philosophic bent that had led
him to science was now more pronounced than ever. He was
now habituated to seeing things whole, attempting to detect the
patterned likenesses and paradoxes that are the order and es-

sence of nature. He would, therefore, take an immunologic approach to viral disease, studying the interactions between the chemistry of the infecting virus and the protective facilities of its host, rather than separating the two. To do this at all successfully he would have to win acceptance among men just as short-fused as Joe Smadel and far more resistant to innovation. His first bid for acceptance had been a fiasco, and an augury.

Donna was working at the Jewish Child Care Association of New York. They saw less of each other than they wished. Interns worked on Saturdays and Sundays, and this particular intern's burdens were enlarged not only by the gravitational attractions of various research laboratories but by his responsibilities as spokesman for the house staff. On Sundays wives were allowed to visit the house-staff dining room for the weekly steak. Donna attended frequently, and they managed to get away from the hospital to socialize with friends occasionally, but they were apart as much as they were together.

Toward the end of his internship, Salk became embroiled in the kind of ruckus for which Mount Sinai had become notorious. The house staff, in common with other Americans, was anxious to help defeat Hitler. The United States was not yet at war, so Americans helped the Allies by contributing funds to war-relief organizations. "All hell broke loose one day," reminisces a physician, "when the hospital director noticed one of us wearing a celluloid button that meant he had contributed to Allied war relief. The director asked what it was and, having found out, said, 'Don't you know that your uniform belongs to Mount Sinai and you are allowed to wear no extraneous decorations other than the one that the administration has authorized—the Red Cross button?'

"Then the director called Jonas down and read him the riot act. Jonas came out of there angrier than I'd ever seen him— I mean he was pale and tight-lipped. He called a meeting of the staff. We all voted to wear the button. Those of us who didn't have buttons went out and got them. The administration then announced that anyone caught wearing unauthorized buttons would be dropped from consideration for subsequent staff appointments. We continued to wear the buttons, and along comes Pearl Harbor. Do you think that stopped the administration? It did not. I remember one session in which we were asked to remember our duties to our patient. 'Suppose the patient is brought in off the street and happens to have German sympathies. Suppose he wakes up and sees you wearing a button that means you support the Allies. He'll think you're his enemy! This will interfere with his care!'

"Jonas was a very staunch guy. He never took a backward step on that issue or, for that matter, any other issue of principle between us and the hospital. In this case, you could see him seething, but his voice remained calm and his words were always reasonable. He merely kept reminding the administration as patiently as possible that there was a war on and that we were in it and that we interns and residents had the right to express ourselves with buttons. The whole thing finally became so embarrassing to the administration that the president of the hospital revoked the threats."

Few threats could have carried less force than one to deny interns and residents more prestigious appointments to the hospital staff. Nobody expected to get such an appointment, anyhow. "The hospital always had an amazing pool of young talent but was famous for discarding it, like a drunk wasting his wealth," says one of the most important physicians at Mount Sinai. "The best way to get to the hospital has always been to go somewhere else first. Even Jonas didn't have a prayer of getting on here after completing his internship. I remember he approached Gregory Shwartzman, the distinguished bacteriologist, in hope of joining his group, but got no offer worth considering."

Salk wanted to stay in New York. It was his home and Donna's and as good a place as any to begin the research career he had been planning. With Tom Francis' help, he sought a residency at the hospital of the Rockefeller Institute. Dr. Thomas M. Rivers, the dean of American virology, headed the hospital and would someday become a most important person in Salk's life. But now Rivers wanted none of him. Salk also was turned down by one or two other institutions. He learned later that one of the celebrated figures who did not want him on a certain famous staff had said with mild indignation to the person who nominated him, "Next thing you'll be bringing niggers in here." Attitudes of that kind were by no means unusual in the medical-scientific brotherhood of that period, and are only somewhat less pronounced today. (The colorful Tom Rivers, for example, was constitutionally incapable of discussing Salk without observing that he was "a young Jew." On the other hand, Albert Sabin was "a smart Jew.") One who canvasses Salk's former peers for their reminiscences and assessments of him can count on being reminded by several, and not always delicately, that he came, after all, "from a certain background," or "from the wrong side of the tracks," as if such knowledge might limit and simplify one's expectations of the man. In this general connection Elaine Whitelaw, director of women's activities for the National Foundation, remembers a lady volunteer who sat next to her at a meeting addressed by Salk when he was still at work on the polio vaccine. He was trying to help the Foundation's cause by showing its volunteers what a scientist looks like. His amiable, self-effacing description of his research and his immaculate, energetic youthfulness aroused considerable delight. Her neighbor turned to Elaine and bubbled, "That Dr. Salk! Is he Jewish or something?" To which Elaine replied happily, "Darling, he's Jewish and something."

Salk's inability, even with his brilliant record, to obtain a suitable position in New York was dreadfully disappointing to him. He needed help and advice. He got it from Tommy Francis. After long negotiations, complicated by enticing offers from Harvard and Columbia, Francis had moved to the University of Michigan in July 1941 to take over the department of epidemiology at the University's new School of Public Health. He was continuing his investigations of flu and, under special grants from the National Foundation for Infantile Paralysis, had tooled up for studies of polio epidemics. In October, Salk paid him a visit at Ann Arbor.

"I thought I would like to study the pathology of virus diseases for a few months, perhaps with Ernest Goodpasture at Vanderbilt, and then join Francis at Michigan," he recalls. Francis welcomed the idea and wrote a letter to Dr. Don W. Gudakunst,

Medical Director of the National Foundation for Infantile Paralysis:

> Dr. Jonas Salk worked with me as an interval fellow between the end of his medical school course in July 1939 until March 1940, when he began his internship at Mt. Sinai Hospital, New York. During that time I found him extremely able and interested in virus problems. His internship will end in March and he wishes to come to Michigan to work with me again or to continue his work. He has just come to Ann Arbor to discuss the possibility with me. His desire is to work on problems related to cellular factors which are involved in immunity to virus infections. He has suggested the possibility of spending three or four months training in special pathology and then coming here for the ensuing year. I have suggested that he might apply for one of the fellowships sponsored by the National Foundation under the guidance of the National Research Council. I thought he might be able to spend four months with Dr. Goodpasture and then come here for the year beginning July 1942.
>
> I have asked Dr. Salk to get in touch with you to discuss the probabilities of such a course of action. I hope you may consider this favorably. . . .

Within the week Salk spoke to Gudakunst. He also spoke to Dr. Homer Smith, administrator of the National Research Council fellowships which the polio foundation was subsidizing. And Smith spoke to Gudakunst. The fellowships were supposed to cover a year apiece. Would the National Foundation stretch the rules so that Salk could work with Goodpasture for a semester and with Francis for a year? Gudakunst was impressed by Salk's academic credentials and by Tommy Francis' interest. He was equally impressed by the aggressiveness with which the young man sought to get his career organized and rolling. He said he would see. On November 20, 1941, Salk wrote to Gudakunst to restate his desires and supply other information already familiar to Gudakunst. The letter merits inclusion here as a fair sample of the ramified prose to which Salk resorts when he suspects that his own appreciation of a situation exceeds that of his reader. He tries to encompass all possibilities, like someone trying to tell a Martian how to get through a revolving door on a pogo stick:

> *My dear Dr. Gudakunst,*
> I have just received a copy of a letter from Dr. Goodpasture to Dr. Francis in which he expresses willingness to have me come to his laboratory for a period of training. In view of the fact that a tuition charge would be required, I am now writing Dr. Goodpasture for more specific details. I shall forward a copy of his letter to you as soon as I receive it.
> Incidentally, since seeing you last, I have spoken with Dr. Homer Smith. His advice about arranging the necessary funds for work with Dr. Goodpasture was to get the assurance of the National Foundation that such help will be forthcoming, and to state this fact in applying to the National Research Council. Then, if a fellowship were granted, the National Research Council would make the necessary arrangements for an extension of such a fellowship with the funds so provided. Since I hope to be able to work with Dr. Francis at Ann Arbor, on some other basis, if I am not fortunate enough to be granted the fellowship, I hope the National Foundation will find it possible to permit me to spend the contemplated period with Dr. Goodpasture, independently of a National Research Council fellowship.
> Since the time is growing near for the meeting of the Education Committee of the National Foundation, I hope to be able to write to you again shortly.

The outbreak of war a few days later erased some of these complications. Tom Francis' work on influenza, a matter of military importance, had now become urgent. Salk would skip the excursion to Goodpasture's laboratory and proceed directly to Ann Arbor after completing his internship.

On April 12, 1942, exactly thirteen years before the day on which he would become a world celebrity, Salk arrived at the University of Michigan to begin work under a National Research Council–National Foundation grant of $2,100 for the year, which divided out to roughly forty dollars a week.

4

JONAS AND DONNA SALK RENTED AN OLD FARMHOUSE ON THE outskirts of Ann Arbor. She joined the Family and Children's Service as a social worker, and the newly ordained research scientist plunged into one of Tommy Francis' laboratories to see how many laws of nature he could discover. In their spare time they rusticated. "They reminded me of one of those back-to-the-land movements you used to hear about during the depression," says a New York friend who visited the farm. "The last human being I expected to see using a wood-burning stove was Donna Salk, but there she was cooking on a wood-burning stove. And canning the produce he raised in their huge vegetable patch. He was all fired up with the novelty of it and full of marvelous excitement about his work at the University."

Although Salk's fellowship was paid for by the National Foundation for Infantile Paralysis he undertook no polio research at Michigan. His assignment was influenza, with special emphasis on the development of an effective vaccine. In 1918 the disease had killed 850,000 Americans, including 44,000 soldiers. With the nation again at war and its susceptibility to epidemic increased by mobilization and migration, the need for a flu preventive was acute. "Jonas was a blessing in those days," says Francis. "Workers with his initiative and talent were even scarcer than usual because of the war, but our scientific opportunities and responsibilities were more pressing. Someone willing to take hold, as Jonas was, could move ahead rapidly. I was continuing with my epidemiological studies for the National Foundation and also was head of the Army group which later became the Armed Forces Epidemiological Board. It was a busy time, the pressure was on, and Jonas fit right in."

During his five and a half years at Ann Arbor, Salk became an acknowledged expert on the immunology of influenza. Free at last to give rein to his thrusting curiosity and his remarkable talents for scientific generalization, he overturned some orthodox concepts and helped Francis simplify what until then had been a frustratingly unmanageable problem of disease prevention. They developed an influenza vaccine that was given successfully to millions of American troops. En route to this achievement Salk acquired the administrative polish, the technical virtuosity, and, above all, the philosophic grasp of viral disease that later enabled him to cope with polio as expeditiously as if he had worked with it all his days.

One of the complications of flu research was the widespread but unproved supposition that recovery from one attack and resistance to the next depended mainly on a mysterious phenomenon called "tissue immunity." According to this theory, the antibody that circulated in the blood of recovered flu patients was an unreliable index to future immunity. It was felt that infection provoked chemical changes in the cells of respiratory tissue and that here, beyond present reach, lay the key to a reliable vaccine. In checking out some animal experiments with which Francis had seemed to strengthen this unproved hypothesis, Salk was unable either to prove or disprove it but delighted himself by proving something else. He found that the degree of immunity against any type of flu virus was directly proportional to the amount of antibody that circulated in the blood. The higher the level of antibody, the greater the immunity. When Francis and he demonstrated that vaccines made of killed flu viruses could stimulate the development of antibody levels as high as those that resulted from the disease itself, it became clear that the influenza vaccine project was an entirely reasonable undertaking.

One of the facts disseminated after Salk's canonization in 1955 was that he had helped develop the killed-virus vaccine used against flu during World War II. In the general brouhaha, the word "helped" was sometimes overlooked. Inference enshrined

Salk as the father of his science. This kind of thing causes dyspepsia in Salk's former colleagues. The modest public conduct expected of scientists fails to suppress their human wish that the record be straight on who accomplishes what. Tommy Francis, who would be polite about such matters even if the traditions of his calling did not require it, points out with ever the slightest tinge of wistfulness that he had been working on the Formalin-inactived flu vaccine before Salk got to Ann Arbor, and that other Formalin-inactivated vaccines had been used for years, especially in veterinary medicine. Francis had long been one of the few leading virologists who conceded promise to the killed-virus principle. Most virologists believed that if a virus were exposed to Formalin long enough to kill it and destroy its infectivity, it would also lose its antigenicity—the power to stimulate protective antibody. Reasoning that "you can't improve on nature," they sought to employ the immunizing processes of natural infection. They favored vaccines made of living viruses which, selectively bred or chemically modified or both, would remain infective but would cause only minimal symptoms in the patient.

Francis had been experimenting with these so-called attenuated flu viruses, but the Army dared not take the risk of trying them on the troops. Flu viruses were notoriously unstable, prone to all kinds of genetic mutations. The possibility that a supposedly attenuated strain might revert to virulence and start a flu epidemic after being injected into people who thought they were getting protection was more than the government could tolerate. In any event Francis and Salk were never able to stimulate higher antibody levels with attenuated flu vaccines than with the safely killed ones.

One of Salk's feats that Francis remembers admiringly as "basic work" was a technique for measuring the amount of flu antibody in blood. A New York virologist named George K. Hirst had recently discovered that certain viruses, including those of flu, caused red blood cells to clump, or coagulate, in test tubes. The phenomenon was a great time-saver for workers who needed to know whether viruses were present in a solution. All they had to do was add blood and look for clumps. Salk enlarged on the idea. He showed that the antibody titer (approximate concentration of antibody) of a blood sample could be calculated by adding virus to the sample and interpreting the clumps that formed.

"This was as active a period as any in my life," says Salk. "At the age of twenty-nine I took over in Tom's absence as acting director of the Army Influenza Commission. It was quite a responsibility. Meanwhile various thoughts were developing about the nature of the influenza problem and how to cope with it."

One of the thoughts that were developing (in him) was that influenza vaccines should contain more types of flu virus than were customarily included in those days: "In the spring of 1943 there was an outbreak of atypical pneumonia at Fort Custer. I went up and discovered it was really influenza. The virus was the Weiss strain, a Type A virus that was not being included in our experimental vaccine. Its appearance in this outbreak suggested that it might appear again later and should be guarded against. After some discussion, perhaps argument, the strain was included in the vaccine and accounted for its success. The Weiss strain caused an epidemic against which the vaccine was highly effective."

As usual, he was considering nature in terms of its trends. He thought, as he still does, that flu vaccines were far more effective than most scientists and physicians realized. "Once it was established that antibody level was a reliable indicator of immunity, the problem was well in hand," he declares. "Naturally, one had to bear in mind that people are living creatures and differ from one another. What might seem to be a high level of antibody could provide one person with less protection than a numerically lower level of antibody might provide in someone else. So what? That's the nature of life! It can be handled! The trick in flu is to give everybody the highest possible level of antibody. In most people that will be so much that the antibody will spill over from the blood into the nasal and respiratory secretions where the blocking of infection actually takes place. So far so good, but if the next epidemic is going to be caused by the Weiss strain, your vaccine will be useless if there are no Weiss strain viruses in it. To avoid surprises of this kind, and the failures so often ascribed to flu vaccines, you must cram your vaccine with every strain you can lay hands on."

The low repute of flu vaccines depresses him. He shakes his head ruefully, wrinkles his nose, and raises his upper lip, like a man trapped at a showing of someone else's home movies. "To understand why so many people think so little of flu vaccines," he says, "you have to put yourself in their place. If you had built your career on the belief that only live-virus vaccines can give durable immunity and that killed-virus vaccines are at best a stopgap, you would begin your consideration of the flu vaccines, which are killed ones, with the assumption that they are only a stopgap. Right? You then would ascribe the occasional failures to all sorts of factors other than that which explains the failures. For example, if an individual is vaccinated but gets influenza a few weeks later, these people decide that the vaccination gave only brief immunity. But this is seldom so. The truth is far more likely to be that the vaccine was incomplete. Is that the fault of the vaccine principle or is it a fault of planning and execution?"

During a flu epidemic during the winter of 1943–1944, Tom Francis subjected an experimental flu vaccine to field studies so carefully controlled that they still are cited as models. They were the prototypes of the 1954 trials that proved the efficacy of Salk's polio vaccine. Twenty-five hundred students in the Army Specialized Training Program participated. Half of the group was inoculated with the vaccine, the others with an inert substance. Until the study was completed, neither the students nor their physicians knew who had been vaccinated and who had been injected with the placebo. It was found that the incidence of flu among the vaccinated was 75 percent lower than among those who got the neutral substance. This statistic was quite impressive, but the vaccine had actually been even more effective than that. At the University of Minnesota, for example, it was found that the attack rate among students who lived on campus but did not participate in any phase of the study was more than four times as great as that of students who had been injected with dummy shots. A similar phenomenon was noticed at the University of Michigan. Salk and Francis explained that the immunization of some students had limited the spread of flu virus in their dormitories, thereby reducing the risk of illness among

their unvaccinated roommates. This manifestation of what immunologists call the "herd effect," whereby vaccination of only
part of a population interrupts transmission of the disease sufficiently to abolish it throughout the population, had been seen
in smallpox and diphtheria. It would be seen again in polio and
would underlie one of Salk's most bitter controversies.

Although Francis was head of the laboratory and director of
all its projects, Salk's name appears first on many of the collaborative articles that he and Francis and various other members
of the group published in scientific journals. This was significant.
It happened often enough to mean that Francis, the arbiter of
such matters, believed that Salk's role as leader deserved professional recognition. Despite the air of self-effacement that they
feel obliged to waft toward the public, scientists are often capable
of ferocious argument about whose name should be first, or
whether certain names deserve mention at all in the literature in
which the team's work is reported to the scientific world. Like
factories, offices, and royal courts, scientific laboratories can become hotbeds of discontent if the chief is considered too parsi-
monious with credit. A Nobel laureate was sued several years
ago and settled out of court with a junior colleague who deemed
himself codiscoverer, at the very least, of the marvel on which
the Nobelist's fame rested. One device whereby senior investigators
limit disgruntlement of that kind is the parceling out of professional credit, awarding published by-lines to their subordinates.
Sometimes the boss man puts his name first just because he is
the boss man, even though his connection with the published
achievement may have been only nominal. Too much of this
causes trouble. Sometimes he may put his name last or leave it
off altogether. He may do this even though the whole undertaking
was his idea and his collaborators were stumbling around in a
kind of blind man's buff, getting nowhere until he showed them
how to get the work done. Sometimes he puts everybody's name
down, giving almost as much credit to junior technicians as to
qualified scientists, a subtlety that does not always delight the
qualified scientists, since it seems to diminish the importance of
their contribution. In short, laboratory workers are seldom at a
loss for conversation during coffee breaks.

During his Ann Arbor period, the dawn of his professional prominence, Jonas Salk wanted his name to come first as often as possible. Francis recalls with a small smile, "He used to tell me, 'Everyone knows who *you* are. It doesn't matter whether your name is first or last.' You couldn't really dislike this in the man, you know. You've got to admire ambition, especially when it's combined with the kind of ability this fellow had. Sometimes, of course, his ambitions carried him a bit far. I remember one paper he wrote that didn't seem to me to substantiate some of the conclusions he drew. I told him so, but he said he thought the inferences were warranted by reason if not by hard data. He said other people were always publishing things without having all the evidence. I told him we didn't do things that way in our place. Then he said he thought he'd send the paper in anyhow. I told him if he did he had better go with it. That was that."

"My striving was strong and unconcealed," agrees Salk. "I wanted to do independent work and I wanted to do it *my way*. There may have been times when I made more of my data than might have been expected, but I was not functioning in the expected way. I was supplying *immunological* insights. I was attempting to elucidate the *interaction* of man and virus in a field which was accustomed to viewing the two separately. I engaged in extrapolation because I had always felt that it was a legitimate means of provoking scientific thought and discussion. I engaged in prediction because I felt it was the *essence* of scientific thought. The fact that neither extrapolation nor prediction was popular in virological circles seemed to me to be a shame."

Salk was promoted to an assistant professorship in the department of epidemiology somewhat less quickly than he wished. Before the promotion was announced in 1946 he began to think of leaving Ann Arbor altogether, a sentiment which he kept no secret and which, some believe, accelerated the promotion. At the end of the war, the government had sent him to Germany to organize diagnostic laboratories in anticipation of flu epidemics. He enjoyed the trip, enjoyed the work, and enjoyed the realization that he, of all members of the Influenza Commission, had been tapped for the responsibility. When he returned, relations with Tommy Francis were civil and correct but perceptibly strained.

Salk was ready to set forth on his own, think his own thoughts, and put them into action. He had numerous ideas about flu, not all of which coincided with his superior's. He needed to find a place where he could set up his own shop.

There were vacancies at the University of California and at Western Reserve, in Cleveland, but his active interest elicited offers from neither institution. He negotiated briefly with Mount Sinai Hospital about establishment of an immunological laboratory, but the hospital was unwilling to give the facilities he wanted. His mother often urged him to come back to New York and set himself up in private medical practice, a wish she cultivated to her dying day, and he would have been thrilled to return East—though not for private practice—but he could find no openings.

Opportunity finally arose in a most unlikely quarter during 1947. The University of Pittsburgh School of Medicine was known far, wide, and justifiably as a dump. The faculty consisted almost entirely of part-time instructors who earned their living in the private practice of medicine and had neither time nor inclination for basic research. A faculty member recalls, "The medical school had a grant of about $1,800 from the American Society for the Study of High Blood Pressure in 1947. I think that was the entire research program. The University's physics department was doing more biological research than the medical school. It had been at least twenty-five years since an animal had been used in the medical school for what we call chronic, or long-term, experimentation. Furthermore the place was filthy. Pittsburgh had not yet attacked its smog problem and the air was full of cinders. You had to bring an extra shirt with you in the morning. You had to cover your desks and tables with cloths at night unless you wanted to dig them out of the soot the next day."

Dr. William S. McEllroy, dean of the medical school, was trying to upgrade the institution by employing full-time faculty members capable of scientific work. He was particularly keen on virus research, leading practitioners of which were bringing large grants and much prestige to their universities. He had hired one virologist, who remained only briefly before quitting in disgust. He now canvassed the field for another and heard of Salk, who was described as a bright, ambitious worker whose association with the flu vaccine would lend unwonted luster to the medical school.

"I went down for a visit and saw nothing but opportunity," says Salk. "Here was a metropolitan area east of the Mississippi River, a wealthy community which was talking about environmental and cultural rehabilitation. Right next to the medical school was a city hospital with plenty of unoccupied space, some of which I was told I could have and more of which I immediately hoped to have. McEllroy promised me every possible assistance in developing my own virus research program. Those were the only assurances I had. I was insane. I fell in love with the place. Tommy Francis thought I was making a mistake. So did everyone else. I can remember someone asking me, 'What's in Pittsburgh, for heaven's sake?' and I answered, 'I guess I fell in love.' What I was in love with, of course, was the prospect of independence."

When he left Ann Arbor, it was agreed that he could return after a year if Pittsburgh turned out to be as impossible as predicted.

5

"WHEN JONAS FINALLY GRASPED THE REALITIES OF HIS SITUATION here," recalls a friend who joined the University of Pittsburgh medical faculty at about the same time, "he saw that he was worse off than he'd been at Michigan. The Municipal Hospital, where he had expected to set up a large research facility, belonged to the city, not to us, and although there was plenty of vacant space in the building, Jonas was shunted into basement quarters too small for his needs. This was a very trying disappointment. After all, he wasn't a conventional academic looking for the kind of security one gets from abiding by other people's rules. He had come to Pittsburgh in October 1947 for only one reason, to create. He could not just retire to his cubicle, make do, and wait for someone to toss him a bone. So he began waging a kind of guerilla war for lab space. He maneuvered with Dean McEllroy, who was on his side but not all-powerful, and he maneuvered with the Mellon family and with David Lawrence, the mayor, and with the National Foundation, and he inched his way into that unoccupied hospital space. It was a gradual conquest—a closet this week, an extra office next week, the auditorium next year."

Working space was only half his problem. The independence for which he hungered had also been withheld. The University's virus research had for some years been conducted by Dr. Max A. Lauffer, a biophysicist distinguished for studies of viruses that attack plant life. The local choreography required that this arrangement continue, at least for the time being. Accordingly, the medical school's new Associate Professor of Bacteriology and

[54]

Pathology, the promising young man who had helped develop a flu vaccine, found that his administrative superior was Dr. Lauffer of the University's physics department. "I was bound and gagged," says Salk. "The rules decreed that Lauffer sign all requisition forms. He even was responsible for deciding how much I should pay my secretary. Naturally, protocol required that my secretary earn less than his. I mention these details only to summarize the relationship, which was formal, awkward, and not at all what I had envisioned when I left Michigan. Another part of the awkwardness was that I was interested in animal viruses, such as influenza viruses, and Lauffer was a plant-virus man. These interests did not necessarily coincide, to put it mildly."

One day Salk telephoned the medical department of Westinghouse Electric Corporation to see if he could be kept informed about outbreaks of flu and other respiratory ailments among the firm's employees. "Where's your office?" asked the physician at the other end of the line. Salk answered, "As I said, I'm at the Pitt medical school. My office is in the Municipal Hospital."

"No, I don't mean that," said the physician. "Where's your *office?* Are you in the Jenkins Arcade? In the Medical Arts Building? Where do you practice?"

"I don't. I'm full-time here at the medical school."

"Oh? What are you? A Ph.D?"

A doctor of medicine who worked for a medical school and did not supplement his income by treating private patients was in this wilderness a queer bird indeed. In love with Pittsburgh? Salk shuddered. It crossed his mind more than once that he could always return to Ann Arbor. And play second fiddle. It would be the first backward step of his life. A sensible man does not take backward steps before exhausting all possibilities in the other direction. The sympathetic dean, Billy McEllroy, was one such possibility. He had agreed from the first that Jonas should be independent. Sooner or later he might find a way to unravel campus procedures. Sooner or later the medical school's virologist might be liberated from the University's physics department, installed in suitable laboratories, and allowed to exercise the promise that had attracted the medical school to him in the first place.

Salk's long experience in the art of making the best of a bad bargain—while scheming to improve it—permitted him to contain his disappointment. He resumed his influenza studies under a grant that the Armed Forces Epidemiological Board had given him when he left Michigan. He set up modest animal quarters at the hospital and began work on an improved vaccine containing an adjuvant, a mineral-oil emulsion that enhanced the vaccine's potency. Use of an adjuvant would mean that many virus strains could be included in a single injection of tolerable size. The trick was to decide exactly which components, in exactly which proportions, and assembled in exactly what fashion, would give most salutary results. The work enchanted him. To search an apparently formless welter of variable and conflicting factors for the central unifying truth was the work that had always excited him most. His talent for analysis of that kind would enable him less than six years later to make two historic revelations within a single week. One would announce the successful testing of a new, unprecedentedly potent flu vaccine. The other would disclose the existence of a polio vaccine which had already been given to human beings with highly promising results.

Being Salk, and only human, he could not have achieved all this so rapidly had he remained in cramped quarters and administrative bondage. His deliverance from these handicaps was delayed until 1949, but its certainty became apparent many months earlier. In fact, substantial expectation broke leaf toward the end of 1947, when one of the shrewdest, most colorful figures in polio research came to Pittsburgh, conferred with Salk, McEllroy, and Mayor Lawrence, and made an offer.

Of the staff that O'Connor had assembled after the war, the most important to the eventual conquest of polio was Harry M. Weaver, a jut-jawed, razor-keen administrator whose vast self-esteem was fortified by an extraordinary ability to anticipate scientific trends. Weaver had been a grantee of the Foundation while an assistant professor of anatomy at Wayne University in Detroit. He had been recommended to O'Connor by Dr. Don W. Gudakunst, the Foundation's Medical Director, who recognized

him as ideally suited to the up-and-at-'em research campaign
O'Connor was planning. Weaver joined the organization early in
1946 and was named Director of Research in October. The
title provoked disapproval among virologists, several of whom,
including the preeminent Tom Rivers, argued with O'Connor
that you can't "direct" research without offending scientific tradition, estranging the researcher, and defeating your own purposes.
They were wrong.

Weaver spent his first months boning up on the current state
of knowledge in the polio field. Also, as he put it years later in
a retrospective memorandum to O'Connor, "Made special effort to
become intimately acquainted with the thinking (or lack of thinking) of: (a) senior staff of NFIP, (b) members of advisory committees on research, (c) grantees of NFIP and (d) nongrantee
investigators in the scientific disciplines pertinent to poliomyelitis."

During 1947 he instituted a series of round-table discussions
at which the Foundation's grantees regaled themselves and him
with their elaborations of the conventional wisdom about polio.
The conferences had two purposes. The first or long-range purpose was to encourage communication and intellectual cross-fertilization in a field notable for its lack of both. The second, short-
range purpose was to complete Weaver's orientation to his job.
As he later wrote to O'Connor, these conferences persuaded him
that "only an appalling few . . . were really trying to solve the
problem of poliomyelitis in man." On another occasion he wrote,
"It became evident that, if real progress were to be made, more
exact methods of research would have to be instituted, objectives
would have to be clearly defined, procedures and techniques would
have to be developed to permit attaining these objectives, and
individual groups of workers would have to sacrifice to some
extent their inherent right to 'roam the field,' so to speak, and concentrate their energies on one or, at most, a few of the objectives."

The tone and content of these private observations were pon-
tifical enough to send the virological brotherhood shopping for
tar and feathers. But virologists did not know that the new research
director felt as he did. His mode of address to working scientists
was ineffably suave. He knew his way around. He knew that he

was not confronting schoolboys but professors heavily weighted
with academic and scientific dignity and the prerogatives thereof.
They would not accept the dictates of a research director. Weaver
had to be an infiltrator, an agent provocateur. He saw with perfect clarity, as he once said to O'Connor, "that an administrator
of science could not effectively exploit his own ideas without
having them first enunciated in a piecemeal fashion by independent
scientists." He and his assistant, the patient, encyclopedic Dr.
Theodore E. Boyd, spent much of their time visiting the laboratories of Foundation grantees, coaxing, exciting, luring—but
never directing—the scientists toward fresh territory. Weaver
quickly overcame the disadvantage of his title as "director" and
the further handicap of being "only" a doctor of philosophy at a
time when leading virus-research workers were usually doctors of
medicine. He soon had most virologists eating out of his hand,
having demonstrated knowledge, discretion, administrative power,
and access to huge amounts of grant money.

Uppermost in Weaver's mind during the first years of his
maneuvering was the unconventional belief that "prevention, as
contrasted with cure, was the only promising avenue of approach"
to polio. Polio workers had been profoundly impressed by the
ruination of Joseph Kolmer and Maurice Brodie after the deaths
of children inoculated with their vaccines. The scientists had
been so impressed that many had made a hallowed principle out
of what previously had been mere theory—the theory that vaccination against polio was impractical. One of their most telling
arguments, on the rare occasions when anyone so much as introduced the subject, was that the poliovirus would grow only
in the nervous systems of monkeys (and by now, certain rodents).
Everybody knew that (a) it was impossible to remove all the
animal-nerve cells when harvesting the viruses for preparation
of a vaccine and (b) human beings injected with foreign nervous
tissue of that kind sometimes suffered fatal allergic inflammations
of the brain. Moreover, the age of "wonder drugs" had dawned:
Virologists were generally more comfortable seeking a chemical
cure than experimenting with hazardous vaccines.

Weaver mistrusted this line of thought. In the first place, no
drug had ever cured a virus disease and none seemed likely to

at the time. It was reasonable to investigate chemotherapy, he felt, but unreasonable to rule out vaccination. Also, he considered it silly to persist in the assumption that poliovirus grew only in nervous tissue. Much circumstantial evidence to the contrary had been discovered. As early as 1911 European workers had found the virus in human feces, which implied that the disease organism multiplied in the alimentary tract. Several American virologists, such as the first Foundation grantees, Drs. James D. Trask and John R. Paul of Yale, had repeated the observation. In 1940 David Bodian and Howard Howe of Johns Hopkins had given chimpanzees polio by feeding them the virus. In 1947 Joseph L. Melnick and Dorothy M. Horstmann, of Paul's group at Yale, had demonstrated that the animals developed antibody and resistance to reinfection after such feeding. To the gimlet eye of Harry Weaver, polio looked like an intestinal infection. If this were as true as it seemed, it almost certainly meant that the virus grew in nonnervous tissue and that one of the main objections to vaccination was baseless. All that was needed was proof. If virus could be grown elsewhere than in the spinal cords of monkeys, it could be harvested for use in a vaccine.

Before the end of 1947, Weaver had a most rewarding chat with Dr. Robert G. Green, Professor of Bacteriology at the University of Minnesota. Weaver denies that he prodded Green toward the question of whether poliovirus might multiply in nonnervous tissue. He acknowledges that he may have "stimulated" the discussion. He says contentedly, savoring a job well done, "Green pointed out that patients with nonparalytic polio excreted huge amounts of the virus in their stools. 'That much virus *must* multiply in the alimentary canal,' he said. 'Such quantities obviously could *not* grow in the nervous systems of these people. They show no signs of nerve damage.' "

If Green had lived long enough to publish the results of the experiment that resulted from this conversation, he might have won a Nobel prize. The experiment was based on the established knowledge that poliovirus could not grow in the eyes of rabbits. But when Green implanted bits of human intestinal membrane in the rabbits' eyes and added poliovirus, the virus multiplied. Q.E.D. poliovirus grew in nonnervous tissue. Not only that, it could be grown in cultures of *human* nonnervous tissue under laboratory conditions. After Green's death his assistant, Dr. Charles A. Evans, buttoned up the experiments but was beaten into print (and therefore into immortality) by Dr. John F. Enders of Harvard, another National Foundation grantee.

While experimenting with the growth of chicken-pox viruses in test-tube cultures of nonnervous tissue taken from human embryos, Enders and two young associates found themselves with a few extra, unused flasks. Offhandedly applying the same concepts that had motivated Green and Evans, they put some poliovirus into the flasks. When the virus established itself and grew, Enders, Thomas H. Weller, and Frederick C. Robbins pursued the matter. In 1954 they got the Nobel prize. Their discovery eliminated two barriers to polio immunization: It made possible the laboratory cultivation and harvest of unlimited quantities of poliovirus for experimental use, freeing research workers from their dependence on the infected spinal cords of expensive monkeys; and it therefore permitted the preparation of a vaccine devoid of foreign nervous tissue dangerous to man.

The likelihood that all this could be done was by no means the only prophetic notion that crossed Harry Weaver's mind during his first months as the National Foundation's research director. Another was his recognition that polio was probably not one disease, but two or more, in that two or more types of polioviruses were implicated. In 1931 Macfarlane Burnet of Australia had reported that animals immune to polio infections caused by one strain of virus could be brought down by another strain. John Paul and James Trask, the Yale team, made similar findings two years later. If a polio vaccine were to work it would have to give immunity against all the types of virus to which man was susceptible. Nobody knew whether there were two, three, or twelve different types. Weaver proposed to find out.

Weaver recognized that the job of classifying all available strains of poliovirus according to their immunologic differences or similarities might take years. It would entail immense cost in laboratory space, equipment, technical assistance, animals. He also knew that well-established polio experts would disdain the work and refuse to do it but would insist on having the last word about it before accepting the results. A senior virologist might postulate the existence of more than one type of virus. He might even study a dozen samples and say that he had found two distinct types (although by 1947 nobody had even bothered to do that). But to ask him to classify *all* known strains was to suggest that he give his laboratory and several years of his life to mechanical, highly unstimulating work. For this kind of drudgery Weaver needed some able youngsters sufficiently hungry for accomplishment to sense, as he did, that the typing program represented an opportunity. Whoever did the work would develop the kind of laboratory team, the kind of laboratory space, the kind of familiarity with poliovirus, and, therefore, the kind of running start that might, on completion of the drudgery, find the drudges ready to scoot home free with experimental polio vaccines.

Weaver had heard of Jonas Salk. He then discovered that Pittsburgh's Municipal Hospital was full of empty space now that penicillin and the sulfa drugs had diminished its role as a center for the treatment of infectious diseases. Weaver was advised that Salk was in the basement there, working on flu and aching for more space and more independence. Some of the upstairs wards were now being used for treatment of polio cases—prime sources of virus samples. Weaver needed to hear no more. He went to Pittsburgh.

It will be recalled that Elijah "lay and slept under a juniper tree, behold, then an angel touched him, and said unto him, Arise *and* eat. And he looked, and, behold, *there was* a cake...." Harry Weaver made an absolutely angelic impression when he suggested to Salk and Dean McEllroy that Municipal Hospital might be just the place to conduct part of a virus-classification program. Provided, of course, that the medical school was willing to accept several hundreds of thousands of dollars in grant money. And provided Dr. Salk was willing to head up the Pittsburgh end of the project. Was Dr. Salk at all interested in polio? Was the medical school at all interested in polio? Could the city of Pittsburgh be persuaded to yield additional hospital space to the medical school for Dr. Salk's important work? Was he kidding?

"Weaver represented a liberating force," Salk says. "The

original attractiveness of Pittsburgh had been the apparent openness of the situation there, but then the openness had proved illusory. And now Weaver came along, willing to provide me with funds and work and people and facilities to be administered and organized by me. This was liberation. He also made it clear that the virus-typing work could lead to something very much larger. Even if it did not become that 'something very much larger,' it was an opportunity to learn something about polio, get facilities that I could do other things with, and assemble an adequate staff."

The studies could not begin until 1949. Weaver calculated that it would take all of 1948 to staff and equip the project, get the consent of the Foundation's Scientific Advisory Committee, and conclude preliminary discussions with the leading virologists who would plan and supervise the work. McEllroy and Salk had better see what they could do about getting the extra space in the hospital. It would also help if Salk began familiarizing himself with poliovirus.

Accordingly, Dr. Max A. Lauffer explained in his application for the 1948 renewal of the National Foundation grant which helped support the University of Pittsburgh's virus-research program, that most of the $35,900 would be for "work carried out in the virus laboratory under the supervision of Dr. Jonas E. Salk." Lauffer and his colleagues in the biophysics laboratory would try to determine the best way of purifying poliovirus grown in the central nervous systems of monkeys, using an ultracentrifuge machine and other physical apparatus. Salk would then check the biological aspects of the purified virus, seeing how infectious it was in laboratory animals, while Lauffer's group studied it under an electron microscope.

During 1948 Salk attended several meetings with celebrated virologists who blueprinted the procedures for him and three other lesser lights to follow in carrying out what plainly was considered stoop labor—virus classification. Among those present at his first meeting, on January 7 and 8, in Washington, were:

—Dr. Charles Armstrong of the United States Public Health Service, discoverer that the Lansing strain of poliovirus would grow in cotton rats. Because other strains would not, Armstrong's discovery had helped call attention to the differences among the viruses and the need for a virus-typing program.

—Dr. W. Lloyd Aycock of Harvard, a polio pioneer who, like Armstrong, had warned against Kolmer and Brodie.

—Dr. David Bodian of Johns Hopkins, who had already made fundamental contributions to polio research more numerous than those of any other worker. He would make still more. The criticisms of polio investigators by Harry Weaver and his predecessor, Don Gudakunst, had not been directed at Bodian, a man for whom gratification lay in work and thought rather than prerogative or visions of empire. Although Bodian would never have listed Salk among his favorite human beings, he welcomed Jonas' success when it happened. Indeed, he made invaluable contributions to it and later risked his reputation in defense of it.

—Dr. Herald Cox, of the drug company Lederle Laboratories, a veteran developer of virus vaccines, who was already attempting to develop modified strains of poliovirus for use in a live vaccine.

—Dr. Thomas Francis, Jr., Salk's teacher.

—Dr. William McD. Hammon, of the University of California at Los Angeles, who would shortly join the University of Pittsburgh and become a thorn in Salk's side.

—Dr. John R. Paul of Yale, another pioneer, who would never see things quite as Salk saw them.

—Dr. Albert B. Sabin, of the Children's Hospital, Cincinnati, a nimble genius with a vulpine face and a silver tongue. After fighting the Salk vaccine and losing, he would at last present the Sabin vaccine and win—but neither completely nor permanently.

After the Washington conference it was decided that the supervisory committee on typing would be composed of Armstrong, Bodian, Francis, Sabin, Harry Weaver, and the four hewers of wood who had agreed to do the actual work—Salk, Herbert A. Wenner of the University of Kansas, Louis P. Gebhardt of the University of Utah, and John F. Kessel of the University of Southern California. Weaver once said, "I know of no single problem in all of the medical sciences that was more uninteresting to solve. The solution necessitated the monotonous repetition of exactly the same technical procedures on virus after virus, seven days a week, fifty-two weeks a year, for three solid years." What was even worse was that the last remaining hope of adventure and discovery departed from the program even before it started. During 1948, Bodian and his colleague Isabel Morgan screened fourteen strains of poliovirus and discovered that they divided into three distinct immunologic types. Working independently, Kessel and Charles F. Pait discovered the same thing. For all practical purposes, the task of the virus-typing program would be simply to see into which of the three categories each of more than one hundred available strains belonged. The chance of finding a fourth type was vanishingly small.

Salk disliked being looked on as a scut worker but, as Weaver had hoped, he found more good than bad in the arrangement. The University of Pittsburgh and its well-wishers in finance and municipal government were overjoyed. The new National Foundation grants would approximate $200,000 a year, a sum unprecedented for this medical school and seldom surpassed at any other. Anybody with half a brain knew that the objective of Salk's project was, sooner or later, a polio vaccine. There was no assurance that he could get that far, but the possibility was there and it shone. Mayor Lawrence heard the tale, punched a few buttons, and Salk got additional space in the basement and on two upper floors of the city hospital. Paint shops, storage closets, and a former morgue were included. All that remained was to convert the hodgepodge into usable space, a costly project. The city could not make an appropriation of that kind without political and administrative deliberation which might take months. The National Foundation said it would award funds only for operations and certain equipment, not basic construction. It was incumbent on McEllroy to seek philanthropic gifts elsewhere.

Much to his joy and Salk's they learned that the local March of Dimes had accumulated tens of thousands of dollars and was eager to give some to the medical school for polio research. After negotiations were underway and Jonas was beginning to count on a large grant, he and McEllroy discovered that they had run into a deadfall. The local polio chapter, an appendage of David Lawrence's political machine, was proposing to give the University money that it had been withholding from Basil O'Connor's national headquarters. The National Foundation requirement that

half of all money raised in fund drives be remitted to New York
had always been distasteful to the Pittsburgh group. Its leaders
were uninspired by the Foundation's connection with Franklin
D. Roosevelt, whose name they omitted from their own literature.
In 1947, when the National Foundation treasury was drained by
expenses incurred during polio epidemics, O'Connor directed all
local chapters to replenish the epidemic fund by turning over half
of their cash reserves. Pittsburgh balked. National headquarters
cited past experience: A centrally administered epidemic fund
could function more efficiently. For example, if Pittsburgh suffered
an epidemic, the central funds would be available without delay
and, if necessary, would give Pittsburgh far more money than the
city had contributed to March of Dimes campaigns. This sort of
thing had happened repeatedly, throughout the country. Pittsburgh
still balked. O'Connor smoldered.

The news that McEllroy and Salk were soliciting alms struck
the leadership of the Pittsburgh polio chapter as the perfect
solution to its difficulties with New York. Pittsburgh for the
Pittsburghers! The chapter would give $35,000 to its own Univer-
sity! The refusal of the national organization to build Jonas
Salk's laboratory for him was an outrage. Was not the National
Foundation supposed to be interested in research? What kind of
hypocrisy was this? When the noise reached New York, O'Connor's headquarters emitted a shower of sparks. Pittsburgh was
placed on notice to reorganize itself and stop the hanky-panky
with Foundation funds unless it wanted its charter annulled. There
was talk of civil suit. There was talk of prosecution. Harry
Weaver came to Pittsburgh and explained to McEllroy and Salk
that the Pittsburgh chapter's money was tainted. Even if it
owned the money, which it did not, the chapter was forbidden to
make research grants, a national responsibility. He advised McEllroy and Salk to extricate themselves, which they did, but not
before Salk spent several depressing hours in conferences, watching his $35,000 go up in smoke. Fortunately, McEllroy was well
regarded by members of Pittsburgh's first family, the Mellons.
The Sara Mellon Scaife Foundation responded most warmly to
the fix he was in and agreed to come to the rescue. Jonas Salk
mopped his brow.

His wife, who has seen him sweat through crisis after crisis
in a career that has seldom been free of crisis or ordeal, remembers
his campaign for *lebensraum* in Municipal Hospital as one of the
most intense, its outcome as one of the more gratifying. "He wants
nothing second rate," she explains, "and is willing to pay the price
in his time and his energy. This perfectionism seems to consume
and exhaust him but it doesn't really. He has amazing inner resources. He perseveres and perseveres and things eventually work
out, by which time he begins to persevere at something else. As
soon as it became possible to remodel the space in the hospital,
he took charge of the work. He designed the new laboratories himself. He had the first and final and in-between words on everything from electric outlets to paint to plumbing to office furniture.
He not only knew what was on the floors but was intimately
acquainted with the undersides of the desks. He can't work any
other way."

They now had two sons, Peter, who was three, and Darrell, an
infant. Their home was in Wexford, a suburb about eighteen
miles from the University. Peter did not like going to the barber
and Jonas, unwilling to inflict on his children the endless imperatives that had governed his own youth, cut the boy's hair, lavish-
ing on that periodic, companionable chore all the intensity given
to electric outlets or virus studies or the problem of whether to
wear a black tie to the campus dinner (would it be preferable to
arrive and find that he was the only one in a tuxedo or better
to be the only one in a business suit?).

An unresolved question among numerous scientists, journalists,
and others curious about the rise of Jonas Salk is whether he
was chosen to make the polio vaccine, like a Sherpa chosen to
carry somebody's duffel up Mount Everest, or whether his eye
for the main chance was so acute that he elected himself to the
job, obviating decisions by anyone else. The question is on a par
with the one about John Alden and Priscilla. Who proposed to
whom? A concise answer is possible, but lacks the fibers and
juices that make truth more nourishing than ordinary fact.
Nothing on earth could have stopped Salk from experimenting

with polio vaccines as soon as he had the opportunity to work in
polio at all. Was this because he was forever eyeing the main
chance? Yes, but for him the main chance was not an opportunity
to become world-famous by means of a polio vaccine. For him the
main chance was an opportunity as head of his own laboratory
to explore and elucidate the immunology of polio so as to augment
humanity's store of knowledge about itself and its diseases.

In the process, he hoped to become identified in the scientific
community as the creative individual who had contributed the
knowledge. But nothing could have been further from his mind
than the possibility that, if he played his cards well, matrons
someday would fling themselves to their knees and get all tangled
up in their minks while attempting to kiss his hand. In his scheme
of things there was no such thing as *the* polio vaccine, *the* brass
ring. He would experiment for years with many polio vaccines,
not regarding them as ends in themselves but as instruments for
the clarification of basic questions about the immunology of the
disease. When asked about this by someone whom he suspects
of thinking in terms of brass rings, he loses color, writhes in his
chair, curls his upper lip, looks at his watch, and otherwise
demonstrates the wish that either he or his questioner were elsewhere. "I wanted to be a scientist," he says, "not a vaccine manufacturer. I was an immunologist, not a product developer. The
thought that vaccination against paralytic polio might be feasible
naturally arose. One of the objectives of the immunologic work
was to see whether this was so and, if so, how and why and to
what extent, and what scientific generalizations could be drawn
from it. And what principles advanced. As we now know, the
selection of one of our experimental vaccines for commercial
manufacture and field testing subsequently became a matter of
urgent, humanitarian concern, and occupied a good deal of time
and attention. This transformation of a scientific worker into a
product developer was most unusual. It happened because of the
unique nature of the given situation, but was not planned or
plotted or looked forward to, nor could it have been."

His perspective on the virus-typing work and its possible
aftermath was set forth quite candidly in a letter he wrote to
Harry Weaver on August 24, 1948:

> As I visualize the problem in its long-term aspect, I antic-
> ipate that the solution of the immediate task of classifica-
> tion of the available strains will be followed by a series of
> other problems. In planning for the future I find it difficult to
> separate the earlier and later phases. . . . There will logical-
> ly arise from these studies the question of immunization,
> both with respect to the development of refined and potent
> vaccines as well as field trials. All these problems, it seems to
> me, would best be carried out according to the same co-
> operative plan which thus far gives promise of success.

By this he meant the joint effort of four laboratories, including
his own, to classify viruses according to prescriptions laid down by
senior virologists. He was not asking Weaver to let him make a
vaccine. He was not warning Weaver that he would make the vaccine, regardless. But he was promoting his own professional interests, getting on record as a man alert to possibilities most attractive
to the National Foundation, the organization that he hoped would
continue to look favorably on him and sponsor his work. The
punch line arrived in the next paragraph of his letter: "For this
reason I should like to propose tentatively that we enter into some
agreement that would enable us to plan for the next five years." At
this stage in his life, the prize he coveted most was assurance of
uninterrupted, long-term support. He had won physical elbow
room. Now he wanted time.

Weaver saw that he got the time, even though not on Jonas'
own terms. He cherished Jonas. "There was nobody like him in
those days," says Weaver. "Perhaps one other young man was his
equal as a laboratory worker, but not more than one. His approach was entirely different from that which had dominated the
field. The older workers had all been brought up in the days
when you didn't accept a grant of more than four or five hundred
dollars from an outside source without having a long conference
with the dean. Everything was on a small scale. You made do with
one or two laboratory animals because you couldn't afford to pay
for the twelve which were needed. Jonas had no such psychology.
He thought big. He wanted lots of space, was perfectly comfortable with the idea of using hundreds of monkeys, and running
dozens of experiments at a time. He always wanted to expand his

program so that it would encompass as much of the subject as possible. He was out of phase with the tradition of narrowing research down to one or two details, making progress inch by inch. He wanted to leap, not crawl. His willingness to shoot the works was made to order for us. Furthermore, he was entirely without fear of the concept of vaccination. You could talk vaccination to him without having Kolmer and Brodie thrown back at you. Jonas could accept a possibility which so many old-timers could not—that, regardless of prior theory, you might be able to immunize human beings against polio if you put antibody into their blood. You cannot imagine how gingerly these ideas had to be broached in those days. Why, old Tom Rivers acted as if I were a foreign agent during my first two years around the Foundation. He challenged everything I said. If I had said he was good-looking, he would have argued with me. Later, of course, the evidence began piling up in favor of experimental vaccination and he came around."

When not elaborating his views to Weaver or disentangling himself from his brief romance with the leadership of the local chapter of the National Foundation, or breathing down the necks of painters, plumbers, and electricians, or pursuing his flu experiments, Salk began assembling a staff for the polio project. His chief technician, Byron L. Bennett, was already on the grounds, having come to Pittsburgh to work with him on influenza. Bennett, a hard-drinking, highly emotional, self-educated Texan, had left the Army Medical Corps with the rank of major after earning professional renown and at least one military decoration for helping control typhus during the war. He had met Salk during the young scientist's days as acting head of the Armed Forces Influenza Commission and had been enormously impressed. To join Salk he quit Walter Reed Hospital, where he was an assistant to the famous Dr. Joseph E. Smadel—the same Smadel who had ridiculed Salk's first scientific paper. Because Bennett lacked a doctorate, Salk called him "Major" and insisted that everyone else in the laboratory do so. The Major was sometimes more than slightly under the weather, but he was a pillar of technological strength. "Salk was Bennett's joy," recalls a colleague of that time. "His devotion to Jonas was positively doglike. Jonas held him together with spit and chewing gum, making him feel important—which he was—and somehow managing to keep the drinking within tolerable limits."

Another admiring member of the team was Dr. Julius S. Youngner, a microbiologist, who came from the University of Michigan at the beginning of 1949 to be Salk's senior research associate. Only twenty-eight years old, Youngner had been awaiting the call from his fellow New Yorker for several months. "He would have followed Salk to Timbuctoo," says an expert on the subject. "Salk was his hero. He admired Jonas' ability to get things done, his command of situations, his unvarying calm, his talent for keeping the goal in view. More than that, he admired the sweep and scope of the man's scientific ambitions and the warmth with which Salk included him in the plans. Salk talked about 'we' and what 'we' were going to do, and how democratically and reasonably 'we' were going to get it done. It was never 'I.' In time Youngner discovered that there is a point at which 'we' leaves off and 'I' begins. He began to feel differently about Jonas. Much differently. So did Bennett." But that was several years and numerous crises later.

Two other members of the Salk work force were Dr. L. James Lewis, a bacteriologist who had worked in the laboratories of several leading pharmaceutical companies, and Elsie Ward, a zoologist whose enthusiasm for the Salk way of doing things never flagged. "He knew what he wanted done and we did it," she says of the old days in her amiable, matter-of-fact way. "It's easy to work for someone who tells what is wanted. Sometimes we'd figure out how to do it, and sometimes he helped, but no matter how you accomplished the task you felt his appreciation. We were there to work, to get our satisfaction from what we did, and his appreciation was the something extra that made it a very special place to be. In those days he had only us and the lab. Now he has so many other people and so much else to do. He was happier then."

Of all those who joined Salk at the beginning of his virus-typing work, none brought less sense of personal commitment than his secretary, Lorraine Friedman. This tall, equable Pittsburgh girl was curious enough about medical science to think the job might be interesting, but she had no intention of staying more than three years. She did not think anyone should stay on a job longer than that. In 1964 she began her sixteenth year with Salk, dispensing warmth to those for whom he felt it, inscrutability to those whom he preferred to keep in suspense, and efficient brusqueness to the downright unwelcome. Since 1949 she has partaken of his every triumph and disappointment and has known about a few of them even before he did. She is his sounding board, litmus paper, confidante, and alter ego, a true believer in the ultimate rightness of his theories, methods, and motivations. An associate of theirs remarks, "As far as his daily professional life is concerned he trusts her more than he trusts anyone else, knowing that talking to her is almost like communicating with his identical twin. Naturally she doesn't always tell him what he wants to hear, but her reactions to things have by now become so much like his, and therefore so reliable from his point of view, that he even gets a certain amount of comfort when she disagrees."

With a staff so worshipful, his research quarters designed and executed *au point,* and a promotion to Research Professor of Bacteriology assured by a medical-school administration grateful for the prestige that it would gain from his large undertaking, the thirty-four-year-old Jonas Salk put aside forever the pick and shovel of the scientific peon. The senior thinkers of the National Foundation's virus-typing committee might suppose that he was embarking on menial work, but he now had his own laboratory, his own. He would run it in his own way.

6

ARCHIMEDES STEPPED INTO THE PUBLIC BATHTUB AND NOTICED that water displaced by his bulk sloshed over the sides. The first law of hydrostatics erupted in his mind. "Eureka! Eureka!" he cried, running naked through the streets of Syracuse, "I've found it! I've found it!"

A full-time sage, Archimedes had few professional duties beyond the cultivation of wisdom. When he felt like it, he could spend his entire day thinking sagely. A modern scientist would not dare. He has too many other things to do. His hours of reflection are hard-won. When he steps into the bath, the telephone rings. If it does not ring, he wonders why. He wonders what might be going on behind his back in the laboratory, or in somebody else's laboratory, or in the sanctum of the dean, or in the committee considering his grant application, or in the negotiations over the new retirement plan. Thoughts of this kind hamper scientific reflection.

The principle enunciated by William James, "Decide what important thing will be done in the next twenty years; then do it," accounts for the enlistment of some of the world's most relentlessly active minds in the biological sciences, where important things are done every week. To cry "Eureka" in that field, substantiate the claim, and get due credit, even the most gifted individual must first hoist himself into strategic position. He must win sufficient autonomy to pursue his own ideas rather than another's. He must have the assistance of an able staff. He must have full access to modern instruments. His budget must be adequate. He acquires and retains these powers and perquisites at the expense of scientific reflection, mastering the skills of the salesman, the writer, the public speaker, the traffic manager, the personnel director, the bookkeeper, and, in some instances, the propagandist. Exceptions are too rare to alter the case.

Thus, when Jonas Salk finally became boss of his own laboratory at the University of Pittsburgh School of Medicine, more than time and reflection stood between him and the cry of triumph. Only at intervals did his job resemble the cinematic image of science with which all nonscientists are familiar. He spent more hours dictating letters than looking into the microscope and saying, "Hmmm" or "Aha." For example, he wrote dozens of letters about monkeys.

One of Harry Weaver's complaints was that polio research had been delayed for years by a monkey shortage. Experiment after experiment had been botched by scientists who used too few monkeys or made the error of reusing monkeys whose systems were misleadingly immune to one or another type of the virus. The goal-oriented Basil O'Connor replied, "We'll go into the monkey business." He had done this kind of thing before, putting the National Foundation into the iron-lung business to assure an adequate supply of the life-saving devices during polio epidemics. The Foundation now obtained export clearances in India and the Philippines, respective homes of the rhesus and Java (cynomolgus) monkeys, hired experts to develop new methods of trapping, transporting, and nourishing the creatures, and acquired the Okatie Farm at Hardeeville, South Carolina, where the monkeys were conditioned for laboratory purposes. Before the $1,190,000 virus-typing program ended, Salk and the other scientists used 17,500 monkeys in their tests. The Foundation's procurement plan was a great time-saver, but in early 1949 its details had not yet been completed. Monkeys and other administrative problems consumed enormous amounts of Salk's time and energy.

January 19, 1949
(WEAVER TO SALK)

In accordance with our previous discussions, may I ask that
you now place an order with the Midway Trading Company,
c/o Watkins and Exner, 90 William Street, New York 7,
New York, for the purchase of seventy-five monkeys on the
first and fifteenth of each month beginning February 1, for
the year 1949. As I have indicated to you the cost of the first
thousand monkeys purchased through this company will be
$35 each, f.o.b. New York. The cost for the next thousand
will be $30 each, f.o.b. New York. The first thousand costing
$35 each will include all monkeys purchased by the various
grantees participating in this plan. In other words, in late
March or early April monkeys will start costing you $30
each, f.o.b. New York.

February 7, 1949
(SALK TO MIDWAY TRADING)

Your letter of February 3 explained the unannounced arrival of the monkeys on the morning of February 3. Their
hunger and thirst is partially explained, I presume, by the
three-day delay in reaching LaGuardia Field.

Two of the animals were dead on arrival. In one instance
there was obvious head trauma; in the other case the cause
was not apparent to us. Very shortly after arrival a third
monkey died, and here again we could not determine the
cause of death.

We have your invoice for seventy-five monkeys, which I
will transmit to the bursar of the University. However, I
should like to know whether or not I am correct in my understanding that you will furnish three extra monkeys on
the next shipment or that you will credit us for three monkeys, two that were dead on arrival and one that died thereafter apparently due to the effects of transportation.

February 22, 1949
(SALK TO MIDWAY TRADING)

I have just received your letter of February 18 confirming
shipment of seventy-five monkeys from Newark Airport by

Capital Airlines. The monkeys arrived on the 18th, but the shipment did not contain seventy-five animals.

Here he lists each box number, the number of animals supposed to be contained in each, the number actually contained in each, the number of dead, and the number of missing. He says that there were only sixty-nine animals in the consignment, of whom "one died day after arrival" and "one has been sick and is morbid today."

In addition to the three monkeys from the first shipment that were dead on arrival, we have lost three more. The three that died were rather puny to begin with and never did straighten out. The latter three animals died within the first week. I wonder whether we are to take the loss in such instances or whether you will replace animals that die so shortly after receipt and before they can be used for experimentation.

I shall call the bursar of the University and ask him to remit payment of the first invoice if payment has not yet gone forth, and I shall hold the most recent bill for seventy-five monkeys until I have heard from you as to whether we should authorize payment for receipt of seventy-five monkeys; if you wish us to . . . it would be agreeable if you would then send us additional monkeys so as to bring up to seventy-five the number of monkeys in the second shipment.

The monkeys that arrived on the 18th seem to have been in much better condition than those in the first shipment. They were cleaner, more content, and evidently well fed; however they seem to be very small.

March 10, 1949
(SALK TO WEAVER)

Thank you very much for sending me the abstract of Dr. Sabin's article on "Fatal B Virus Encephalomyelitis in a Physician Working with Monkeys."

I have been meaning to write to you to inquire as to whether or not we may have your permission to purchase a $10,000 life insurance policy for each of the individuals who will be engaged in this extra-hazardous work. This is some-

thing that is done at other institutions, and I would feel somewhat more comfortable if we could do it here, too.

March 15, 1949
(WEAVER TO SALK)

The National Foundation has always operated on the policy that individuals compensated with funds of a National
Foundation grant are considered employees of the grantee institution and not of the National Foundation. It is our feeling that the question you have raised relative to life insurance
policies is therefore one which should be directed to the
administration of the University.

May 11, 1949
(WEAVER TO SALK)

With regard to your last paragraph in which you stated
that you believe you can save considerable money by continuing your present arrangements for obtaining monkey diet
locally, may I write as follows: The price of the diet prepared by Okatie is just sufficient to pay for materials and
labor. In this circumstance considerable savings are accomplished by buying ingredients in carload lots. In view of this
fact I am wondering if the low cost of your diet is not due to
the fact that there has been some substitution in content. If
that has already occurred or if there is a possibility that it
may occur some time in the future, you are, of course, well
aware of the fact that it could be a very expensive venture.
I cite this only because I do not think it possible for any
substitutions to be made in the diet prepared at Okatie Farms.

October 14, 1949
(SALK TO WEAVER)

When the budget estimate was made for support of the
first year of our participation in the program on immunologic typing of poliomyelitis viruses, as many of the requirements were included as could be anticipated. As you are well
aware, estimates are gross approximations at best. In the
conduct of the work we have tried to stay within the limits

set for the respective items but we have found that in some instances the allocation is in excess of our needs and in others our needs exceed the allocation. In any event it appears now that we will be able to complete the tasks set for the year, including construction of necessary quarters and facilities, within the total amount of our grant. In fact, there will be an unused portion that will be returned to the Foundation.

The purpose of this letter is to ask your permission to make the necessary revisions in the distribution of the funds in accordance with our best judgment for accomplishing the purpose of the grant. Were it not for the fact that you visited the laboratory recently and have some basis for decision I would not have asked for such broad license.

October 17, 1949
(WEAVER TO SALK)

I regret to advise you that it is not within my province to grant blanket permission to allow revision in the distribution of the funds carried in any budget covering a grant in support of research. My authority is limited to specific situations. In your case, I should have to have a detailed statement as to what revisions are desired, the extent of such revisions, and the reasons for such revisions before I could consider the request you have made.

October 20, 1949
(SALK TO WEAVER)

No doubt you gathered from my letter some reservation on my part in making the request of the 14th of October. You can hardly blame me for trying; the alternative will require the preparation of a detailed statement as to what revisions are desired, etc. Needless to say, I understand your position in this matter and will, of course, comply.

If he is a peace-loving type, the new kid on the block is careful not to challenge local customs. He wears a friendly smile and bides his time. Later in life, when he gets a job as a messenger boy, he knows better than to spend the first day writing notes to the corporation's suggestion box, no matter how irrational the established routines of the place may seem to him. Anyone attuned to the civilization knows that you catch more flies with honey than with vinegar; and you have to crawl before you can walk; and when in Rome—

In January 1948, at his first formal meeting with the eminent virologists who were designing the National Foundation's virus-typing program, Jonas Salk, the new kid on the block, wore a friendly smile and bided his time. His principal feeling was the trepidation of the newcomer, a feeling that intensified as the meeting droned on. Here he was among Brahmans of polio research, invited by them to share their wisdom that he might later do their bidding with efficiency and dispatch. He was impressed by their professional stature and by the certainty that his future in this field depended greatly on his ability to achieve their good-will. Could he achieve it? Would it demand of him the kind of conformity that he had been trying to outgrow? He remembers, "I wanted the acceptance of these people. I wanted to be a colleague among colleagues. Who wouldn't? Wenner, Gebhardt, Kessel, and I had been engaged to do work that the others considered beneath their own dignity. This was a barrier to quick acceptance, of course, but not insurmountable. The real question was how the senior members of the committee would react to innovation. We were to classify the viruses according to methods designed by them. But suppose a better way arose?"

The possibility that a "better way" might arise was, of course, taken for granted by Salk. One of his most cherished responsibilities as a scientist was to question prevailing assumptions. It would have been easier for him to stop breathing than to accept the dictates of the National Foundation's typing committee without critical appraisal. At that first meeting, where he judiciously kept his opinions to himself, it seemed to him that the virus-typing methods most favored by the committee were complicated, expensive, and time-consuming, as if overelaboration were both a virtue and a necessity. Thousands of monkeys would have to be infected with viruses already identified as belonging to one of the three known types. Then laboriously measured doses of *unknown* viruses would be tested in groups of these monkeys, or in samples of their blood, or in both. For example, a number of animals would be infected with a virus strain known to belong to Type I. Those that recovered from the illness would be immune to all Type I strains. They now would be inoculated with virus of an unknown type. If they proved susceptible to infection it would mean that the unknown strain belonged to Type II or Type III —otherwise the immune monkeys would have resisted the challenge. The tests then would have to be conducted all over again, using the same unknown virus to challenge monkeys immune to Type II or Type III. The most wearisome part of the procedure was the work that would have to be done with the unknown viruses before they could be used in this way. To challenge a monkey's immunity one had to make sure that one knew how large a dose of each unknown virus was needed to pose a meaningful challenge. Some strains of poliovirus are highly infectious, others far less so. To give an overdose of a highly infectious strain might give results as misleading as those obtained with an underdose of a less infectious one. It would be sheer drudgery to classify all these strains according to their infectivity before being able to get down to business and discover the immunologic types to which they belonged. No wonder Harry Weaver had warned that the virus-typing project would be endlessly dismal.

One means of bypassing some of the scut work was suggested to the gathering by the distinguished Dr. Thomas B. Turner, Professor of Microbiology at Johns Hopkins. During a brief colloquy with Albert Sabin, who had been dominating the proceedings with his carefully wrought, eloquently defended proposals, Turner remarked without emphasis that it might be useful to reverse the procedures that Sabin had been advancing. The same notion had occurred to Salk. Why not infect a monkey with an *unknown* virus first and then check its blood against samples of *known* viruses? When Sabin showed no enthusiasm, Turner dropped the matter and the discussion moved to other things.

The idea had been well worth exploring, whether Sabin and Turner and the rest thought so or not. How simple it would be, Salk thought, to give a normal, previously uninfected monkey a massive dose of an untyped strain. Infection would undoubtedly occur. Antibody would appear in the animal's blood. Then one would merely check to see which of three different *known* viruses—one of each of the three known types—was neutralized by samples of the monkey's blood. The unknown virus would then be classified. Simple. Thousands of monkeys and many months of time would be saved. Salk would look into this. In the meantime, of course, he would keep his own counsel. If a Tommy Turner could be brushed aside by Sabin, imagine what might happen to a Jonas Salk!

He found out what might happen to a Jonas Salk just six months later, when the typing committee reconvened at the Waldorf-Astoria in New York. Laboring in the vineyard of Dr. Lauffer and waiting for 1948 to pass, Salk had performed experiments which demonstrated, in his opinion, that the plans of the committee were even less sensible than he had thought. "The differences between my approach and the other," he says, "were the differences betwen the immunologist and the virologist. I saw virus classification as an immunological problem, the answer to which could be found in the relations between virus and host, antigen and antibody. Those whose thinking was virological rather than immunological were not necessarily indifferent to the dynamics of the virus-host relationship. But they were more virus-oriented, shall we say, and when confronted with an unknown virus were beguiled by questions such as the organism's infective properties—questions which did not bear directly on our problem of immunological typing, or did not need to. When the virologists worked up these elaborate procedures for determining the infectivity of unknown viruses so as to determine the proper dosages with which to challenge the immunity of monkeys, they encountered another luxuriant, virological problem which detoured them still further from the basic, immunological question of virus-typing. This additional problem was most perplexing: Some viruses were so feebly infective that it was difficult to demonstrate that laboratory animals had actually *been* infected. How, then, could these viruses be typed? I answered the question in what I thought was a most plausible way. On the basis of observations reported by others but more or less overlooked by the virologists, I conducted some simple experiments. I took variants of the Lansing virus, which I got from Tommy Turner, Dave Bodian, and Charles Armstrong, and inoculated mice. I was able to show that, even though the infectivity of the different viruses varied by as much as a hundredfold, and that some of the infections were hardly detectable when sought by conventional means, each of the viruses produced generally equal amounts of *antibody* in the mice. In other words, the viruses were about equally *antigenic*. It seemed to me that this phenomenon—this dissociation between infectivity and antigenicity—should be borne in mind now that it had been proved. It seemed to me that it revealed once again the disadvantages of a typing procedure which concentrated on the difficult problem of infectivity rather than availing itself of the convenience of antigenicity. It was now plain that a large dose of unknown virus, regardless of its infectivity, would induce antibody formation. Why not take advantage of this? Why not just see which *known* virus the unknown antibody neutralized?"

As tactfully as possible, because he was still the newcomer, Salk tried to introduce these ideas to the typing committee at its New York meeting. "All I did," he says, "was ask a question at an appropriate time. They were again discussing the problem of viruses of low infectivity or, as we call it, low infectious titer. Some infectivity experiment or other was being analyzed. And I asked, 'How much *antigen* is actually present in the suspension of mouse or monkey spinal cord?' I was asking, you see, whether it had occurred to the committee that a virus of low infectious titer might provoke formation of as much antibody as would a closely related virus of higher infectious titer. I was suggesting that our purposes might be served better by testing an unknown virus' capacity to immunize, rather than worrying about its capacity to infect. Albert Sabin sat back and turned to me and said, 'Now, Dr. Salk, you should know better than to ask a question like that.' It was like being kicked in the teeth. I had offered an oblique challenge to one of the assumptions, you see, and now I was being put in my place. I could *feel* the resistance and the hostility and the disapproval. I never attended a single one of those meetings afterward without that same feeling."

He made matters worse by offering some preliminary results of his mouse experiments, the ones that he thought demonstrated the advantages of the immunological approach to virus-typing.

There were no takers. A scientist present at the time says, "I don't recall any actual hostility toward Jonas so early in the game. I do remember that he was a lot more vocal at that meeting than at the earlier one and that he and Sabin seemed to rub each other the wrong way, but people were always rubbing each other the wrong way in polio meetings. We knew so little and were often too devoted to what little we thought we knew. We'd argue about details at the drop of a hat. If Jonas felt any hostility that day, perhaps he was more sensitive than the occasion warranted. Perhaps he was full of unconscious hostility himself. In any event, he had a way of worrying an idea to death. He'd buttonhole you in the hall. He'd call you on the phone. He'd write you letters. This particular idea about reversing the typing procedure was a good one and he finally persuaded the group to let him carry through with it, along with the regular methods."

Salk did not await their permission. "They had their fixed procedures and it was my job to comply, so I did. But there was no reason why I could not also do the work in my own way, and I did. The typing program was to take three years, but our laboratory had the whole thing solved before the end of the first year. Everything that happened during the last two years was merely confirmatory. What could I do? I couldn't slap those people in the face and call them dumb bunnies and shriek that they were doing their job ass-wise. Even if I could have, I would not have wanted to. They had their way of looking at things and I had mine and it was incumbent on me to try to win them over. That first experience, with the backlash from Sabin and the indifference of the others, made me more careful than ever of their feelings. When I finally published a paper about the alternative method of typing viruses I wrote it in such a way as to minimize the possibility of anyone thinking that I considered my method best. I was as conciliatory as possible, always. But as far as my own work was concerned, I went ahead and did what I pleased and ignored the committee."

"He was one of the kindest, most considerate men I have ever known," says a nurse who worked in the polio wards at Munic-

ipal Hospital. "There was some resentment against him when
he took over the hospital auditorium, which had been used for
staff dances and other social events, but he took time to explain
why he had to have that room and what his use of the room might
mean someday to all of us. This was one of the remarkable
things about him—his generosity with time. When you talked to
him you felt that you were getting his undivided attention, even
though you knew that he had his flu laboratory and his polio
laboratory and his staff to think about. Whether you ran into
him at six in the morning or at midnight you could count on a
friendly greeting, the offer of a lift up or down the hill, the willingness to discuss a problem. I can remember how concerned he
was because the smell of his animal quarters was almost as-
phyxiating some of us. He saw to it that ventilators and air
conditioners were installed, and kept rearranging his facilities
until the problem was solved. He was just plain downright nice."

John Troan, who was science writer for *The Pittsburgh Press*
in those days, made a routine call to Dr. Campbell Moses of the
medical school one day to see if anything was new. "Why don't
you see Salk?" suggested Moses.

"Who?"

"Jonas Salk, over at the virus-research lab in the hospital.
Tell him I said it's okay."

The reporter found Salk most reluctant to talk about his
work. "He was already thinking about polio vaccines," says
Troan, "but was afraid that a news story might cause premature
public optimism, which would embarrass him personally and
harm him professionally. Finally he said he'd let me interview
him about the general problems of polio research, provided I let
him see the story before we printed it. But then he told me that
he was on his way to Fort Dix, New Jersey, where he was doing
flu experiments with the soldiers, and wouldn't be available to
review my piece until after the weekend. I needed the thing for
the Sunday paper. 'Let me write it,' I said. 'If you don't like what
I print, never talk to me again.' He looked at me for a while and
said, 'All right.'

"On Sunday afternoon I was home taking it easy when a telegram came from Salk in Atlantic City. 'You did a splendid job,'

it said, 'Jonas E. Salk.' I almost fainted. He must have been pacing the boardwalk waiting for the Pittsburgh papers to come in. I'd been in the newspaper business for almost fifteen years and that was the first time anybody ever sent me a thank-you wire."

In the fall of 1949, Elaine Whitelaw, the National Foundation's Director of women's activities, was putting together a program for a Washington meeting to help drum up enthusiasm for the next fund-raising campaign. The meeting was to be attended by her leading volunteers and the presidents of various national women's organizations. "I knew just whom I wanted to speak to the group about polio research—a certain scientist who had proved on other occasions that he could talk to a relatively uninformed audience without seeming to patronize. But when I went to Harry Weaver to arrange it, Harry insisted that I use Jonas Salk. I'd never heard of him. Harry said, 'Someday you're going to be grateful to me for this suggestion. Have I ever given you a bum steer? Take Salk or I won't help you get anyone!'

"The meeting was at the Wardman Park in November 1949. Helen Hayes was there. Her daughter, Mary MacArthur, had died of polio only two months before and Helen had just agreed to be chairman of our Women's Division. This was her first appearance in public since Mary's death. I'll never forget Mr. O'Connor coming across the room to her and saying, 'We did all we could, but it wasn't enough.' A year later Helen spoke to another meeting of the same group and said, 'At that moment I knew one day he'd be able to say that we did all we could and it *was* enough.' I think that Jonas' talk at the Washington conference was most inspiring to Helen. It was to us all. He was nervous at first, not having spoken to an audience of this kind before, but he won us over immediately with his charming directness and his unmistakable desire to help plain people understand polio research. Afterward some of us got the chance to meet him socially and appreciate his remarkable scope as a person—his delight in music and the theater and especially in other people's values and opinions. Anyone who doesn't admire Jonas simply does not understand him."

By the fall of 1949, when he had demonstrated to his own satisfaction that he would have the answers to the virus-typing questions within a few more months, Jonas Salk had exhausted that investigation of what little intellectual excitement it held for him. The rest would be dull routine, possibly as much as two and a half years of it, if the typing committee insisted on strict adherence to prescribed ritual. The job was not taxing enough to keep him warm. It could be done by his staff. He could supervise it with the back of his left hand. Fortunately, Harry Weaver was his ally and, it was clear, would eventually help the committee appreciate Salk's unorthodox tests. As soon as that happened (and it could not happen until the statesmanly Weaver was sure the ground had been prepared), the typing program could be shortened. Salk might then be able to disengage himself and move to more stimulating projects. He had polio immunization in mind.

Shortly before Labor Day, 1949, Salk and Weaver talked about vaccines. Two recent developments had convinced Weaver that immunization against paralytic polio was now only a matter of time and that intelligent planning could bring him to the goal sooner rather than later. The first of these developments had come from Isabel Morgan, of the brilliant Johns Hopkins group. Trying her hand at an experiment that had intrigued and frustrated other adventurous workers for four decades, Dr. Morgan succeeded in immunizing monkeys with injections of killed poliovirus—virus rendered noninfectious by treatment with the formaldehyde solution known as Formalin. As Jonas Salk had realized while still a medical student, and as he, Tom Francis, and a few others had demonstrated in scientific practice, there was no particular reason why noninfectious preparations should not be as effective against certain viral diseases as they were against bacterial diseases such as diphtheria and tetanus. By now, of course, killed vaccines had been found useful in influenza and certain viral diseases of animals. But the principle had attracted only tentative, widely scattered interest among leading polio workers. Simon Flexner, who had been Tom Rivers' boss at the Rockefeller Institute, had ruled that only an infectious vaccine compounded of living viruses could protect against polio. The opinion had become law: Until polioviruses could be bred selectively for vaccine purposes, so as to infect without causing paralysis, a polio vaccine was regarded as entirely out of the question.

There were other reasons why the judicious Dr. Morgan could not propose that her success with monkeys had opened the door to development of a vaccine for humans. In the first place, monkeys were monkeys. Polio was not a natural disease of theirs and could be given them only under laboratory conditions, by injection or feeding. Nobody could tell whether a preparation which immunized them against this artificial disease would immunize people. Worse, Tom Rivers had shown years earlier that viruses grown in the nervous systems of animals could not be injected into human beings without danger of fatal allergic brain damage. And finally, it was all very well to talk of a Formalin-inactivated virus vaccine immunizing monkeys, but polio research was full of dignitaries who would invoke tradition to say that since an inactivated virus could give no lasting immunity, Morgan's vaccine was not really inactivated—there must be live viruses in it.

Shortly after Dr. Morgan's modest report, an even more exciting but equally modest announcement came from the Boston laboratory of Dr. John F. Enders. He, Thomas H. Weller, and Frederick C. Robbins had succeeded in growing a strain of poliovirus in test tubes containing cultures of minced, nonnervous, human tissue. This was what Weaver had been waiting for. By the time their report appeared in the magazine *Science,* Enders and his group had grown other types of poliovirus in the same way. Vaccine could now be prepared without the contaminating nerve tissue of animals. Safe human experimentation was just a hop and a skip away. Not that Enders would make such a claim or even contemplate it.

This slightly rumpled, professorial, self-effacing man was regarded as the paragon of orthodox virology long before he grew polioviruses in cultures of nonnervous tissue and won a Nobel prize. He was independently wealthy and had come late to science after a short career in languages and literature. He had chosen biology for the best possible reason. It interested him. He could afford to indulge the interest on his own terms, advancing with measured tread toward whatever objective attracted him, fully independent of and stubbornly resistant to outside influence. His laboratory was small, because he wanted it that way. His work was precise, his published reports direct and to the point. He never upset his colleagues by speculating in print about matters that had not yet been investigated. When he committed the revolutionary act of proving that poliovirus would grow in non-nervous tissue (a possibility embraced by a handful of workers and already proved, but not yet reported, by Charles Evans), his admiring peers received the news with equanimity. They judged his experiment a superb piece of work, quite in his tradition. It occurred to few of them that a revolution had begun: In their conservative way, some reasoned that there was a huge difference between growing viruses in test-tube cultures of nonnervous tissue and proving that it multiplied in the nonnervous tissue of a living man. Later, when evidence became overwhelming that Enders had successfully challenged one of their dearest assumptions about the poliovirus, his peers took up his tissue-culture technique themselves and became quite excited about its potentialities. They did not begrudge Enders his revolution, nor was there any reason why they should. He had given them a new tool with which to work. He had strengthened rather than weakened orthodox polio research. Enders therefore was a congenial, professionally compatible revolutionary, a revolutionary different from young Jonas Salk. Salk's revolution, when it came, would threaten to annul certain indispensable presumptions of orthodox polio research. Far from giving polio workers a new tool it would undermine the theoretical grounds on which many of their careers rested. By developing an effective polio vaccine according to principles that orthodoxy could not accept, Salk would embarrass and estrange its leaders.

Assertions of this kind undoubtedly shock some readers and strain the credulity of others. The processes of science are mysterious to most of us. Its practitioners are so remote and speak to us so unintelligibly that our kinship with them becomes obscured. We forget that scientists are living creatures. They resist change.

Like moles, biscuit manufacturers, and authors, they vest their interests in whatever state of affairs provides prosperity, security, and survival. When something arises to alter the circumstances, threatening their prosperity, security, and survival, they react negatively. Thomas Kuhn writes of this thoroughly familiar way of life, "No part of the aim of normal science is to call forth new sets of phenomena; indeed those that will not fit the (preformed and relatively inflexible) box are often not seen at all. Nor do scientists normally aim to invent new theories, and they are often intolerant of those invented by others." In his classic compilation *Resistance by Scientists to Scientific Discovery,* published in *Science* on September 1, 1961, Dr. Bernard Barber, Professor of Sociology at Barnard College, Columbia University, points out that Michael Faraday's electrical discoveries were rejected or otherwise unappreciated for years. Von Helmholtz, commiserating with Faraday, philosophized that "new ideas need the more time for gaining general assent the more really original they are." Yet Helmholtz himself gave the back of his hand to Max Planck when that genius elaborated the second law of thermodynamics. And another Faraday sympathizer, Lord Kelvin, denounced X-rays as a hoax. The great astronomer Tycho Brahe refused to accept the theories of Copernicus. Abbe Mendel's peers thought he was insane to apply mathematics to botany. In his autobiography, John Enders' mentor, Hans Zinsser, remarked, "That academies and learned societies—commonly dominated by the older foofoos of any profession—are slow to react to new ideas is in the nature of things. . . . The dignitaries who hold high honors for past accomplishment do not usually like to see the current of progress rush too rapidly out of their reach."

Be that as it may, the differences between revolutionary Enders and revolutionary Salk were polar. In some of his interviews with the press, Salk acknowledged his technological debt to Enders by saying with a diffident smile, "He threw a forward pass and I caught it." That wasn't all Enders threw at him. The Harvard virologist found Salk's theories of polio immunization so out of phase with his own beliefs that he opposed public use of the Salk vaccine. Indeed, Salk says that Enders once confronted him across a table and called his work "quackery." All of which would seem to indicate that today's successful revolutionary is tomorrow's defender of the throne and that the phenomenon is probably too universal to be moralized about.

A scientist who knows Enders and Salk extremely well cites differences in their personalities as proof that there is room in science for people of all kinds. "A man's personality," he says, "is a poor indicator of whether he has anything to contribute to a science. Social psychologists are always doing personality profiles of groups of scientists. It's a waste of time. Enders and Salk, both of whom have made important contributions, have practically nothing in common so far as personality goes. During the time it takes Enders to proceed from step to step Jonas has made several passes at the moon. The rush of things bothers Enders. You hint deadline at him and he balks. But Jonas reacts with enthusiasm to pressure and even encourages it. He gets a lot out of it, psychologically. Also, Enders has always hated to accept more financial support than the irreducible minimum. He would ask the National Foundation for $3,000 when everybody knew he'd do better with $25,000. Salk, on the other hand, is always up in six or seven figures because he needs to operate on a larger scale. About the only thing they surely have in common is a quality for which Salk is seldom credited: They both like to ruminate about generally accepted facts. They like to say, 'Is this fact really a fact? Is there a way of proving that it is not really a fact?' And I think they may share one other quality, though neither of them would concur in the opinion: They both are ambivalent toward fame, fearing it and craving it at the same time."

In 1950, Enders deployed some of his attitudes in a letter to an official of the National Foundation. Except for the quality of its prose, the letter might have been written by Salk, whose sentiments were identical:

> I do want to make it clear that I had no objection to participating in the presentation ceremony. I did object to being photographed in the act of receiving the grant . . . and having such photographs published. I objected for two reasons, one of which is personal. I know that most of my colleagues would not themselves care to do this and would

be inclined to criticize me if I agreed to do so. The other rests on my conviction that teachers and investigators should not be directly concerned in and obliged to devote a considerable portion of their time to raising money to support their work. Nowadays I see so many of my associates drawn away to assist in raising funds for their institutions. Perhaps this is an inevitable necessity. I hardly think so, however. It is certainly not a trend which I want to appear to support.

I do, however, wish to make it equally evident that I am deeply appreciative of the indispensable assistance of the Foundation and the efforts of people like yourself who have made this possible. I have a real sense of obligation and shall always be eager to cooperate with you in any way I can from the standpoint of scientific information. . . .

Fourteen years before the Enders discovery that poliovirus grew in nonnervous tissue, Albert Sabin had reported that it did not. Shortly before Tom Rivers died, the old warrior told the National Foundation's historian, Dr. Saul Benison of Brandeis University, about the Sabin experiment: "Sometime in 1935 or thereabouts, Dr. [Peter] Olitsky's laboratory obtained from one of the New York hospitals a three- or four-month-old dead human embryo taken from a Caesarean section. Using tissue from the brain, cord, kidney, lungs, and liver of the embryo, Sabin and Olitsky prepared several different tissue-cultures and inoculated them with a filtrate of the [Rockefeller] Institute's MV virus. They soon discovered that while the virus multiplied readily enough in nervous tissue, it would not grow in the presence of nonnervous tissue. That work was so meticulously done that I believed it was absolutely correct. Hell, it *was* correct and every working virologist that I knew believed it, with the possible exception of Dr. John Enders at Harvard.* To this day I don't know why John didn't believe that work. I suppose it's his nature. He is a great old skeptic who never believes anything right off and I expect he just didn't take this work as proved. In 1949 John made everybody sit up when he reported that he was able to grow poliovirus in nonnervous tissue. . . . I read his paper over

* By the time Enders came along, this belief was not quite unanimous.

and over looking for a flaw. In the end I had to believe he was right. It wasn't easy because I damn well knew that Olitsky and Sabin were also right." Rivers finally reasoned that Sabin and Olitsky's downfall had been the virus they used in their experiment. As Sabin subsequently proved, possibly at Rivers' suggestion, the MV virus was the only poliovirus that would *not* grow in nonnervous tissue. Rivers pointed out, "If Olitsky and Sabin had worked with another strain . . . the chances are that . . . we would have had a breakthrough of major proportions in making a vaccine. As it turned out we had to wait fourteen years. . . ."

Before finding out why Enders had succeeded where he and Olitsky had not, Sabin unburdened himself of some pointed comment about the tendency of the National Foundation to regard the Enders discovery as a stepping-stone to vaccination. Here, with italics added for emphasis, is what he wrote to Basil O'Connor:

> I am writing this letter to you because I am deeply disturbed about the policy recently pursued by the information and publicity divisions of the National Foundation in leading the public to expect the imminent development of a practically useful vaccine for poliomyelitis. The enclosed publication No. 35, which is being distributed by the various chapters throughout the country, has come to my attention as a member of the Medical Advisory Board of the Cincinnati Chapter. I wish particularly to call your attention to the section entitled "On the Research Front," which contains the following statement:
>
> > Scientists have already successfully vaccinated laboratory animals against the three known viruses that can cause polio in man. Many others may exist. March of Dimes funds are supporting research to determine exactly how many are capable of causing the human disease. This project should be completed within the next three years.
> > In the past year a method was discovered for growing virus in test tubes. This development, financed by

the March of Dimes, offers real hope that the need for large quantities of virus can be met. When these two projects are finished, scientists will be ready to attempt production of a vaccine against all known types of polio.

The chief objection to this and similar statements is that it misrepresents to the public the significance of research carried out by grantees and promises, even if only by innuendo, something which, on the basis of available information, *cannot possibly be delivered.*

The available data on the immunization of monkeys with "killed-virus" vaccines may indeed be interpreted as *pointing to the hopelessness and impracticability* of the ultimate prevention of poliomyelitis by this means. Although I have not spoken to Dr. Enders in the last few months, I strongly doubt, knowing him as I do, that the interesting experiments at present in progress in his laboratory, would lead him to say that they offer "real hope that the need for large quantities of virus can be met." The unfortunate thing is that even if the need for large quantities of virus could be met there is no valid reason for believing at this time that "killed-virus" vaccines can be of any practical value in the control of a disease like poliomyelitis. That is not to say that work along these lines is not worthwhile. However, premature and irresponsible promises to the public, in my opinion, are not only unwarranted and unkind, but ultimately may also constitute a serious hazard to the important efforts of the NFIP. . . .

It is impossible to read this outburst in 1965 without exercising hindsight. Killed-virus vaccines have for all practical purposes eradicated paralytic polio wherever they have been used properly. Sabin's letter therefore seems more amusing now than it did in 1949. When Harry Weaver absorbed the message contained in the carbon copy that Sabin had thoughtfully mailed to him, he realized once again that although a vaccine might at last be within reach, concurrence of the nation's leading virologists was remote. Leading figures such as Sabin, Tom Rivers, John Enders, and John Paul did not usually depart from convention until it was shot out from under them by a broadside of irrefutable proof. Even then it sometimes took them a while to accept the proof as irrefutable. On the other hand, the spirited Salk was already talking about vaccine experimentation of a sort that might bring results. If he were allowed too much rope, he would strangle himself and the National Foundation in the scientific community. But if the leash were held too taut, discontent might drive Salk right out of polio into something more imminently rewarding. He was a problem.

On September 7, 1949, Salk told Weaver in a letter how pleased he was to have talked to him about polio vaccination the week before. With regard to Weaver's fears that a vaccine contaminated with nervous tissue would be unsafe, Salk mentioned the work he had done years earlier, purifying influenza virus with calcium phosphate. More recently, other workers had purified rabies vaccine with calcium acetate. Salk suggested that this "might be worthwhile investigating in relation to the over-all problem of immunization in poliomyelitis. If nothing is done in this regard before we get to it on our long-range agenda, we propose to see what there is to it." Having suggested this possible means of eliminating the problem of nerve-tissue contamination, Salk continued, "I would be much more hopeful, however, if we could investigate the immunizing capacity of tissue-culture virus. You mentioned Dr. Enders' work on virus grown on foreskin tissue-culture. If you could arrange for us to get some of Dr. Enders' material, we would like very much to try to immunize a few monkeys with it. You appreciate this is something that we could do very easily along with the other work we are doing; because of the setup that we have it would be no effort at all. I believe you had suggested this yourself in the course of the conversation," he went on hopefully, "but we never did get back to it to arrange anything definitely. Whenever you have a chance to think about this I shall be glad to hear from you."

On September 12, Weaver tightened the leash. He wrote to Salk that the purification of poliovirus grown in monkey brains was already being attempted by another grantee, whom he did not name. "I have reason to believe that this job will be done very well," he added, implying that Salk should desist. As to Salk taking recesses from the costly and already sufficiently contentious virus-typing program to play with John Enders' tissue-culture technique, the time apparently was not yet ripe for that, either —at least, not under Weaver's aegis. "I feel certain," he told Salk, "that Dr. Enders would be very happy to furnish you some tissue-culture virus if you would care to ask him for it. Why don't you write directly . . . ?" This answer was not what Salk had hoped for. The indifferent suggestion that he write a letter to Enders signified official unwillingness to help him take up the tissue-culture technique and put it to quick use. But expansion of that kind was essential. It now was imbecilic to study the poliovirus without the Enders technique. How could Salk's friendly liberator, Weaver, fail to see this?

The truth was that Weaver saw it very well. He had been trying, with depressingly small success, to induce other polio workers to embrace tissue-culture research. Many were interested, but their tempo was academic, which is stately. Some of the ablest would not install tissue-culture apparatus for years. Weaver would have been pleased to juggle the budget to expedite Salk's plunge into the new work, knowing that the young man would absorb the technique with Salkian rapidity and begin exploiting it to advantage on a multitude of fronts. But Weaver had other things to worry about. Salk recalls, "When I pressed the point Weaver told me that the typing committee would frown on me going into tissue-culture. I was supposed to be too heavily involved in their program to attempt anything new. I thought this was ridiculous, but I did not feel like making an issue of it."

Besides overseeing the virus-typing activities of his staff, he had entered high gear with his influenza studies at Fort Dix, New Jersey. This was a huge undertaking. The respiratory ailments and the reactions to experimental flu vaccines of thousands of soldiers were being scrutinized closely, and the data were fed into an IBM machine. Whenever flu or an illness suspected as flu broke out at the camp, Salk rushed there, sometimes spending half his week in New Jersey and half in Pittsburgh. Reminiscing about the pace he set, Salk shakes his head, shrugs his shoulders, and smiles brightly, "I must have been crazy but the volume of work suited and satisfied me. I was often tired but seldom exhausted and I knew I had plenty of time and attention to give to tissue-culture."

After Weaver explained his reluctance to associate himself with these ambitions at this time, Salk turned elsewhere. "I didn't fuss or fume," he says. "I just went to Dean McEllroy, pointed out the importance of the tissue-culture technique, and told him what I wanted to do about it. He got me seventy-five hundred dollars from the Spang Foundation to help pay a tissue-culture technician's salary and buy an incubator and a roller drum and other supplies, and we prepared to go to work. The technician was Elsie Ward, whom I hired for this purpose in December 1949. It took several months to launch the program, what with waiting for the financing and the equipment.

"One day Harry Weaver visited our place and wanted to know what was going on in the lab where Elsie was working. I told him, 'tissue-culture work on polio.' He walked in and saw what was happening. I hadn't deliberately concealed the work from him but I didn't think it was any of his business, because he was only interested in the virus-typing program, you see. After he noticed what we were doing and where we were headed, he arranged for the National Foundation to support that aspect of our program. It was very much like the other episode, when we developed the different way of typing viruses. That too, I was told, would be frowned on but I went ahead and did it anyway. I had a way of doing things 'anyway.'"

On June 16, 1950, Salk wrote Weaver a letter that will surely find its way into a museum someday. He announced that he was ready to begin studies of polio prevention. Weaver had requested the letter, to build a record of intent. He, too, was ready to shoot the moon. By doing things "anyway" Salk had run too fast and too far to be opposed any longer. He wrote:

> Some time ago I promised to write to you giving an outline of my thinking about the program of research that we would like to undertake in the next several years. It is much easier to think first of the objective and then to consider how it may be achieved. My orientation at the moment is to see if we can develop a satisfactory procedure for the pre-

vention of poliomyelitis by immunologic means. The approaches to the realization of this solution are obvious
enough. The problem at hand is that of devising ways and
means whereby it can be accomplished. . . .

Under the rules, Tom Rivers and the medical advisory committee would have to approve the proposed experiments before
the National Foundation could sponsor them. Although Rivers
was still skeptical about polio vaccination, he had been impressed
enough by the Morgan and Enders reports to concede that immunologic experiments were now well justified. Salk designed his
prospectus to match, hoping to propitiate Rivers and other virologists whose orthodoxy inclined them toward live-virus vaccines, if any. His first effort, he promised, would be to hunt for
the kinds of viruses from which such vaccines might be compounded—"a virus that possesses the capacity to multiply and
induce immunity without necessarily inducing disease." If such a
safari proved successful, so much the better. His willingness to
try it might minimize the inevitable grumbling about his second
suggestion, which he proposed to implement along with the first:

> We are studying Enders' tissue-culture virus . . . and find
> that high titers of antibody are developed in monkeys in-
> oculated with a mixture of the virus with adjuvants [oil
> emulsions which enhance the antigenicity, or antibody-in-
> ducing capacity, of viruses]. . . . Without much further
> thought I think we could consider inactivation of this ma-
> terial with ultraviolet light for immunization of children. I
> have investigated the local possibilities for such an experi-
> ment and find that not too far from here there are institu-
> tions for hydrocephalics and other similar unfortunates. I
> think that we may be able to obtain permission for a study
> of immunization using tissue-culture material. If a prepara-
> tion could be made available which was noninfectious in
> chimpanzees by oral administration as well as by [injection],
> then permission could be obtained for inoculations and
> antibody studies at least. . . . This is more of a dream than
> a reality but something that might be considered. Some of
> the earliest experiments that might be tried, both in chim-

panzees and in the institutionalized children and, perhaps, inmates of prisons who might volunteer for such studies, would be vaccination followed by the administration of active virus after the titer of antibody has increased and become stabilized.

The suggestion was premature—hair-raisingly so. A man less sure of his own wisdom and skill would not have dared offer it. Tom Rivers, custodian of the National Foundation's scientific conscience, would be repelled by the idea of human experimentation at this stage in polio history. Only a few months earlier he had fought and, so far as was known, had defeated an effort by Dr. Hilary Koprowski, of Lederle Laboratories, to get official New York State approval for tests of an experimental live-virus polio vaccine in institutionalized children. Most other leading virologists shared Rivers' outlook. Unlike Salk they did not yet believe that polio resembled other virus diseases in all essential particulars. Neither did they believe that an inactivated vaccine could immunize human beings except, perhaps, briefly and unreliably. Nor did they assume that a living poliovirus which infected and immunized monkeys without paralyzing them would necessarily produce the same benign results in a man. These things remained to be proved to the scientists.

Harry Weaver, a master tactician, knew that evidence in favor of modest human experiments was mounting. He believed that Salk or someone else would try them with impunity in the next year or two. But not yet, not yet. And certainly not the kind of experiments projected by Salk. To be sure, it was an ancient medical custom, born of necessity, to experiment on persons mentally incapable of appreciating the consequences of experimental failure, or on felons eager to purchase lenience with self-sacrifice. To inject a noninfectious polio preparation into such subjects was conceivable. But to return several weeks later and feed these same subjects living poliovirus, as if testing the responses of expendable animals, was a maneuver that the National Foundation would never approve. Salk could undoubtedly muster impressive arguments in favor of his proposal. So could Weaver, for that matter. But after he read this section of Salk's letter he scrawled "No" in the margin.

The third plank in Salk's research platform was experimentation with so-called passive immunization—supplying ready-made protective antibody instead of depending on a vaccine to induce formation of antibody by the human system. He wrote to Weaver:

> Our thinking . . . has been concerned more with the usefulness of a preparation that we may be able to develop from yolk of immunized hens than in preparation from human or animal serum [meaning gamma globulin]. Our thinking has gone one step further. We have been considering the immunization of cows with the idea of developing milk with a high content of specific antibody. We already have inoculated some cows with influenza virus and adjuvant to see whether antibody levels of any significant degree are found in the milk of such animals. We know, of course, that milk does contain antibody to a variety of antigens during the early phase of lactation and even in lactation later. It is not unreasonable to expect, therefore, that we might be able to alter the situation and exploit this to our advantage. To carry this idea to the logical conclusion might be to suggest the possibility that milk itself or perhaps an . . . eggnog containing the proper ingredients from hyperimmunized animals might be used to maintain an environment in the gastrointestinal tract that would neutralize the polio viruses. . . . As you can gather from the foregoing I consciously have not restricted my thoughts to any one phase of the broad problem nor have I limited myself to a discussion of details whereby the problem proposed may be solved. What I have done essentially is to outline all of the conceivable means whereby we may be able to solve the polio problem by immunological means. I realize the enormity of the task and that in lieu of having at one's disposal unlimited resources and assistance it is something that can be accomplished only over a period of years. Needless to say it would be well to determine which of the several approaches might be most profitable and which might yield the earliest solution. Within certain limits considerable flexibility will be necessary.

To achieve this flexibility, he informed Weaver, it would be helpful if the work were done by an investigator free of the kind of supervision that Salk had been suffering from the typing committee. "That group had a very useful purpose," conceded Salk, luxuriating for a moment in the past tense, "but I would prefer the flexibility and wider latitudes that would be permitted by the alternative method of operation." Meaning independence. "Although the work should be pursued as expeditiously as possible," he went on, "it will not be possible to rush a program of this kind. The details as to the amount of financial support and the duration of such a program is something that we can work out together."

He ended with organ tones, as if conscious that history was looking over his shoulder: "I think the time has come for initiating the critical experiments for immunologic prevention and more than that, the time has come for these experiments to be carried out in man."

He was right. Human experiments were already under way. In utmost secrecy the audacious Hilary Koprowski had circumvented Tom Rivers' objections and had fed a live-virus vaccine to institutionalized children.

7

HARRY WEAVER SHOWED JONAS SALK HOW TO PARE THE INDI-
gestible elements from his proposal and make of it a fillet likely
to appetize Tom Rivers. Thus, when Salk submitted a formal
application for a new National Foundation grant on July 12,
1950, he made no mention of using mentally defective children for
experimental purposes.

"It is proposed," wrote Salk on the application form, "to
undertake studies with the objective of developing a method for
the prevention of paralytic poliomyelitis by immunologic means."
Referring to experiments by Morgan and Bodian at Johns Hopkins, he pointed out that "a correlation exists between the level
of serum antibody . . . and the degree of immunity in monkeys. . . . Thus, the immunological principles that apply to other
infectious diseases also apply to poliomyelitis. It should, therefore, be possible to devise for use in man a method for active or
passive immunization." Earliest emphasis would be given to conservative experiments. Salk would use monkeys to test the protective properties of gamma globulin, the blood fraction that contains antibodies. He also would test the effects of eggs from his
immunized hens and milk from his immunized cows. If passive
immunization of this kind showed promise, "field trials in epidemic
areas and possibly in families in which paralytic cases are occurring might be considered."

As to active immunization with experimental vaccines, he
spoke only in orthodox terms: "It will be necessary either to
discover, or to develop artificially, strains of low pathogenicity

that would still retain the capacity to infect and immunize without producing the paralytic consequences. . . ."

The grant was awarded. Work was to begin in 1951. Salk's simplified method of classifying polioviruses had now been accepted and, although the old, more complicated procedures were not abandoned, Sabin and other members of the typing committee agreed that the problem of typing no longer seemed as monumental as it once had. Salk could take time for other work without endangering the program.

He spent much of the last half of 1950 tooling up the tissue-culture procedures on which he counted for production and testing of viruses. He also traveled frequently to Fort Dix, where some of his influenza-immunization theories were beginning to display the promise he expected. There were, of course, several flies in his ointment. There always are. "Discontent was one of his paramount virtues," says Harry Weaver. "No matter how well his affairs seemed to be going, he was always sufficiently unhappy with himself or his situation to keep driving. The harder he drove himself, the closer he came to the unattainable perfection he sought."

The chief foreign object in Salk's craw during this period was a new arrival on campus, Dr. William McDowell Hammon, a veteran grantee of the National Foundation who had become Professor of Epidemiology in the University's new Graduate School of Public Health. One of the world's most celebrated public-health physicians, Dr. Thomas Parran, former Surgeon General of the United States Public Health Service, had come to the University about a year after Salk, had taken over as Dean of the School of Public Health, and had set about trying to recruit a respectable faculty. "He was confronted with the problem of getting somebody for the chair of epidemiology and microbiology," says Salk. "Because I had come from a school of public health and a department of epidemiology, it seemed to me that my background and experience brought me within reason as a candidate for the job. At the time I was only remotely connected with the medical school and the situation there was still speculative, and I really hoped something might happen for me at the School of Public Health. I remember being quite upset at not having been considered. Or perhaps at having been considered and rejected. It actually was fortunate that I did not get the post because it would have set me in a mold. I was really much better off in the unstructured environment of the medical school, where McEllroy was trying to arrange freedom for me and later, when I got it, would take steps to protect it for me. But I can remember thinking how unreasonable they were to bring in somebody like Hammon, whose interests were so closely related to mine. He even was given space in the same building. It was most uncomfortable. Perhaps I was reacting in somewhat the same way that people react to me when I come on the scene for the first time. There is a feeling of territoriality and of competitive antagonism."

Hammon, a Harvard man who had been a missionary before he became a virologist, had collaborated with John Enders on a vaccine that protected cats against distemper. Later, as Professor of Epidemiology at the University of California and associate of Dr. Karl F. Meyer in the Hooper Foundation, he had conducted classic studies of encephalitis epidemics. Like so many other prominent virologists, senior or junior, he was known as a stubbornly patient worker. Before transferring to Pittsburgh, he had been applying that quality, and his others, to studies of polio antibody. He was especially interested in the possibility, appreciated by several other investigators for many years, that gamma globulin might possibly defend humanity against polio by supplying ready-made antibody.

"I won't say that Jonas' nose was out of joint," says a former Pittsburgh colleague. "I won't even say that he felt threatened by the older, better-established man's presence. But I do know that he was upset as hell. And I do know that he wasn't the only one who thought he should have been made Professor of Epidemiology and Microbiology. Several of us thought so. Anyhow, there was a rivalry between Hammon and Salk from the minute Hammon arrived. It was a perfectly natural rivalry in one sense, because they both were able, ambitious workers and saw their work from diametrically opposite viewpoints. Hammon was pretty much a traditionalist and Jonas a kind of D'Artagnan in a white smock. The rivalry was not entirely wholesome and caused a stir around the campus now and then. But maybe it had constructive elements, too—stimulating each of them to see who could get somewhere first."

November 14, 1950
(SALK TO WEAVER)

You will recall my talking to you . . . specifically about the possibility of conflict with Hammon in relation to studies related to passive immunization. At that time I had made some broad, as well as specific, suggestions; to a great extent these were the result of conversations that we had together earlier. I wanted from you at that time a clear understanding so that there would be as little duplication as possible to avoid any complications. I was willing at that time to forgo the initiation of any work if you had had any prior commitment to Hammon as a result of his expressed interests.

I thought the matter was quite clear until just yesterday when Hammon inquired of one of the people on our staff about the various instruments that we use for autopsying monkeys, and various other technical questions. At that time he also inquired about "stomach tubes" or catheters that might be so used in monkeys. He went on to say that you had asked him to see what happens when gamma globulin is administered in this way.

As you know I described to you in some detail, in a letter written to you in June and subsequently in the application for our grant, about experiments dealing with the administration of poliomyelitis antibody by the oral route. Our thought was, as you will remember, to try to employ egg yolk and, perhaps, milk—each containing antibody—for this purpose. You might be interested to know that we have already fed antibody to monkeys and have made plans for extending these studies. Before doing so I would like your comments with regard to the incident cited and any pertinent developments since our last conversation.

I am well aware of the fact that we are working not only on problems that we have conceived but on problems that have been suggested to us, that others have also thought of, and, in fact, that others are pursuing in very close parallel.

I am well aware, also, of the fact that many persons can arrive at the same stage of thinking and can get the same idea all at the same time.

I look forward to your usual frank and honest comments, and you can understand, I am sure, the reason for this communication.

November 24, 1950

(WEAVER TO SALK)

Pursuant to my telephone conversation of a few minutes ago, I wish to advise that the program of research described in the third paragraph of your letter of November 14, 1950, is not to my knowledge being carried out or contemplated by any other worker at the present time.

December 16, 1950

(SALK TO WEAVER)

In confirmation of our conversation of December 14, I should like to indicate that we plan to modify the program outlined in our Application for Grant for 1951 to the extent that we will not engage in studies on passive immunization which we understand are in progress in other laboratories. . . .

Bill Hammon quickly became a public figure. In 1951 he and others showed that gamma globulin protected monkeys against paralysis. Basil O'Connor reacted with typical promptness, launching a gamma globulin program that cost the National Foundation $14.5 million. Tests on 55,000 children in Houston, Sioux City, and Provo, Utah, demonstrated that the shots provided several weeks of immunity. A few lives were undoubtedly saved in the process. The press began fitting Hammon for halos. In 1952, when Salk was starting his first human experiments with inactivated vaccines, O'Connor cornered the American gamma globulin market. He bought up every drop. He then turned the material over to the Office of Defense Mobilization for free distribution to public-health officers in communities threatened by epidemic.

O'Connor's immense expenditure on gamma globulin has been mentioned more than once as an example of the National Foundation's profligacy. The criticism was especially sharp in scientific circles, where the limitations of the substance were clearly understood. Tom Rivers, who had favored those parts of the field trial that showed what gamma globulin could do, was appalled at O'Connor's insistence on sinking additional millions in the stuff. "If there had been any scientific grounds for opposing the program, you can bet I'd have opposed it to the end," he once said. "But there wasn't much I could do. That O'Connor is a stubborn old man and knew that gamma globulin was better polio protection than nothing." Indeed, the outlay of $14.5 million was simply an example of O'Connor's determination to do whatever he could to prevent paralysis while awaiting further developments. He did not want gamma globulin to become a black-market item, so he bought it himself and distributed it for free.

"Wouldn't you have done the same?" he challenges. "Why do you suppose the people gave us money? They wanted us to fight polio. So we fought polio."

"Along about that time," says a Pittsburgh friend of Jonas Salk, "Hammon was getting a lot of publicity. The importance of gamma globulin was being exaggerated terribly. The protection it gave was too costly and too fleeting to make it a practical means of fighting polio, except in certain emergencies. What the trials demonstrated, of course, was that antibody—even small amounts of antibody—would protect human beings against polio. This was tremendously important, a great feather in Hammon's cap. I can remember somebody mentioning all this to Salk, sort of rubbing in Hammon's success and prominence. After listening a while, Jonas smiled and said, 'Just wait a few months. Just wait.' "

Salk's desire to begin tissue-culture studies of polioviruses became an absolute craving when John Enders performed a stunt for him. Within days after getting fourteen strains of virus, which Salk had already classified as to type but which he sent to Enders without labels, the New Englander accurately identified each one. He had done it by infecting and challenging the immunity of tissue-cultures, not monkeys. He had completed in a week the kind of investigation that had been taking the virus-typers several months.

As soon as all the necessary machinery and glassware had been delivered to Pittsburgh and installed in the laboratory, Julius Youngner and Elsie Ward set to work trying to duplicate Enders' feats. The first time they tried they failed. "What the hell are you guys doing?" asked Salk. "We can't seem to repeat Enders' work," they said. "Great," said Salk.

"Then I asked them whether they were doing exactly what Enders did," he recalls. "Of course they weren't. They were trying to *improve* on his work. So I pointed out that the first thing to do was to repeat his procedures precisely. After that would be time enough to improve on them."

Elsie Ward reminisces, "There was so much excitement. It was such pure joy to come to work in the morning. Every day brought new progress. To look into the microscope and see what we saw was a great thrill. Dr. Salk was in the lab morning, afternoon, and night. He couldn't wait to see what was going to happen."

Theirs seems to have been the first group outside of Enders' laboratory to master the new technique. "One thing evident," says Salk, "was that some of our difficulties had to do with the strains of virus we were using. As we had already seen in the typing program, different strains behave in different ways. Some are less infectious than others, for example. So we went to the dry-ice chest and got a bunch of virus samples and began trying to grow them. We just put them in a race to see which performed most satisfactorily in tissue-culture. Three of them gave brilliant, startling results, destroying monkey and human tissue right before our eyes. It was thrilling. These three strains, chosen at random to see how they might behave in the test tube, were obviously the best candidates for our subsequent experiments with mice and monkeys. Lo and behold, they then turned out to be the strains best suited for the experimental vaccines we later tested in human beings. They were the most antigenic strains, the most stable, the most reliable. It was a fantastic accident, choosing those particular strains as we did. Others have spent years trying to find better ones. So have I. But nobody has found one."

The Mahoney strain, a Type I virus, had been isolated by Tommy Francis from a nonparalytic patient of that name in Ohio. The MEF–1 (Type II) had come from Egypt, where scientists attached to the American Middle East Forces had found it in 1942. The Saukett strain (Type III) had been discovered in one of the wards in Municipal Hospital, Pittsburgh. The donor was a paralyzed small boy named James Sarkett, whose name was misspelled by whoever labeled the stool sample.

A nurse recalls, "Once in a while Dr. Salk made rounds in the hospital, especially if one of the physicians wanted diagnostic help. He certainly knew what was going on upstairs, and anyone who understands how sensitive he is to suffering can imagine how all his scientific and technical problems must have goaded him under those circumstances. He knew that children were dying within a few yards of him because the problems had not yet been solved. A lot of people thought he was an awfully cold fish. They thought he was remote from the everyday life of the hospital and indifferent to it. This was unfair. His job was to understand polio, not to treat it. He knew what polio did to people and their families. He had been present often enough when decisions were made to remove a child from a respirator because she was going to die anyhow and someone else might benefit from the apparatus. Dr. Salk didn't need to be exposed to that kind of thing repeatedly. He was keyed up enough to begin with."

Another nurse: "In all my career there has been no experience like Municipal Hospital before the Salk vaccine. One year the ambulances literally lined up outside the place. There were sixteen or seventeen new admissions every day. One of our resident physicians never went to bed for nights on end, except for stretching out on a cot in his clothes. We nurses could never get home on time, either. To leave the place you had to pass a certain number of rooms, and you'd hear a child crying for someone to read his mail to him or for a drink of water or why can't she move, and you couldn't be cruel enough just to pass by. It was an atmosphere of grief, terror, and helpless rage. It was horrible. I remember a high school boy weeping because he was completely paralyzed and couldn't move a hand to kill himself. I remember paralyzed women giving birth to normal babies in iron lungs. I remember a little girl who lay motionless for days with her eyes closed, yet recovered, and I can remember how we all cried when she went home. And I can remember how the staff used to kid Dr. Salk—kidding in earnest—telling him to hurry up and do something."

To enliven the tempo of polio research without seeming to prod, Basil O'Connor and Harry Weaver staged round-table conferences at which National Foundation grantees reported their work, tested their ideas, exacerbated each other's competitive feelings, and, in effect, prodded themselves. No longer encapsulated in their individual laboratories and no longer dependent for information on reports published in learned journals months or years after the developments described in the reports, polio investigators now marched to an unprecedentedly brisk cadence. For example, at a meeting held in the chocolate redolence of Hershey, Pennsylvania, on March 15, 16, and 17, 1951, it suddenly became clear that, regardless of individual qualms and reservations, the time for human experimentation had come, just as Jonas Salk had insisted to Weaver nine months before.

It was a remarkable meeting. Isabel Morgan Mountain (who had left Johns Hopkins after her marriage and was working at the Westchester County Department of Laboratories and Research in a suburb of New York) reported monkey experiments in which poliovirus inactivated with Formalin—a killed vaccine—produced antibody levels and immunity comparable to that achieved with live viruses. Howard A. Howe, of Johns Hopkins, reported similar findings in chimpanzees. David Bodian, his colleague, demonstrated in monkeys what William McD. Hammon would later show in humans, that the relatively low levels of antibody supplied by gamma globulin injections were protective against paralysis. Jonas Salk, whose work with tissue-culture viruses had begun only recently, was already thinking in concrete terms of experimental killed-virus vaccines, but contented himself with a brief, inconspicuous report on the virtues of gamma globulin and, more emphatically, the usefulness of mineral-oil adjuvants in enhancing the antibody-provoking capacities of poliovirus preparations. Bill Hammon, who had been urging a human field trial of gamma globulin for more than a year, urged it again, this time getting approval on principle, if not on every detail. Before Hammon spoke, Howard Howe addressed the group on "Tentative Plans for Field Tests to Determine the Effectiveness of Active Immunization in Man." The experiments he had already reported to the conference, combined with those of Dave Bodian and Isabel Mountain, had been sufficiently dramatic to make "tentative plans" of human trials a matter of considerable interest. Furthermore, Hilary Koprowski had set off a firecracker earlier that day, reporting human experiments totally devoid of the tentative.

In a field cluttered with singular personalities, Koprowski manages with only slight effort to be the most singular of all. A conservatory-trained pianist, a medical graduate of the University of Warsaw, a gifted linguist and litterateur, and a master of polemic who enjoys swamping his adversaries in polylingual quotations and mythological allusions, Koprowski is a hard man to handle. In 1944, at the relatively tender age of twenty-eight (two years younger than Salk), he had commandeered an independent existence for himself in the research department of the pharmaceutical firm of Lederle Laboratories. His nominal superior, the accomplished Dr. Herald R. Cox, was a wise enough administrator to leave him alone. Having done significant research on rabies and yellow fever during previous sojourns in England and Brazil, Koprowski turned to polio about 1946 and by 1950 deemed himself ready to try an experimental vaccine in human beings. Because his investigations were financed by an industrial concern, his orbit rarely intersected that of Harry Weaver and the National Foundation's squadron of grantees. But he turned up at Hershey for the March 1951 round-table discussions to report some of his rabies work and to drop his firecracker.

During a lull in the proceedings, the chairman of the moment, Dr. John R. Paul of Yale, by prearrangement said to the fun-loving Pole, "Dr. Koprowski, did you have some data to present at this time?"

"Data which I want to acquaint you with," replied Koprowski, "represent a summary of clinical trials based on oral feeding of children with the TN strain of poliomyelitis—living virus." He went on for several quiet paragraphs, explaining that the preparation had sometimes been mixed with chocolate milk and given on a spoon, and that each of twenty children and two adults had developed antibody without the slightest symptom of illness. His memory of that day continues to tickle him. "I reported just after lunch," he grins, "and everyone was somnolent. Tommy Francis listened to me droning away and said to Jonas Salk, 'What's this—monkeys?' and Salk answered, 'Children!' Francis sat up and gasped, 'What?' Albert Sabin got all perturbed and said to me later, 'Why have you done it? Why? Why?' "

Koprowski's subjects were the first people on earth to be fed live, authentically attenuated poliovirus for purposes of immunization. His definition of attenuation is instructive, and typically Koprowskian: "To compare the attenuation of a virus with Heracles' task of taming the Ceryneian Hind," he once wrote, "is to indulge in what might seem to be exaggeration, but the two tasks are both arduous and time-consuming. Attenuation of poliovirus can most easily be defined as loss of pathogenicity for man but retention of all antigenic qualities for immunization purposes." He had obtained a sample of the Brockman strain of Type II poliovirus from John Kessel and, after growing it in monkeys, had passed it through successive generations of cotton rats until it no longer would paralyze monkeys when injected into their brains. This meant, of course, that adaptation to cotton rats had eliminated, at least for the time being, the infective organism's virulence for monkeys. Koprowski named the attenuated strain "TN," in tribute to his assistant, Thomas W. Norton, and began looking for institutionalized children to try it out on. When Tom Rivers tried to stop him, he disappeared from Rivers' view and went ahead with the project, regardless, feeding his first human subject on February 27, 1950.

The Hershey assemblage behaved toward Koprowski as if his daring were more impressive than his laboratory techniques. Several of the conferees were annoyed because Koprowski was not quite sure whether the Brockman strain he had obtained from Kessel was actually the Brockman strain or something else parading under that banner. Nor was Koprowski entirely sure that the strain had not become mixed up with another unidentified virus in his own laboratory. He looked upon this sort of thing as both trivial and irrelevant, and was content to rest on his results, which were, to say the least, striking.

The true importance of his achievement was noted by Howard Howe during his remarks about plans for field-testing experimental vaccines. "I am tremendously interested in Dr. Koprowski's report," he said, "because in feeding a [Type II] virus to his unusual group of experimental subjects, he got roughly the same levels of antibody that we have obtained in feeding either the Lansing or the Wallingford strains to chimpanzees. All of which suggests, then, that the human is certainly not less—or shall I put it this way—the human is *at least* as sensitive a reactor to the poliomyelitis antigen as is the chimpanzee." Koprowski had taken a giant step. Vaccine experimenters could now approach human trials considerably more secure in the hope that a vaccine that protected a chimpanzee would also protect a man.

Howe, who differed with Tom Rivers and most other virologists about the dangers of polio vaccines prepared from viruses grown in nervous tissue, was also a strong protagonist of inactivated vaccines. If an inactivated polio vaccine could produce adequate levels of antibody without danger of infection, why take chances with attenuated living viruses, which might revert to virulence at any time? For every thousand persons who contracted a natural polio infection in the course of their lives, perhaps one suffered paralysis. The rest thought they had intestinal flu. "The vaccine has to be pretty safe to beat that," said Howe. "I think perhaps we are approaching the point where some sort of effort should be made to get some preliminary data on the responses of children to inactivated virus."

The subsequent debate about ways and means of designing such a field test and about what strains of virus to use in the experimental preparation was inconclusive. It was clear, however, that Howard Howe intended to inoculate a few children himself. It also was clear that Tom Rivers would fight to the death against any large-scale use of the Howe preparation, because of its contamination with nervous tissue.

A visitor recently asked David Bodian why he and Howe had not adopted tissue-culture techniques with the alacrity of Salk; why, in short, they had not capped their multiple contributions to polio research with a Bodian-Howe vaccine. "That wasn't our field and it wasn't our taste," answered Bodian. "We had a small, manageable, academic research facility and were not attuned to the kind of large-scale developmental project which was required. Nor would we have wanted to be. Our job was to learn what we could about polio, including polio immunization. After the basic determinations had been made, it seemed to us that actual development of a vaccine was essentially an industrial process." John Enders felt the same way. In most essential respects, so did Jonas Salk, the main difference being his preference for operations of a large scale so that he could try to bite all sides of the apple at once.

He had entered the most gratifying phase of his career. He was doing what he wanted under conditions which he had prescribed. Regardless of the written terms of his National Foundation grant, he was as free as any other scientist to break new ground, so long as the ground lay in the neighborhood of polio immunology. This was exactly what he intended to do. The awful possibility of failure never crossed his mind. "What was there to fail at?" he asks. "We were studying the immunology of polio. We had recognized that it was a disease like other diseases. If we did no more than demonstrate certain similarities and certain differences with other diseases the time would have been well spent. We were under no compulsion to produce a vaccine. We would have incurred no criticism if animal tests had shown that human use was inadvisable. Any of a thousand problems could have prevented human experimentation, possibly for years. This would have been no reason for self-reproach or even for personal disappointment. People who doubt this are not just cynical, they are uninformed. They think of science in terms of pills and products, which are not the concern of science. The scientist asks questions of nature and induces nature to answer them. My questions were three: 'Is not polio like other infectious diseases?' and 'Is it not possible to immunize human beings against this disease?' and 'Will not an inactivated preparation immunize as effectively as the natural infection does?' Whether the answers were yes or no, the inquiry would have achieved its purpose."

The positive pleasures of this kind of work were enhanced for Salk by a delicious new sense of professional acceptance. He and Enders had engaged in respectful correspondence, exchanging information of mutual interest. Sabin had begun to treat him less offhandedly, as if he might soon qualify for The Club. In acknowledgment of his extraordinarily resourceful contributions to the virus-typing program, the committee elected him to describe its work at the Second International Poliomyelitis Congress, held at the University of Copenhagen in September 1951. An honor of that kind was meat and drink to a young scientist. He accepted with relish. Nevertheless, being Salk, he perceived that the feast had aspects similar to those that engrossed Damocles when Dionysius sat him beneath a sword suspended from the ceiling by a single hair. Salk was still guarded and uneasy in the presence of most other polio workers, as if the hair were about to snap and the blade about to fall. His views were hopelessly divergent from theirs. He knew how bitter their resentment would be if events ever compelled them to confront the differences. Ever? The confrontation was inevitable.

"I sailed to Europe on the *Stockholm*," he remembers. "John Enders and Albert Sabin and some other workers were aboard. They were having caucuses together and I spent a good deal of the time by myself, although we all sat at the same dining table with the ship's physician. I had plenty to think about in those days and welcomed the solitude. I spent hour after hour standing alone in the bow of the ship, watching it cut through the water. A nice feeling, standing up there in the breeze. Once Albert came and put his arm around me and talked about establishing a polio research institute. How great it would be to have Joe Melnick and me with him, Melnick being the other 'bright young man' in polio work. We'd have meetings every morning and we'd decide what to do and what not to do. One big happy family. I was rather laconic about it, I suppose. I was busy laying plans for my own work, and the prospect of submitting to Albert in a kind of institutionalized typing-committee arrangement was not what I had in mind for myself. He really is a remarkable fellow. During the voyage on the *Stockholm* it became obvious to anyone who had not heard of it before that I was a nice young whippersnapper from Pittsburgh, going to Denmark to report on some drudgery I had performed. I might have failed abysmally, it seemed clear, if Albert had not been up in the flies, pulling the strings and setting the standards. I was not quite Charlie McCarthy and Albert was not quite Edgar Bergen, but you can't have everything. It was an amusing trip."

On Tuesday, September 4, in Copenhagen, John Enders reviewed his tissue-culture discoveries for the world's foremost virologists and immunologists. As usual, his paper was a model of concise, scientific prose, illustrated with lucid charts, graphs, and statistical tabulations. Also as usual, it was gracious: "Dr. Jonas Salk has kindly allowed me to say that vaccination experiments carried out by him in rhesus monkeys using Lansing tissue-culture virus combined with adjuvants gave rise to a level of resistance comparable to that induced by vaccine consisting of suspensions of . . . monkey [spinal] cord." Salk's experiment had shown that viruses grown in test tubes could make potent animal vaccines. Enders was happy to give him the credit and Salk was pleased to receive it.

During the ensuing discussion Salk took the floor to praise Enders and to show how greatly the new method of growing viruses had facilitated his own investigations. "When this conference is over we shall all remember vividly Dr. Enders' brilliant presentation," he declared. "The work that he has done stands out in the last years as one of the most outstanding contributions in poliomyelitis research. It has been possible, simply by following Dr. Enders' technique but using monkey testes as a somewhat more available tissue, to isolate virus quite readily from human stool suspensions. . . . Using monkey testes it has been possible also to grow virus readily. . . . The value of this tissue —and I am sure that there will be many others that will be discovered in time—has made it possible to extend immunologic investigations rather broadly. We have been able to prepare from the testes of a single monkey two hundred tubes which, for immunologic studies, would correspond to two hundred monkeys, using the same number of tubes as one would use animals."

Now came Albert Sabin, warning against undue optimism by young whippersnappers. "The contribution that Dr. Enders and his co-workers have presented represents a milestone in poliomyelitis research," he agreed. "Like all milestones, they stimulate the imagination and sometimes the imagination begins to travel much beyond the territory that is safe to travel," he warned. He turned now to the fascinating question of why Enders had been able to grow poliovirus in nonnervous tissue fourteen years after he and Peter Olitsky had failed. Not until 1954 would he be able to publish a report showing that the MV virus, which he and Olitsky had used, was a freak and would grow only in nerve cells. As of now, in 1951, before his peers in Copenhagen, he took recourse in conjecture: "A personal qualm comes to my mind," he said. "Dr. Enders was kind enough to remark on the work that Dr. Olitsky and I had done . . . showing the multiplication of poliomyelitis virus in human embryonic nervous tissue. At that time we also used nonnervous tissue. When Dr. Enders made his interesting observations, I naturally asked myself: 'What did we do that was wrong? Why did we fail to make the observation that Dr. Enders has made? . . .'

"When I look at Dr. Enders' work," he continued, "it seems to me that what he did was that he kept his cultures of nonnervous tissue *longer* than we did. We made our passages every three or four days and failed to show multiplication. His tissues were kept longer. Now I am not remarking on that simply because I want to satisfy my conscience. I am remarking on that because I think it is of basic, fundamental importance. . . ."

The room was filled with connoisseurs of Sabin's dazzling ability to discern possible flaws in the reasoning of others. They now sat forward and paid attention. The ball was on its way to the plate. "Possibly something which happens in tissue-culture does not happen in the human body," said Sabin. He was beginning to map the territory beyond which it might not be safe for Salk's young imagination to travel. "Possibly," he went on, "certain changes in the metabolism occur in these nonnervous cells which then permit a reaction to occur . . . which does not occur in the human body. Therefore," he continued patiently, "it remains to be shown that what can occur under the artificial metabolic conditions of tissue-culture will also occur in the human body." He then directed his analytic powers to Salk's use of monkey testicles. In case the audience thought that Salk was the only one ingenious enough to use such tissue, it was misled. In case the audience thought that Salk was somewhat overoptimistic about the implications of his work with the tissue, it was right: "Preliminary results reported by Dr. Evans only a few months ago at a meeting in the United States indicated that while he could also get multiplication on the monkey testis as Dr. Salk has done, he could not demonstrate multiplication in the testis *within the body of the monkey.* . . . I think that we must keep in mind the possibility that we must also continue with work in the animal because the metabolism may be different in the animal than it is in the tissue-culture."

Salk, who is capable of secret chortles, chortled secretly. Sabin had obviously not yet mastered the Enders technique. His explanation of his failure of sixteen years earlier was a trifle anemic, lacking the solidity it might have derived from an attempt to grow the virus according to the Enders method, the Enders method already mastered by Salk. As to the refusal of poliovirus to grow in the testes of a living monkey—so what? The object of the game was to grow and harvest large quantities of poliovirus. If the virus grown in laboratory flasks was able to immunize mice, monkeys, and finally men, who cared whether it would grow in a live monkey's scrotum?

As long as Salk lived, he would never forget Sabin turning on him in 1948 and saying, "Now, Dr. Salk, you should know better than to ask a question like that." What had chilled his bones on that occasion was not the mere upstaging, the assertion of superior rank and seniority; far more disturbing was the ineluctable feeling that here was a man who would defend his views with every available weapon. Those views would not, could not be compatible with Salk's own. Here, Salk felt, was his philosophical adversary, his professional bête noire, the man whom he could pacify only by surrender. Although the feeling that had originated in 1948 had not become more intense by

1951 and would not until open warfare broke out in 1953, the "amusing" voyage on the *Stockholm* had refreshed it. Salk was incapable of a conscious desire for retribution and, for that matter, incapable of conceding himself any other motives that he knew to be small or unworthy, but he enjoyed Sabin's slight discomfiture at Copenhagen.

The rationalizations of Sabin elicited a predictable response from Enders. "I certainly agree with Dr. Sabin," he said, "with regard to extreme caution in transferring inferences from the observations on these isolated cells . . . to the effects of the virus on the animal body. It is possible, as Dr. Sabin suggests, that the metabolism of these cells is altered profoundly . . . enabling the virus to multiply in them, and that possibility must certainly be investigated. . . . Probably in some places in the body, as in the intestines, the virus does grow in nonnervous tissue. These two hypotheses must be considered." It was the kind of statesmanly answer that Salk would have given had he been in Enders' statesmanly place—the soft words which doth not necessarily turn away negativism but throw thumbtacks in its path.

Salk's own formal report to the congress was a short summary of the virus-typing program and concluded circumspectly.

> As the number of strains examined increases without uncovering more than three immunologic varieties, the likelihood of greater immunologic complexity diminishes. It would appear at this time that the development of a procedure for the control of poliomyelitis by immunologic or other means need only be concerned with the three antigenic types that have been found so far.
>
> The number of monkeys involved and the time and energy expended were enormous; nevertheless, the task has been accomplished and the new knowledge that will derive therefrom will reward the interest and effort of those who conceived, planned, and contributed to these studies. The consequences that will follow are self-evident and perhaps can be expressed most justifiably in terms of the many aspects of the problem of poliomyelitis that will be enlarged as the result of these studies, which are to be continued into the future.

Nobody could quarrel with that.

The friendship between Basil O'Connor and Jonas Salk began during the voyage home from Europe. They had exchanged civilities at Copenhagen and at other scientific gatherings but had struck no sparks in each other. To Salk the older man was a pleasant curiosity, a modern Maecenas who swept in retinue from place to place and event to event like the champion of the world, dispensing patronage more bounteous than any Maecenas could, because the funds were replenished annually by a faithful public. Salk? O'Connor knew who he was: a young worker from Pittsburgh whom Harry Weaver praised highly. O'Connor had seen promising young workers before and supposed that he would see many more. People were always plucking at O'Connor's sleeve, making promises. A man in his position was better off at arm's length and let's get on with the work.

Weaver now advised O'Connor that Salk and John Enders were also aboard the *Queen Mary*. Courtesy suggested that the two scientists be invited to join the O'Connor table, a scene of expansive hospitality and light banter. Salk went with fascination, Enders without. One of the group was O'Connor's younger daughter, Bettyann Culver, not yet fully recovered from a recent attack of "Daddy's disease," paralytic polio, and distressed by the feeling that she should have made more rapid progress than she had. Salk, whose preference for research coexists with prideful ability to use his medical art in relief of other people's doubts, discomforts, and pains, gravitated to Mrs. Culver just as if she had had a cinder in her eye or needed advice about headaches. O'Connor had been deeply troubled by his daughter's unhappiness and was relieved when Salk, through patient counsel, seemed to restore the young woman's perspective. He adjudged him what he calls "a fine young fella." One day he and Salk stood waist-deep in one of the ship's swimming pools, and the small talk became a lengthy exploration of ethics, philosophy, and the values of science. O'Connor discovered that the fine young fella was proprietor of a formidable and most engagingly unfettered mind. They had more in common than either had dared expect: social

indignation, mistrust of ritual and protocol, a humanistic faith
in man and democracy. Salk's villain was unreason, O'Connor's
was unintelligence. These overlapped, at least. Perhaps they
coincided. The men took long walks around the deck, probing
and testing each other and delighting in what they found.

Science and the world it serves have not yet totaled the results
of this friendship. The accounting is years away because all the
returns are not yet in. In the meantime, the friendship attracts
attention only in the parishes of biological science and philan-
thropy, where dispassionate evaluation is hard to come by. For
every Enders who goes his own way there are a dozen scientists
who wish that they, with their superior talents and attainments,
had been admitted to the place of honor and privilege that Salk
occupies at O'Connor's right hand. For O'Connor's oversight in
this regard, they blame him or Salk or both. The friendship, one
hears, is symbiotic, each using the other to pry open the vault
of immortality for himself. Or the friendship is strictly psychological, the father-son relationship. And there are embellishments,
about each compromising his own best and most essential interests
rather than loosen his opportunistic hold on the other, or about
each being entirely ready to discard the other when the time is
ripe.

"I try to put things in biological terms," says Salk, declining
to discuss O'Connor in the back-fence or dumbwaiter-shaft style
that typifies most conversations about the friendship. "We have
to get away from the metaphysics of personality, the metaphysics
of Freud," he says, soliciting the depersonalization of a subject
most personal to him. Yet his version is compelling. "We have
to think in operational terms of a scientific kind," he insists. "It
can be said, for example, that Basil O'Connor and I brought out
the best in each other. The statement describes a result, an operational result. O'Connor had a potential and I had a potential.
Each of us complemented the other in the sense of constituting an
environment which allowed the other's potential to develop. I
believe that the fundamental relationship in all living things is the
relationship between the organism's biological potential and its
environment. The organism's potential is revealed and developed
only under environmental influence. The environment educes,

draws out, causes the potential to be expressed—if the relationship is appropriate. Thus did O'Connor provide opportunity for me and thus did I provide opportunity for him."

Salk acknowledges that the polio vaccine would have been obstructed for years if it had lacked sponsorship as puissant as O'Connor's. He agrees with misted eye that the magnificent Salk Institute for Biological Studies at La Jolla, California, could scarcely have been conceived, much less planned, built, and staffed without O'Connor. They often traverse the continent to visit each other. They speak frequently by long-distance telephone. Salk's letters to his friend are effusions of warmly solicitous admiration, appreciation, and love. Yet Salk denies a sense of personal indebtedness. He sees the relationship as larger than that. He prefers to depict himself and O'Connor as compatible instruments of nature, each propelled by powers beyond his control, and each working most effectively in tandem with the other.

"I decided long ago," Salk says, "that my role in life is to *find out*. If people do not like what I find out it is just too bad. They should then attack nature, not me. That I chose to ask the right question and was able somewhat artfully to expose the answer was likewise a phenomenon of nature. I have no control over my motivation to do this sort of thing. I am as much at the mercy of forces over which I have no control as others are when they have to contend with me. It's the same with O'Connor. He represents a phenomenon in nature too. He can't help himself any more than I can help myself. He is programmed and coded to deal in two commodities, health and humanitarianism. I didn't make him that way, nor did he make me the way I am. Only God can make a tree."

He peers at his questioner, sees perplexity there, and edges closer to the heart of his professional difficulties. "So somebody says that O'Connor is a layman and therefore not quite respectable and that when I associate myself so closely with him and accept so much assistance from him I am selling out to him, selling out to the laity," he complains. "Not respectable? By what social or scientific standards? It is precisely O'Connor's assistance that makes it possible for me to do more than could possibly be done

without his assistance. From the standpoints of science and society, then, O'Connor is an invaluable facility, a rare item of
human equipment. Name another like him. There is none. In
him are combined self-interest and social interest in ideal proportions. He can't satisfy the first without fulfilling the other. And
I come along and we hit it off and we discover that the relationship enables us to be more creative than we could have
been without it. Obviously, I honor his great qualities but it is
irrelevant to speak of 'indebtedness.' We do not do favors for
each other like a pair of ward-heelers. We try to get work done
in biology."

O'Connor's affection for Salk is entirely unconcealed. "Jonas is
a remarkable person," he says. "He sets high standards for himself and refuses to lower them in the interests of expediency. I
admire that. I wish the characteristic were more widespread than
it is. We'd all be better off. Something else I admire and have
admired from the beginning might not be appreciated by someone who has had less opportunity than I've had to be around
scientists. Jonas is in touch with the world. I don't mean that he's
worldly. He's not. In some ways he reminds you of a girl who's
never been in a bar before. But he is a human scientist, or call
him humane or humanitarian or humanistic. He is aware of the
world and concerned about it. He sees beyond the microscope.
He takes an overview. He tries to see how things fit together,
not just in the laboratory but in the whole shooting match. He's
a generalizer and a synthesizer. For someone with a legal mind
like mine this is impressive. I am less impressed by the sort of
mind that gets bogged down in fringe details. These were the
reasons, along with his friendly, modest ways and his unmistakable
sense of honor and rectitude, that I liked Jonas. Before that ship
landed I knew that he was a young man to keep an eye on. Not
that I had anything directly to do with him making the vaccine.
At that stage my contact with the scientific activities of the National Foundation was limited to meetings, where I tried to keep
abreast of developments and asked a leading question once in
a while. I had always known that I'd better learn all I could
about the work, because I might have to try the case someday.
But I didn't really get my feet wet until 1953 when Harry Weaver

left and we had to shake ourselves up to arrange field trials for the Salk vaccine."

By 1964, having endured many hellish ordeals and several victories together, O'Connor and Salk were as close as father and son and had occasionally irritated each other as much. The father-son analogy unsettles them both, partly because it is accurate and intimate and nobody else's business, but mainly because it has been cited as an explanation for O'Connor's unflaggingly generous support of Salk's ambitions. The implication is clear that the generosity might well have been directed elsewhere. O'Connor grits his teeth. "The National Foundation has granted millions of dollars to scientists I don't like personally," he says. "Scientists I *do* like have won Nobel prizes for work done under our grants, and other scientists I like can't get a penny from us because our medical advisers don't think they deserve it. I tell you, I don't know how Jonas has been able to tolerate the abuse and obloquy he's suffered in his profession. It's a wonder they haven't destroyed the poor kid's spirit by now. They won't even elect him to the National Academy of Sciences. It's a scandal. He shows the world how to eliminate paralytic polio and you'd think he had halitosis or had committed a felony."

8

JONAS SALK HAD RETURNED FROM EUROPE AND HAD BEGUN immunization experiments with monkeys, using polioviruses killed by exposure to Formalin. "By the following July we were inoculating human subjects," says Salk in entirely appropriate amazement. "God! It's incredible! The technical questions that had to be worked out!" Before Salk could attempt to inoculate human beings, he had to decide which strains of poliovirus, having been inactivated by Formalin, would produce most antibody in monkeys and presumably might turn out to be correspondingly antigenic in man. Also, he and Julius Youngner and Elsie Ward had to tinker continually with the tissue-culture process, trying to select the specific kind of nonnervous monkey tissue that would yield viruses in the largest possible quantities without spoiling their antigenic powers. Furthermore, Salk had to plan and participate in multifarious experiments with the Formalin-inactivation process, hoping to make an exact science of what for decades had been a mostly slapdash method of killing viruses. To inactivate poliovirus until no further infectiousness was demonstrable—and yet to retain maximum antigenicity—he had to decide the proportions in which virus and Formalin should be combined. And at what temperature should the reaction take place? And how long should it last? And how could he be sure that any single batch of supposedly inactivated virus was really inactivated, thoroughly harmless? Suppose it contained a few living particles, enough to kill a child? Merely to test a small sample of the batch, or even two or five small samples, would not necessarily answer the question: The living particles might be in the untested portion of the batch. The only foolproof safety test would be to inject the entire lot into monkeys and see if any became infected. But a batch of inactivated virus consumed in that way would be consumed forever and no longer available for use in a vaccine. The only fitting solution, Salk concluded, was to discover the principles that governed chemical reactions between poliovirus and Formalin. Having done so, he could inactivate the virus under conditions which abided by such principles. Safety would be guaranteed by the process itself.

"We wanted to know the *nature* of the chemical reaction between virus and formaldehyde, as this would be reflected in the rate at which virus infectivity was destroyed," Salk once explained. "We believed that there must be certain well-defined laws in nature that governed this process, governed this interaction. If it were merely a haphazard thing, it would be contrary to the way things function in nature, and therefore we felt that we should know more about this in order to go the next step beyond which was to be able to prepare vaccine . . . in a consistent manner—so that when we did certain things, there would follow therefrom an expected result."

When you release the clutch pedal too quickly, the automobile stalls; boiling water is essential to the brewing of decent tea; a lock will not open unless you insert the key right side up. Man gets through the day most easily when he has grasped general truths. The alternative would be perpetual trial and error, an unendurable chaos. Yet Jonas Salk's efforts to promulgate the general truths of the reaction between poliovirus and Formalin led to some of the most destructive controversies of his career.

David Bodian tells a story about a stuffy scientist riding on a train: "Look!" said his traveling companion, who was looking out the window, "There is a sheep that has been shorn." The stuffy scientist answered, "Oh. You mean it has been shorn on *this* side, don't you?" At first, Salk's theoretical generalizations about the inactivation process were eyed suspiciously because they rested, in part, on what he safely assumed was the state of affairs on the other side of the sheep; he could not tell for an absolute certainty that every drop of vaccine produced according to his laws was entirely free of dangerously infective living viruses, but his knowledge of chemistry and mathematics and the results of his exhaustive safety tests assured him that this was so. Later, when he refined his understanding of the process and elaborated his theories, he was charged with pretentiousness. The other side of the sheep was still invisible. Still later, after hundreds of thousands and then millions of doses of vaccine prepared according to his principles had been injected into human beings without a single known instance of ill effect, and after vaccine prepared in violation or ignorance of his theories killed and paralyzed human beings, his theories nevertheless remained controversial.

During the winter of 1951–1952, when he studied hundreds of possible variations, Salk decided that the most salutary inactivation method was to combine tissue-cultured virus and Formalin in proportions of 250:1 at the temperature of melting ice (about 1° centigrade—33–34° Fahrenheit). After inactivation periods of seven to twenty-one days, he found himself with preparations that stimulated antibody formation in monkeys but were entirely noninfectious. Meanwhile, he satisfied himself that other methods of inactivating the virus, such as ultraviolet irradiation, tended to destroy antigenicity along with infectivity and were not worth further exploration. He also learned how to grow viruses at an unprecedented rate, using monkey-kidney tissue instead of monkey testes. A synthetic tissue-culture nutrient known as Medium 199, developed by Dr. Raymond Parker of the Connaught Laboratories of the University of Toronto, further increased the yield of virus and simplified other problems as well. Salk soon had a full liter of poliovirus, more than any man on earth had ever seen at one time.

On December 4, 1951, while all this was in progress, Salk went to the Commodore Hotel in New York to attend the Immunization Committee meeting. The committee was composed of David Bodian, John Enders, Tom Francis, Bill Hammon, Howard Howe, John Paul, Andrew J. Rhodes (of Connaught Laboratories), Albert Sabin, Joe Smadel, Tommy Turner, and Salk himself. Basil O'Connor, Tom Rivers, the Foundation's Medical Director, Hart Van Riper, and Weaver were among others in attendance. The first question before the group was ticklish: How could anyone who wanted to make an inactivated polio vaccine be sure that he had really inactivated the virus? After inconclusive discussion of various animal tests, Tom Rivers addressed himself to the other side of the shorn sheep: "I think we will all admit," he rasped, "that there is no test to be sure the stuff is inactive. Why not just accept that? Why kid ourselves?" Salk wondered if the tough old man was now going to suggest a resort to general principles, a search of nature's laws. Instead, Rivers proposed an exercise in semantics: "Why use the word 'inactive?' Why not just say, 'safe for use?' It won't produce disease, and that's all there is to it."

The issue was tabled, pending further scientific developments that might help resolve it. Jonas Salk had a few such developments in his hip pocket but knew better than to introduce them at this point. Under Weaver's tutelage, and from his own experience in the world, he had learned to wait until the ground thawed before trying to plant seed. Later in the day, the sun shone briefly. Joe Smadel delivered a speech recommending that the first human experiments be efforts to increase the levels of antibody circulating in the blood. Tom Rivers argued about some of the details, but conceded, "I think it is time that we got ready to go somewhere, and somebody ought to come up with some concrete experiments that will be done in human beings on a small scale in order to get going." Even John Enders, a live-virus man from away back, agreed, "I believe that in the case of this disease the possibility of using inactive vaccine is very good and one that should be very carefully explored while other procedures that might lead to attenuation are examined."

After Enders concluded with a technical discussion of the difficulties that awaited anyone who hoped to attenuate polioviruses for use in a live-virus vaccine, Jonas Salk took over, boldly. "I always like to listen to Drs. Smadel, Rivers, and Enders think out loud," he said. "Needless to say, they have covered all of the possibilities that the human mind can conceive in approaching this problem, but the question before us now is what to do from here. It is quite evident that there are several lines of investigation that can be pursued simultaneously. . . . Some of the things that we ought to begin to find out about appear to me to be as follows:

first, the relation of antibody level to immunity. This is a very difficult thing to determine. It is something that we talk about in relation to many diseases, but I wonder if we should not begin to formulate some ideas as to what antibody level we want to achieve. . . . I don't know whether increasing circulating antibody will prevent poliomyelitis, but certainly it is one attractive hypothesis with which we can make some progress. . . . The relative value of *infection* versus *vaccination* for inducing antibody increase, and whether or not, at corresponding levels of antibody, immunity from *infection* is superior to that induced by *vaccination*. At the moment it seems, not only from studies we have done but those that have been done by others, that one can certainly exceed the antibody level resulting from infection. . . . We have observations in monkeys well over a year after vaccination with virus plus adjuvant. . . . The level . . . is undiminished from the peak that was reached six weeks after inoculation. It seems to me that there is a way to raise the level of antibody and maintain it.

"I would like to suggest," he continued, "that the first experiments on immunization in humans be done with a noninfectious preparation. . . . It seems that with tissue-culture-propagated virus, rendered noninfectious . . . we are able to induce a high level of antibody. We are in the process of determining for how long the induced level is maintained. . . . I would feel reasonably confident in proposing . . . vaccination of . . . human subjects, as soon as the data are available for examination and we are convinced that the conditions for producing and testing a safe preparation are available."

It was the most direct, concrete proposal of the meeting. Dr. Norman H. Topping, microbiologist and educator associated at the time with the National Institutes of Health of the United States Public Health Service, responded heartily. "Dr. Salk has said some of the things that I wanted to say. I think . . . progress can be made even in light of the fact that we have so little knowledge. It would seem to me the time has come logically to really go at the inactivated material. . . . The live virus is fine, but if you think about it as a public-health measure, it is a difficult thing to use. . . . I don't think you have a good excuse morally to go into infectious material until we have shown that inactivated material was unsatisfactory."

Salk was delighted. A bit of diplomacy was now in order. "I am very glad Dr. Topping brought that up," he said. "I started by saying that there were several lines of investigation that could be pursued simultaneously. While carrying [them] out, we should continue our search for potential attenuated, or shall we say modified, strains . . . that might possibly be used in humans if we fail with the noninfectious material. We should not abandon this approach, and we have studies under way in the search for such strains. I must say that the tissue-culture technique of Dr. Enders has provided the basis for our being able to talk about this today."

Tom Rivers was uneasy about the emphasis on killed-virus preparations. "Let us suppose," he supposed, "we vaccinated everybody in the United States with an inactive virus without knowing too much about how long it would protect, and then forget about it. Perhaps in four or five years from now we might have a big outbreak of polio. We would certainly have a gripe from the public then." He suggested that it might be a good idea to challenge the effectiveness of a killed-virus preparation by feeding live viruses to volunteers who had been inoculated with it. This, of course, was exactly what Salk had proposed in a letter to Weaver in 1950. The idea had been obnoxious at the time, and still was. Rivers offered it only as a debating point, as if risks of this kind would have to be taken by scientists silly enough to trust the immunizing capacities of a killed-virus vaccine.

Tommy Francis came to the rescue, reminding everyone that there was no basis for assuming that natural infection or an infectious vaccine would give immunity more durable than might be achieved with a killed-virus vaccine. The assumption, he said, was "inconsistent with the rest of the evidence." To which Albert Sabin responded with a comprehensive proposal similar to Salk's but oriented toward a diametrically opposite view. He said that all useful lines should be explored, but added, "I agree with many of the general principles that Dr. Francis has laid down, but I am also one of those people who believes that,

if it is at all possible—this is theoretical—to infect an individual
with an attenuated virus, you have got your best immunizing
agent."

Howard Howe then reported on the first human experiments
with Formalin-inactivated preparations since the disaster of Maurice Brodie. "Since many people have said that it was high time
that we ought to try some human volunteers," he said, "it gives
me courage to tell you that some have been tried and the results
are very tentative. That is really why I hesitate to say very much
about them. The rationale of these experiments was as follows:
We felt that Koprowski's experiments with regard to human volunteers were important chiefly because they provided a bridge
from the chimpanzee to the human. We had a great deal of
data on the chimpanzee, and his findings in human volunteers
were similar to what we had found with feeding chimpanzees
Lansing-type viruses. These experiments with human volunteers
are, therefore, really designed to again provide a bridge from
the chimpanzee to the human."

He had injected six institutionalized children with a Formalin-
inactivated vaccine prepared from viruses grown in the spinal cords
of monkeys. The results had been ambiguous. He now proposed
to repeat the experiment, this time increasing the potency of his
vaccine with a mineral-oil adjuvant. The suggestion threw the
conference into turmoil. The inoculation of human beings with
foreign spinal-cord material was frowned upon to begin with;
inoculation with such material plus adjuvant would increase the
danger of allergic brain reactions. Howe did not agree. He and
Sabin debated heatedly. The meeting ended in confusion, shortly
after Howe pointed out, "I am very grateful for suggestions and
criticisms, but this is a scientific question, really, and we cannot
very well vote on it. . . . [You] can say, as Dr. Sabin did a
minute ago, 'You had better not use adjuvant.' It is all right,
because in the end we will have to be the ones to decide. . . . I
will send you a reprint, Dr. Sabin."

Before April 1952, when the Immunization Committee resumed its nervous brawling, Jonas Salk expanded his knowledge

of the Formalin process, the effect of adjuvants, and the use of monkey-kidney tissue-cultures. By the day of the meeting he was only weeks from his first human experiment. "We did not have a vaccine yet," he emphasizes. "There really was not *a* vaccine until an arbitrary decision was made prior to the national field trials of 1954, and *the* vaccine, so to speak, was not developed until even later than that. In 1952 all we had were several dozen different experimental preparations, some with adjuvant, some without, some containing one type of virus, some another or a third or all three, some made with monkey kidney, some with testes, some inactivated for ten days, some for thirteen, some for twenty-one."

He had no leisure and sought none. A Sunday walk or an evening at the movies were chances to think. It has been written that he got home one night, collapsed into his favorite chair, and picked up the thread of his thoughts while Donna, for whom his presence was a luxury, attempted conversation. Noticing that he was abstracted as usual, she said, "You're not even listening to me." The words penetrated. His face brightened, his eyes focused, and he was briefly the Jonas well-remembered. "My dear, you have my undevoted attention," he smiled. National Foundation personnel who met him for the first time during this stage of his career looked upon him affectionately, even paternally, as the very model of a naïve, somewhat fuzzy academician. Nothing could have been further from the truth: He simply paid little attention to such visitors, thinking his thoughts, planning his plans, rejecting intrusions. In the laboratory he was anything but fuzzy. "We worked like dogs," remembers one of his former associates. "It was like a factory, but those of us who knew how unusual that kind of speed-up was in a university lab did not mind, because we felt we were part of a closely knit team engaged in a great effort. Jonas was no longer as warm and friendly as he had been in the beginning, but we attributed that to the strain of the work. The bravery he was showing in going ahead so rapidly toward human experiments was also terribly admirable, we felt. So if one of us accomplished something today but accomplished nothing tomorrow and Jonas' attitude seemed to convey a feeling of 'What have you done for me lately?' we took it in good spirit."

Nonparalytic poliomyelitis is an infection so uneventful that most people recover from it without awareness that they have been significantly ill. In 1952, however, more American children died of *paralytic* poliomyelitis than of any other communicable disease. The virus made its way from their intestines to their central nervous systems, where it destroyed cells on which life depended. Until that year, most polio investigators assumed that the infection spread to spinal cord and brain by way of nerve fibers, although hints that it traveled in the bloodstream had been offered at intervals for more than a decade. The unrecognized possibilities were immensely important. If the virus circulated in the blood during any preparalytic stage of the human disease, it meant that a vaccine might neutralize the infection before it could reach the spinal cord. A vaccine might prevent paralysis.

In 1941 Albert Sabin had observed viremia (virus in the blood) in a monkey but had not pursued the curiosity, nor had anyone else. Supposition was unanimous that the virus had probably just "spilled over" into the blood of that particular animal. The possibility was not considered that the animal's blood might have contained virus during an especially significant stage of infection. As we have seen, orthodoxy regarded polio as a nerve disease, immunity to which depended on mysterious cellular changes in nerve tissues. What took place in the blood, therefore, could not be decisive. Just as viruses could get there only by chance—"spilling over"—antibody appeared there only as a by-product of recovery and immunity, but was helpful to neither.

These doctrines explain why the National Foundation's scientific advisers rebuffed Drs. Sidney Kramer of the Michigan Department of Health and Joseph Stokes, Jr., of Philadelphia Children's Hospital in 1944, when they proposed to try gamma globulin as a polio preventive. Among the arguments against Kramer and Stokes' notion, the strongest was that gamma globulin did not contain enough antibody to "spill over" (that term again) from the blood to the nerve tissues, where meaningful combat with poliovirus supposedly took place.

In 1946 Joseph Melnick, Dorothy M. Horstmann, and Robert Ward of Yale found viremia in a human patient, as did Hilary Koprowski a year later. No significance was attached to the reports. But in 1948, after Sabin and William Hammon each located polio antibodies in the blood during early stages of infection, it became obvious to Dr. Theodore E. Boyd of the National Foundation that the antibody might, after all, be an inherent part of the infectious process. Polio very likely was not as different from other virus diseases as had been supposed. Boyd said to Harry Weaver, "This raises the question of viremia in an early stage of polio." To which Weaver replied, "It certainly does. Let's get someone to look into it."

Easier said than done. Joseph Melnick, their first candidate for the project, was interested in other things and did not get around to viremia. Another investigator attempted the investigation but botched it. Instead of testing individual monkey's blood for virus at each stage of infection, he pooled blood samples from various animals. He therefore got antibody from one animal all mixed up with virus from another, destroying the virus. He found a few cases of viremia, but not enough to be sure about. The turning point came in 1951, when Bill Hammon's preliminary field trial of gamma globulin at Provo, Utah, indicated that small amounts of antibody probably helped to prevent paralysis. At this point David Bodian decided to find out why this was possible. So did Dorothy Horstmann. They each discovered that viremia occurred in chimpanzees and monkeys during the very earliest stage of infection. They then looked for viremia in human beings and found it. It was now permissible to speculate that, if antibody were present in the blood in appropriate quantities, infection might not spread from the intestines to the central nervous system.

When the Immunization Committee reconvened in New York on April 18, 1952, Bodian and Horstmann had already reported their animal discoveries and, much to their astonishment, had landed on the front pages of newspapers. It should be explained that viremia was of greater public interest in 1952 than it can possibly be now. The public of 1952 was desperately helpless against paralytic polio and eager for any substantial good news. The Bodian-Horstmann news was, of course, extremely good. Vaccination was a step closer.

The discussion of this subject at the Hotel Commodore on April 18 was warmly unpleasant. Tom Rivers, who would be a pillar of strength when the time came to test the Salk vaccine, had still not forsworn loyalty to the past. The viremia development shook him. The publicity about it offended him. He was cranky. During Bodian's report he said, "I would like to say that you haven't proved to us yet anything about viremia. You are saying a certain amount of antibody is stopping viremia. I know from the *newspapers* that there is a viremia, but in your discussion here you haven't convinced me yet that you have got a viremia, and yet you say a certain amount of antibody stops it. Let us get this orderly."

Bodian: "Do you mean that I haven't shown viremia?"

Rivers: "You haven't shown that viremia is a common thing. You have shown a couple of chimpanzees there that had viremia, but you haven't convinced *me* with regard to viremia. I know it is so in monkeys, but I don't know it is so in man. You are getting everything kind of mixed up here a little bit."

Sabin (as conciliator): "I think you are getting us mixed up a little bit, too, Tom. I think that Dave has undoubtedly shown . . . that some of the chimpanzees had viremia to a certain level. Now it is true that he has not shown how often that occurs or what the importance of it is for the development of central-nervous-system manifestations."

Weaver, chairman of the meeting, finally had to hammer for silence so that Bodian could get on with his report. A few minutes later, however, after Bodian, with mild demurrers from Sabin, had suggested that antibody could break the chain of infection from the alimentary tract to the nervous system, Rivers got out of hand again. "I would like to make a statement," he said. "In the first place, I don't want to hurt Dave's feelings, but I wouldn't like for him to call monkeys 'he.' "

Bodian: "What?"

Rivers: "You used the term 'he' for a monkey."

Bodian: "Chimpanzee."

Rivers: "I think it is proper to say 'it' when you are speaking about an animal. I yet do not accept chimpanzees and cynomolgus as equal to man, and it kind of grates on my feelings of propriety to have someone keep on calling the monkey a 'he.' "

Bodian (who admired Rivers and was willing to put up with a great deal from the old despot): "Well, he wasn't a she."

Rivers: "Well, it is an it."

And so on and on, and then an argument from Rivers that Bodian should not talk about viremia in poliomyelitis but about viremia in *experimental* poliomyelitis. And finally, Rivers came to what was really bothering him: "The thing that I am driving at is a thing that we are being pushed into, that the National Foundation is being pushed into, that this committee is being pushed into. The papers are saying that this is an accomplished fact. We haven't got a vaccine ready for polio in human beings. We are not absolutely certain yet that gamma globulin works in human beings, and Mr. O'Connor and this committee will be deluged with requests for vaccines and gamma globulin when we are not in a position yet to give them an answer, and I don't know who is to blame, whether it was the newspapers or whether it was organizations. It doesn't make any difference to me as to who is to blame, but I don't think it is fair to be put behind the eight ball the way we are now behind the eight ball.

"I firmly believe," he went on, much to Jonas Salk's joy, "that we have in the near future, a matter of a year or two, a solution to many things that we want a solution to, but if we are to be pushed ahead of time and before we are ready, we will make a terrible mistake and we will get into trouble that we will regret as long as we live. We have got something big here, and unless we handle it right it will be terrible, and I for one don't like to be pushed into that position."

Rivers was that way, capable of his worst and his best within five minutes. Basil O'Connor, whom he liked, feared, and hated by turns, but whom he always respected, has said more than once, "If I had to defend what we did on the Salk vaccine before an intelligent jury, all I'd say is, 'Gentlemen, we had Tom Rivers on our side. I rest my case.' " He means it, although there were times when he could scarcely stand the sight of the man.

The viremia debate at the April 1952 meeting became more amiable after reparative growls by Rivers: "I have done a lot of beefing this morning, but I do want to say that I think the discovery of viremia is an important fact. It is an advance, and I want to agree with Dr. Sabin on that and, in spite of my beefing, I am taking my hat off to the people who have done it." He then went out for coffee.

The next big event of the day was Jonas Salk's report on proposed human vaccination experiments. "I would rather not discuss proposed human vaccination experiments," he began, "but rather present the data that we have gathered over the last several months which may serve as the basis for confidence in thinking about a human vaccination experiment. Perhaps I can do this best by showing some lantern slides which summarize the data that have been gathered on the induction of antibody in monkeys, first with active virus used as a vaccine and then with presumably noninfectious preparations. . . ."

It was a resplendent performance. He showed that solutions of live virus, diluted until they no longer paralyzed monkeys, continued to provoke immunizing antibody in the creatures. He showed that comparable results were obtained with greater safety by killing the virus with Formalin. He discussed his Formalin-inactivation techniques, describing numerous alternative methods. He discussed the potency-enhancing effects of mineral-oil adjuvants. He fielded questions one-handed, backwards, and blindfolded. He was in command of his subject. A complaint about him which has been attributed to John Enders but has been repeated by dozens of other virologists—"We wish Dr. Salk would show us more and tell us less"—could not have been uttered on this day. Where he had no minutely detailed supporting data of the sort his colleagues preferred, he acknowledged it and pointed out that this, after all, was a discussion of trends, of work in progress. When Harry Weaver said, "Gentlemen, the subject is open for discussion," Bill Hammon said with conviction, "I think I will start it off by saying that it was a beautiful job." And Albert Sabin echoed him before calling attention to the other side of the sheep: "I think this is a beautiful example of a systematic study which needs to be continued, and it shows how much more has to be learned before one can even think of beginning to know what kind of test to try in human beings. . . ."

On June 5, 1952, Harry Weaver sent an astonishing communication through channels. "It is the purpose of this memorandum," he announced, "to suggest that there be created a committee to decide what should be the activity of the National Foundation following the conquest of poliomyelitis.

"It is my feeling that such a committee should consist of individuals who cannot possibly benefit personally from their presence on the committee. I would suggest further that the membership consist of individuals whom we can rely on to pick us a subject which is solvable within a reasonable time.

"If you approve of this suggestion in principle, will you please transmit it to Mr. O'Connor."

Jonas Salk had not yet begun experimental vaccination of human beings, but the Research Director was advising the Medical Director to inform the President that the conquest of polio was imminent enough to justify concern about the Foundation's future. Weaver and O'Connor were chums. They dined at Twenty-One together and went to the theater together and hoisted glasses together. They had discussed the conquest of polio as much more than an academic possibility, and O'Connor knew quite well that changes in the National Foundation's socioscientific role would someday be indicated. But now Weaver put it in writing and sent it through channels, thereby calling as much attention to the existence of the channels as to the idea contained in his note. "He was not a lover of channels," says O'Connor. "He is a great man. Great friend of mine. Nothing I wouldn't do for him. Or him for me. But the thing about him was that he knew he could run the National Foundation at least as well as I was running it. Notice, I say I believe he *knew* he could run it. I don't say I believe he only *thought* he could run it. Perhaps he was right. We'll never know. He couldn't be happy just directing research. He wanted a voice in everything. But we weren't set up that way and couldn't reorganize to accommodate his wants. We needed the very best research director we could get, meaning Weaver, and we needed him to put in full time on that job. Hell, he was the best research director anybody *ever* had. Announcing the conquest of polio a month before Jonas began vaccinating children was typical of him. He loved to do things with a flourish. Don't we all, if we can get away with it?"

On June 12, Jonas Salk went to the D. T. Watson Home for Crippled Children at Leetsdale, fifteen miles up the Ohio River from Pittsburgh, and began taking blood samples from children who were candidates for experimental inoculation. The name of the home is bleakly Dickensian but there are no other resemblances. The institution was established in 1920 on a large estate called Sunny Hill, in accordance with the will of the late proprietor, a wealthy attorney named David T. Watson. Under the medical direction of the distinguished Dr. Jessie Wright, the home's superb reputation antedated the celebrity it gained from its involvement in Salk's first human experiments. Indeed, it was a feather in Salk's cap to win cooperation from an establishment of this sort rather than start his work in a public institution.

Lucile Cochran, R.N., administrator of the Watson Home, remembers Salk's first visit. "It was in May," she says. "Dr. Wright and Harry F. Stambaugh, who was chairman of the board, brought him here for lunch. He was charming and gentle —we have never seen him otherwise—and obviously he was not just a scientist on an experiment but a man deeply concerned about the human importance of the experiment. He explained the scientific basis of his work with great care. The first thing he wanted to do was take blood from polio patients, find out the type of antibodies they had, and then inoculate them with vaccines of the same types to see if the vaccines would raise their antibody levels. Since the subjects already had antibody and were immune to another paralytic attack from the one type of virus, the experiment would be as safe as it could possibly be. We all were very much in favor of trying it. So were the parents of the children. It may seem peculiar, but we had no sense of making history. We just enjoyed being part of the project. And the parents and children and staff were so wonderful. Nobody said a single word to an outsider. The experiments remained an absolute secret."

One newspaperman phoned and said he understood that gamma globulin was being tried at the home, and Miss Cochran was able to answer truthfully, "No. That's going on out West."

A medical scientist explains the need for secrecy: "You can't do pioneer human experimentation effectively without it. The news is too exciting. It gets into the newspapers. Your phone begins ringing and does not stop. Part of the public goes haywire with premature optimism and the rest with unwarranted fear. Do-gooders and crackpots of all shapes and sizes try to get into the act, interfering with the selection of experimental subjects and making the terms and conditions of the experiment a matter for public debate."

One of the chief reasons for the Watson Home administration's confidence in the Salk project was Salk's apparent confidence in himself. His earlier unconcern about failure ("What was there to fail at? We were under no compulsion to produce a vaccine") was no longer strictly applicable. He now was going to inject experimental vaccines into children. Rationalizations and animal experiments to the contrary, somebody might die. "I have the courage of my convictions," he once said when complimented on his bravery of 1952. "I couldn't do it unless I was more critical of myself than others were of me. It is courage based on confidence, not daring, and it's confidence based on experience." Which was true enough but becomes more lifelike when juxtaposed to a more recent remark of his about the Watson Home experiments: "You have no chance of succeeding unless you're willing to fail."

On June 12 he took blood from forty-five children and twenty-seven members of the Watson Home staff, eliciting much admiration with his deft manipulation of the needle and his tender, playful behavior toward the children. On July 2, having typed the antibodies contained in these samples, he returned. It was a hot day, but the auditorium of the Watson Home was cool. Hypodermic needles, cotton, disinfectant, and the other im-

pedimenta of inoculation were arrayed on long tables. The first
injections were to be given. Miss Cochran does not remember
for certain which child was first in line, although the distinction
has been credited on occasion to William F. Kirkpatrick, sixteen-
year-old son of an industrial executive. Thirty children got a
Type I vaccine, two were given Type II, and eleven Type III.
"When you inoculate children with a polio vaccine, you don't
sleep well for two or three months," Salk later told a reporter.
Miss Cochran recalls, "He came back again that first night to
make sure everyone was all right. Everyone was."

There were no adverse reactions of any kind the next day,
either. Or any day afterward. "He phoned frequently and returned
again and again in that old rattletrap car of his," says Lucile
Cochran, "taking bleedings and injecting all three types of vaccine into subjects who had no antibody to begin with."

This was risky. Perhaps the earlier subjects had been spared
paralytic infection from the vaccines only because they had
antibody in their blood before the inoculations. Perhaps Salk's
vaccines were not as safe for humans as for chimpanzees. The
only way to tell was to try and then wait. Salk's confidence in
his procedures was great but could not be total. He visited the
home frequently, telephoned persistently. The waiting period
passed without incident. Anybody who was incubating polio as
a consequence of vaccination would have had polio by now, but
not one of the subjects had displayed a single symptom.

Toward the end of that intense summer, Salk and his colleagues in the laboratory at Municipal Hospital found what
they had been hoping to find. Some of the vaccines given to
children whose blood contained antibody prior to inoculation
had produced far higher levels of antibody—an impressive booster effect. And some of the subjects whose blood contained no
detectable antibody before inoculation were now giving samples
of blood replete with antibody. The levels of antibody were high
enough to destroy living polioviruses. Salk saw it under his microscope. Blood samples taken from the vaccinated were de-
posited in tissue-culture that contained virulent poliovirus. If
the virus remained alive, it would destroy the tissue cells. But
in these cultures the tissue cells continued to grow. The antibody

produced by vaccination had killed the virus. Salk's principles had worked out in practice. Of this he was sure. "It was the thrill of my life," he says. "Compared to the feeling I got seeing those results under the microscope, everything that followed was anticlimactic."

"I've got it," he told Donna.

"Hmmm," she said, or something to that effect.

"No other comment?" he inquired.

"I was sure," she said, "Weren't you? I mean, Jonas, when you put your mind to something . . ."

A poetic young patient at the Watson Home later summarized the feelings there:

> Dr. Salk is a happy Man
> I am proud of Him
> he discovered a safe vaccine to fight polio
> and I hope No one else Gets Polio
> and May God Bless Him
> From your pal, Peter Herwatic.

The cook at the Home used to like to know in advance when Salk was coming so that she could make strawberry pie, which he loved. The children, even those who hated the needle, also looked forward to his visits: He remembered their names and what they had talked about last time, and what type antibodies they had and what neighborhoods they lived in. The most envied individual in the place was a waitress who fell and cut herself while he was there and had the cut treated by him, personally. In October he drove out and called the staff of the home together and said, "I've got it. And I thank you. I never thought it possible that so many people could keep a secret this well."

9

THE LAST SIX MONTHS OF 1952, THE PERIOD OF SECRET EXPER-
imentation, were the most rewarding Salk had ever known.
Basil O'Connor, Harry Weaver, and Tom Rivers were the only
outsiders aware of what he was doing. They held their tongues,
allowing Salk truly undisturbed time in which to work. He expanded the Watson Home studies and gave inoculations at the
Polk State School, a public institution. He pursued his influenza
trials at Fort Dix and among students at the University of Pittsburgh; his killed vaccine with adjuvant produced higher antibody levels and immunity at least as durable as resulted from
flu itself. The morale of his staff remained high and grew higher
with the imminence of historic achievement. A few personnel
changes had improved the atmosphere, too. The most important
was the arrival from Australia of Percival L. Bazeley, known as
Val. This physician, veterinarian, and technological wizard had
been recommended to Salk by Harry Weaver, who had heard
about him from the great Australian virologist Sir Macfarlane
Burnet. Among Bazeley's gifts was a penchant for large-scale
production. For example, during the early days of penicillin when
Australia had little and needed much, he had shown how to produce the antibiotic in quantity. He now was greatly interested in
coming to the United States to see if he could help Salk produce
polio-vaccine viruses in unprecedented volume. Which is exactly
what he did, after figuring out how to use larger flasks and how
to improve the efficiency of the tissue-culture process. His liking
for "Doc Salk," as he calls him, was instantaneous and has

endured. He is now principal assistant in Salk's laboratory at the Salk Institute.

"In December 1952," says Salk, "we took new bleedings at the Watson Home and the Polk School and discovered that the subjects' antibody was holding at the September level. There it was! By this time we knew how to make far more potent vaccines and, beyond that, we knew that still more potent ones would be possible in future. To have attained the results we did with material as primitive as we had used was extremely heartening. A couple of months earlier, when we already had the first results from the Watson Home, Howard Howe had been quoted in *Life* magazine to the effect that vaccination was years away. I kept quiet. I remember sitting next to Harry Weaver at a meeting about Hammon's gamma globulin field trials at that time and discussing with him whether I should say something. But I didn't want to show my hand that early in the game. We let Hammon have his field day, to which he certainly was entitled. But when the December bleedings turned out as they did, we knew it was time to move toward more extensive tests. To do this we needed the support of the polio-research community."

Tommy Francis remembers a luncheon at which Tom Rivers said with cryptic jollity, "You better hold on to your hats, boys. We're going to toss a bomb at you." It did not occur to Rivers that a killed-virus vaccine could be the last word in polio prevention, but he was now satisfied that Salk's was safe and might turn out to be reasonably effective. He was for it.

The bomb promised by Rivers was Salk's report on the results of inoculating 161 human beings with various Formalin-inactivated poliovirus preparations. The occasion for the report was a private meeting at Hershey, Pennsylvania. "It was in January," says Salk. "Albert Sabin and I rode to Hershey on the train from Pittsburgh. He'd been on a tour of various labs that were doing tissue-culture work, apparently having had some trouble establishing the procedures in his own place. He spent a day or so around our lab and came to the house for dinner and we talked about things in general. I was busy preparing for the meeting and didn't feel like discussing what was going to be reported there, but he pressed me as to what my approach was going to be, and was I interested only in killed vaccines or was I planning to work on live ones, and so forth. He made it plain that he intended to get to work on a *live* vaccine as soon as he could."

Salk was mistaken in this impression of Sabin as a tardy prospector trying to stake out a claim in areas of polio prevention already being mined by Hilary Koprowski and Herald Cox, to say nothing of Howard Howe and Jonas Salk. The facts were that Sabin had recorded his intent to explore that field long before Salk himself was in polio research and even before the others had begun actual immunization experiments. On November 29, 1946, Sabin had written to Harry Weaver, "After our last discussion . . . I told you that I wanted to have some additional time to think about the broad outlines of a long-range program of investigative work on poliomyelitis that I would be interested in pursuing and directing in the forthcoming years. I should like to set forth in this letter the outlines of the program that seemed most worthwhile to me and the lines of thought which led me to this choice." There followed an exhaustive review of the mysteries of poliomyelitis, and the assertion that ". . . it seems to me that the search for a means to supply . . . immunity artificially at the earliest possible age still offers the most important approach to the control of the disease. To anyone who is familiar with the work that has been done along these lines in the past, it is hardly necessary to point out that many would regard such an approach as rather unpromising." Among the lines of investigation that Sabin himself considered unpromising were killed-virus vaccines, which, he said, "would require multiple doses and yearly reinoculations" and would therefore be most impractical. On the other hand, he foresaw great promise in an infectious vaccine "consisting of 'live' modified or mutant virus, which . . . would undergo *sufficient multiplication* to give rise to immunity of long duration, but not to paralysis." This, of course, is the very principle he later applied in developing the polio vaccine that now bears his name. That he did not begin to implement the idea in 1946 but waited until 1953 is undeniable. On the other hand, as soon as he started, he made up for lost time with a stupendous display of vitality and ambition. So immense were his energies that he not only could attend to his own scientific tasks but also had time to become an ubiquitous public analyst of Salk's problems, many of which he seemed to consider insoluble. During the difficult years of 1953 and 1954, when meaningful national field trials of the Salk vaccine depended on public confidence in the merits of the undertaking, the National Foundation found it necessary to establish a kind of intelligence network to keep itself posted on Sabin's negative utterances at medical meetings and press conferences. Not that anyone questioned his sincerity. Neither did anyone question his right to promote his own theories and advance his own cause. In the game of science, as in other competitive pursuits, one may win honor not only by running faster but also by maneuvering the other fellow into running slower. Thus, a Tom Rivers was able to remain Sabin's staunch admirer throughout this turbulent period, conceding only that his heckling was sometimes "a nuisance."

Having sensed that Sabin's hat was now in the ring, Jonas Salk was not in the least surprised at the quality of the Cincinnati scientist's comments on his report to the Hershey meeting. "It was almost as if he were trying to minimize what I had said," remembers Salk. "His interpretations made my work seem incredible, of no meaning or significance. We hadn't done this and we hadn't done that and this was premature and that was unsubstantiated. I remember asking him later, 'Why do you constantly emphasize the negative?' He answered that this was 'the scientific way of doing things.' John Enders was gentlemanly, but not more favorably disposed to what we'd been doing. And I remember Howard Howe coming to me and saying, 'I feel as I would if I had just lost a child,' referring, no doubt, to the vaccine he had been experimenting with. It was a tense meeting and I was by no means the tensest person there."

In an interview with Saul Benison, the National Foundation's historian, Tom Rivers recalled that those present at the meeting were impressed with Salk's achievement. "This doesn't mean that they accepted everything he said lock, stock, and barrel— not by a long shot—and I can tell you that they put Jonas through his paces. Some . . . were doubtful that immunization

with Formalinized vaccines would give antibody levels higher
than that produced by a natural infection. Others were skeptical
of the use of adjuvants. Many adjuvants at that time were produced commercially and had toxic components that caused rather
severe local reactions. . . . Still other virologists were worried
about the possibility of organ damage caused by inoculating
people with material derived from monkey-kidney tissue. They
examined Jonas closely—that's not surprising. These boys would
have questioned their own mothers if they were foolhardy enough
to give a paper at a conference.

"When the problem of whether Dr. Salk's results warranted his
carrying out a field trial later that spring was brought up, a wide
variety of opinion was expressed. Dr. Smadel got up and asked,
'When are you going to do your Provo test?' " (Referring to the
Provo, Utah, field trial of gamma globulin.) "Dr. Smadel was
bold and at this point I would say was even out in front of
Harry Weaver. From the January meeting forward, Dr. Smadel
consistently preached 'to get going and hold a field trial.' Dr.
Tommy Turner of Johns Hopkins was another who felt that if
an inactived vaccine could be produced under rigid standards
of safety an early field trial was warranted. Dr. Sabin, on the
other hand, counseled against holding a field trial. Like some
others at the conference, he was concerned about the use of
adjuvants and the organ damage that might be caused through
the use of monkey-kidney material. He particularly urged that
more work be done with animals and even suggested that antibody surveys be done in representative communities. Albert
not only looked directly at the question, he looked around it
and examined every possible facet, including a few theoretical
facts that didn't occur to others. A number of other virologists,
while impressed with Dr. Salk's results, were at that time simply
against the idea of holding a field trial of the nature of the
Provo. . . . They recommended that Dr. Salk extend his clinical
studies on a more limited basis than that suggested by a field
trial. Dr. John Enders fell into this category. I think that it might
be helpful if I quoted some of the remarks he made at that
time:

" 'I am afraid that I can't quite agree with Dr. Turner if he

uses the term "Provo experiment." I don't think that we are
ready for it. I think if we do such a thing it would mean that
we would go off half-cocked. What I have heard here makes
me think that, first of all, we haven't decided on the strains of
virus that are most suitable to use yet. Dr. Salk is not quite
satisfied with his test for safety in respect to the virus. Further
work should be done on that, and careful work. The mode of
vaccination, the route and type of vaccination, adjuvant or no
adjuvant . . . we haven't got enough data to decide which to
use on a scale of this magnitude. . . . I would suggest more
experimentation along the same lines that he is doing so admi-
rably at the moment, and not enter into a large experiment which
will inevitably be connected with a lot of publicity and may
jeopardize the entire program. . . .'

"I would like to add here," Rivers continued, "that at no time
during the conference did Dr. Salk push for a field trial. As a
matter of fact, like Dr. Enders he too spoke of extending his
clinical studies rather than doing a field trial on the order of
Provo. He was very cautious."

Salk smiles a despairing smile. "Of course I didn't want a field
trial at that stage," he says. "There was no vaccine, no product
to try out in hundreds of thousands of people. All we had was
a flicker of light, an intimation that the hypothesis about inactivated polio vaccines was valid. The talk by some about
hurrying into field trials was as disheartening as the wearisome
reviews by others of all the facts we had not yet established. Each
school of thought was unhelpful, really. The sense of being
caught between two lines of fire made me ache to retreat to Pittsburgh and continue my work in my own way. I was naïve to
think that this was possible."

The annual March of Dimes was on. Of all seasons, this one
was ideal for revelation of National Foundation progress toward
prevention of paralytic polio. Harry Weaver was alert to such
considerations. Furthermore, he had utmost confidence in Salk's
ability to solve the remaining scientific and technical problems
and produce, within the year, a vaccine suitable for national trials.
Basil O'Connor was similarly disposed. He was not yet close
enough to Salk to know and share the young scientist's view of

the problems of vaccine development. In time, O'Connor would become a ferocious defender of Salk's right to be left alone. But as of January 1953, he knew of no reason to refrain from exploiting the success that lay ahead.

On January 26, at a special meeting of the National Foundation's Board of Trustees in the Waldorf-Astoria, Harry Weaver delivered a speech that made clear to one and all that a polio vaccine was probably in the offing, courtesy of the March of Dimes. "I had stayed in Hershey an extra day on the previous weekend to help Harry work on the text of the speech," says Salk. "The idea apparently was to conceal yet reveal and my problem was to encourage him to conceal as much and reveal as little as possible. I wanted to avoid the hue and cry of publicity so that I could get on with my work undisturbed."

Weaver's speech was full of disclaimers, such as, "I come before you this evening with no intention to state or imply that the means is now at hand whereby all of us can protect ourselves and our loved ones against the paralytic consequences of an infection with the virus of poliomyelitis." But the caution was interspersed with nuggets: ". . . our knowledge about poliomyelitis is, it seems to me, approaching with unusual directness and rapidity, the objective for which we all strive—complete understanding of the disease and ability to control it." And: "I wish I could say that field tests with such a vaccine will be undertaken during 1953. This I cannot say with complete assurance, but I can say that tremendous progress has been made during the past several months—in fact, the kind of progress one is accustomed to see prior to the taking of an important forward step." The word began to get around.

Weaver wrote one of his for-the-record memorandums to O'Connor, advocating prompt preparation for field trials:

> The practice of medicine is based on calculated risk. Where the risk is known, the physician elects to follow the course that provides the greatest benefit with the least risk of incurring any untoward effects.
>
> It is impossible at this stage of development to predict the degree of efficacy, on the one hand, and the degree of safety,

on the other, of the poliomyelitis vaccine that has been developed. These questions can only be determined after injecting relatively large numbers of human beings.

There is no question of the fact that, with additional research:

1. A still more effective poliomyelitis vaccine could be
produced;

2. We would be better informed as to the kind and frequency of untoward effects that might result from the use of
the vaccine; and

3. We would be better informed with respect to the best
route of inoculation and the best time for administration of
the vaccine to obtain maximal protection against paralytic
disease, etc.

If such research is carried out, a very considerable amount
of time will elapse before a poliomyelitis vaccine is made
available for widespread use; with the result that, in the
interim, large numbers of human beings will develop poliomyelitis who might have been prevented from doing so
had the vaccine been made available at an earlier date.
It seems to many of us that we have come to a stage where
the future course of our work must be governed by both
scientific and sociological considerations. . . .

The sociological were as formidable as the scientific. Regardless of O'Connor's desire to save humanity from paralytic polio
by any means whatever, and regardless of Salk's confidence in
the validity of his work, and regardless of Weaver's serene confidence in Salk, which exceeded the scientist's own, experimental
polio vaccines simply could not be injected into large numbers
of people until the way was paved. The Pope had recently in-
veighed against medical experiments which "transgress the right
of the individual to dispose of himself." A case in point had occurred in the United States, where three federal prisoners died
during experiments with viral hepatitis, creating furor in medicine and government. A comparable disaster associated with injections of a polio vaccine would ruin the National Foundation
and hobble medical research for generations. The field trials
should be organized, Weaver felt, but only with the endorsement
of leading figures in American science and medicine.

Tom Rivers agreed with Weaver that the most promising of Salk's present vaccines might as well be tried on a relatively large scale. He also agreed that approval for the trials should be solicited from influential figures. He signed a letter inviting such persons to a special meeting at the Waldorf on February 26. Besides O'Connor, Salk, Rivers, Weaver, Hart Van Riper, Tommy Turner, Joe Smadel, Norman Topping, and Raymond Barrows, Executive Director of the National Foundation, the following dignitaries were there: Margaret A. Hickey, of the *Ladies' Home Journal*; Dr. Louis H. Bauer, President of the American Medical Association; Dr. Rufus H. Fitzgerald, Chancellor of the University of Pittsburgh; Dr. Alan Gregg, Vice-President for Medical Affairs of the Rockefeller Foundation; Dr. Rustin McIntosh, Carpentier Professor of Pediatrics at the Columbia University College of Physicians and Surgeons; Dr. Thomas P. Murdock of the American Medical Association Board of Trustees; Dr. John D. Porterfield, Director of the Ohio Department of Health; Dr. David E. Price, Assistant Surgeon General of the United States Public Health Service; Dr. Richard E. Shope of the Rockefeller Institute; and Dr. Max Theiler, of the Rockefeller Foundation, developer of the yellow-fever vaccine.

"I want to say just these few words," O'Connor began. "We are indebted to you for coming here today. The ultimate problem is to solve polio intelligently and scientifically, and that is the end the National Foundation is seeking. In all activities we have tried to be as intelligent as we reasonably could, invariably calling on the best advice we could get to help us solve our problems, and that is why you have been asked to come today to listen to a story . . . we hope to have the benefit of your advice. . . ."

Tom Rivers outlined the problem. Salk's polio vaccines had been injected into 161 people. More injections were indicated. But the Pope's point of view was scarcely to be disregarded, and the deaths of the federal prisoners should also be borne in mind. "Now I can tell you ahead of time," said Rivers, "that what we are going to discuss today is not in that category, the one that I have spoken of with respect to hepatitis. I would say to all intents and purposes that the vaccine that Dr. Salk is going to talk about is reasonably safe. In the first place, the virus is inactivated. It is dead. In the second place it is made in tissue-cultures instead of brain. Brain material itself is dangerous.

"Now if Dr. Salk's solutions were injected into 10 million children, I am certain something would happen to somebody . . . that would either be the result of that solution or be attributed to it. Actually, I think an occasional person would drop dead if you stuck a sterile needle into him, so that what we are talking about today really isn't so dangerous, but there are social implications. . . .

"Dr. Salk is a very cautious man. Some people want to go much faster than he wants to go. Some want to throw all he has got out of the window and try something else, or they can find a great many objections to what he is doing. In closing my introductory remarks, I would like to say something that Samuel Johnson once said, that 'nothing will ever be accomplished if all possible objections must be first overcome.' Someone is always going to have an objection to everything that is proposed, so let us take this and look at it and decide about it because Dr. Salk himself does not want to assume the responsibility entirely."

These allusions to the negativism of virologists who detested the killed-virus theory were music to Salk. He began his own speech by acknowledging the wisdom of Rivers and Sam Johnson. "I appreciate your remarks, Dr. Rivers," he said, "and I would like to tell you that not so long ago someone pointed out that life is not a popularity contest and I don't think that our purpose in doing the work that we are doing is to try to please everyone. The purpose is to derive as objectively as possible —and that is the only way in which one can function—scientific data in answer to certain questions. The question that is before us is: Can we induce antibody formation in human subjects with preparations containing poliomyelitis virus which have been treated with chemicals in order to destroy their infectiousness for experimental animals? The next aspect of that question is: Can we do this in human subjects and is the material so used equally safe in humans as . . . in experimental animals?"

He showed lantern slides of charts and graphs that summarized the results of his early inoculation experiments at the Watson Home and the Polk State School. He described the in-activation process, taking care to credit Albert Sabin with prior use of a similar method in preparing two viral encephalitis vac-cines. He discussed the advantages of the mineral-oil adjuvant, explaining that it was absolutely harmless and gave far better antibody results than could be obtained with an aqueous vaccine. He revealed that fears about the ill effects of monkey-kidney tissue did not seem warranted by tests he was conducting in his own laboratory.

Tom Rivers pointed out that the newspapers had begun to generate excitement about a polio vaccine and that, when Salk's first official report appeared in the *Journal* of the American Medical Association, which planned publication in its March 28 issue, his life would no longer be his own. "Everybody and his brother is going to want the vaccine, just like everybody and his brother is going to want gamma globulin this coming summer," complained Rivers, "so that there is a question here of what the National Foundation should do and what Dr. Salk should do. Dr. Salk is over a barrel. Terrific pressure is going to be put on him. Terrific pressure is going to be put on the Foundation and there is always the danger of going too fast. There is also the danger of going too slow, because if you have something that is good, the public should have it as soon as possible and at a safe time. That is the problem before the group this morning. . . . Dr. Salk has got to be protected and the National Foundation is going to be harassed, and I think both Dr. Salk and the Founda-tion would be pleased if an opinion could be given by people who are interested. And I might say that with the exception of Dr. Salk, there is not a man around this table that is working on poliomyelitis. We have deliberately left out all those who are . . . because they might be a bit biased one way or another. . . . Wouldn't it be silly to wait fifty years or to wait ten years to develop the ideal vaccine [which he described as a live-virus vaccine] when there is the possibility of a vaccine being developed very rapidly that will last, say, for two or three years with one injection perhaps? We don't know anything about that, but have we the right to wait until the ideal vaccine comes along? Should we go ahead and use this vaccine that seems to be effective right now when people are crying for it?"

Salk: "I don't know that we even have a vaccine yet. That term was used, but I think it should be understood that we are using it as a colloquial expression. We have preparations which have induced antibody formation in human subjects."

Rivers: "I think you have a vaccine, Jonas."

If Salk had chosen to argue the point, he would have undermined the meeting and invited a state of war with Rivers and Harry Weaver and, for all he knew, with Basil O'Connor. He did not have a vaccine suitable for extensive human trials and hated to be put in the position of seeming to. Such a vaccine, the combination of variables most likely to produce lasting human immunity, was two or three years away, he felt. In the meantime, all he wanted was a by-your-leave to give a few thousand more experimental injections. Rivers' sudden willingness to concede merit to an inactivated preparation and endorse large field trials derived from a genuinely humanitarian anxiety to do something about polio, Salk believed, but behind this was the old man's fundamental disdain for the killed-virus concept. To him, a Salk vaccine was nothing but a stopgap, something slightly better than gamma globulin, something by definition imperfectible but worth a try pending the development of a safely infectious live vaccine.

Now was not the time to debate such matters. Nor would there ever be a time when Salk could argue in good conscience against the humanitarian idea that an imperfect vaccine was better than no vaccine at all. He saw on this day what he had only sensed in the past: To respond to the cry of the people for quick relief from paralytic polio while appeasing the diverse scientific prejudices of the National Foundation's advisers and satisfying his own irrepressible need for perfection would demand guile and skill and luck. At the moment guile was required. Guile prescribed the waiting game.

It was an amiable meeting. During a discussion of the allergic reactions that some people feared might be induced by viruses grown in monkey kidneys, Rivers mentioned the damage caused by injecting monkey-brain material into human beings. O'Connor brought down the house: "One cannot help but think what would happen to the poor monkey if you inoculated him with human-brain tissue." And Salk responded, "Think of all the psychological problems you would induce in the monkey." Solemnity resumed when Joe Smadel demanded "a general idea of the next step"—a discussion of what kind of human experimentation should now be undertaken. Rivers replied, "My feeling about it—and . . . I am speaking a little bit for Dr. Salk here—is that he would like perhaps between now and January 1954 to be permitted . . . [with] moral support from this group, to go ahead and vaccinate, let us say, somewhere in the neighborhood of twenty-five thousand children mainly to determine whether the vaccine is safe. I think that those experiments could be done best nearest to his laboratory somewhere in the metropolitan area of Pittsburgh, and they should not be given during the polio season because of the big argument about injections precipitating paralysis. I don't know that that is a very important thing, but certainly if he vaccinates enough kids during the polio season some one of them is going to come down in about two or three days after the vaccination has been given and there will be a big hue and cry that the vaccine caused it."

A lengthy discussion of technical details terminated in an outburst from Smadel: "Now if we have got something that is worth it, let us quit fooling around and get to work on it. If it isn't good enough to go to work on now, then we don't have to discuss the minutiae today, since they will be different next fall.

"If every vaccine that was ever used on human beings, including the few that are worth anything, had been put through half of this," he protested, "we wouldn't have any preventive measures at all because no one would have ever bothered with them. . . . If we are really talking business, I am for knowing that there is no virus present, knowing that there are no bacteria or toxins, and getting on with a field trial in an area where there is a reasonable chance that you might have polio and answering the sixty-four-dollar question: Did it prevent the disease? . . . Believe me, if in the Army I had to go through half of this stuff to get a vaccine to use on somebody in Japan or Korea, the war would be over long before . . ."

O'Connor objected, "Joe, you are working with captive people. . . ."

Smadel shot back, "*You* are working with captive people. These are four-year-olds. Somebody picks them up and brings them down and they get shot."

O'Connor put an end to it: "Somebody has to decide to pick them up and bring them down voluntarily."

A bit later Salk got his opportunity to tell the gathering how he, the man under the gun, wanted to proceed. O'Connor gave him the opening: "What is it that you think you ought to determine . . . by tests in human beings, Jonas?" Salk wanted to keep himself free of any obligation to inoculate twenty-five thousand people. He wanted to be free to feel his way. Now was the time to say so, without necessarily alarming or antagonizing anyone. "I would answer the question," he said, "not in absolute terms but in progressive terms . . . at the very outset to consider the inoculation of not more than two hundred people and increase that in twofold steps until you have accumulated enough individuals so that everyone is satisfied that the number has exceeded whatever the probability is of something accidentally occurring as it did with Kolmer. . . . I don't know what that number is, Mr. O'Connor. I don't know about the twenty-five thousand. I don't know *what* the number is. I can only say, let us move ahead and move ahead cautiously, and when we have the answer, then we know we have it. . . . My own feeling is that I wish we either could have withheld these experiments or this information before the polio season or, if not that, that all this experience had occurred six months earlier. Since neither of these things is true and since we are facing the reality of the time limits, I would like to have the opportunity to do as many people as I can before the season starts. And the moment the season is over to continue right into the next season." The others agreed that flexibility of this kind was sensible. They also agreed that Tom Rivers should write a letter to the *Journal* of the AMA, explaining in the name of everyone present why Salk was proceeding cautiously, and why a polio vaccine could not be ready for mass distribution until much later than the polio season of 1953.

Austin Smith, editor of the *Journal,* had already agreed to publish such a letter in his April 4 issue, one week after the appearance of Salk's report on the first inoculations.

Scientific tradition forbids the individual worker to reveal his discoveries to the public at large before giving his professional colleagues an opportunity to study and evaluate the work. In medicine the chief beneficiaries of this custom are the physician and his patient. Although the physician is highly unlikely to attend the scientific conference at which the new development is revealed and is almost as unlikely to read the learned journal in which the original report is published, the system tends to ensure that his patients will not learn of the new drug, operation, appliance, or vaccine before he does. The chances are that he and patient alike both read about the innovation in the same issue of *Time,* which gives the physician a chance to do additional homework and form some professional opinions before patients begin stampeding into his office to demand the treatment.

Physicians and their organizations are understandably inimical to anyone who complicates the doctor-patient relationship and jeopardizes human health by creating a public demand for medical materials without prior advice to and consideration by the profession. Jonas Salk, Tom Rivers, Harry Weaver, Basil O'Connor, and others involved in the polio vaccine were fully aware of this and of the sound reasons for it. They recognized the urgent need to keep the nation's medical practitioners abreast of developments. Rivers' letter to the April 4 issue of the *Journal* of the AMA, combined with caveats in Salk's article of the preceding week, would, it was hoped, prepare the medical profession for and enlist it against whatever public hysteria might result from newspaper reports that a vaccine was on the way. Later, in the not inconceivable event that some pharmaceutical company attempted to rush into production with a polio vaccine before Salk's laborious testing was completed, the profession would be in a position to judge the wisdom of the move. Furthermore, when time arrived for national field trials of a Salk vaccine, the cooperation—or, at least, the consent—of medical societies would be indispensable. And finally, if the vaccine were found safe and effective and were licensed for commercial production, the attitude of American medicine would determine the extent, the speed, and the efficiency of polio prevention campaigns.

Which are some of the more evident reasons why Jonas Salk became upset when the first news of his work appeared not in the AMA *Journal,* as planned, but in the Broadway column of Earl Wilson: "New Polio Vaccine—Big Hopes Seen." He assumed that an overzealous functionary of the National Foundation had planted the item with Wilson, to stir interest in the March of Dimes campaign. He was furious, and his mood deteriorated further when other newspaper reporters began to sniff after the story. Long before publication of the March 28 issue of the *Journal* of the AMA, he was certain that matters were getting out of control. Tom Rivers' letter and his own careful article, so replete with disclaimers, would be swept away in a deluge of premature enthusiasm.

"I went to New York and told O'Connor how I felt," he says. "I told him that what was already happening and was sure to happen after publication of my paper in the *Journal* was not only embarrassing me among my colleagues but was bound to hamper our work in the future. I said that I thought I might be able to exert a moderating effect if I went directly to the public myself and told them, perhaps by radio, exactly what the situation was and exactly why it was not yet time to count on polio vaccination. He liked the idea and arranged a national broadcast for the evening of March 26 on the Columbia radio network. It was timed, you see, to anticipate and hopefully to affect the kind of newspaper coverage which the *Journal* article would get. The broadcast was entitled 'The Scientist Speaks for Himself.' I slaved over my speech and sent a draft of it to Albert Sabin on the assumption that he, of all people, would be most alert to the problems against which it was directed. He phoned me, incensed. Told me I was misleading the public. Urged me not to do it. I was flabbergasted."

At 10:45 P.M. on Thursday, March 26, Basil O'Connor addressed the nation: "Good evening. At a time when scientific research is engaging the serious attention of all of us, it's comforting to realize that much of this research is being directed toward

the eradication of man's diseases. Never before in history have
scientists and laymen worked together so effectively toward this
great goal. You, the American people, have characteristically made
yourselves active partners—stockholders, if you will—in this co-
operative enterprise which seeks to attain better health for all
the peoples of the world.

"In our efforts to conquer polio, a disease which has increased
through the years in spite of our most heroic efforts, the National Foundation for Infantile Paralysis is the channel for your
voluntary support. In addition to its patient-aid and professional-
education programs dealing with the tragic after-effects of polio,
your National Foundation is vitally concerned with the vast
medical research program which aims to prevent polio.

"The many scientists whose investigations you support through
the March of Dimes recognize that their progress depends in large
part on your sympathetic understanding—not only of the problems they seek to resolve but also of the methods they employ to
reach those objectives.

"So that you may understand the progress made to date toward an effective vaccine against poliomyelitis, the Columbia
Broadcasting System has invited the scientist to speak for himself. Dr. Jonas E. Salk will speak to you about research he is
conducting at the University of Pittsburgh's School of Medicine
under a grant from the National Foundation for Infantile Paralysis. It's a dramatic—an inspiring—story of the contributions by
many scientists in many laboratories, each playing an important
part in a planned attack on polio. In this unique broadcast you
will hear one of these scientists speak for himself and so it's with
great pleasure that I present Dr. Jonas E. Salk. Dr. Salk . . ."

Salk had been fidgety all day but was now composed, a Saint
George ready to wield the weapons of reason against the dragon
of immoderation. His words, he thought, would keep the people, the medical profession, the National Foundation, and his
scientific reputation safe from the hazards and penalties of premature public excitement. He was not entirely wrong, except in
regard to his scientific reputation. The radio broadcast and the
television film made at the time were the beginning of his popularity and his fame, both of which he needed like a hole in the

head. "What adult would be naïve enough to think he could go on radio and television to talk about a polio vaccine he was making and expect to be allowed to retreat to his cloister afterward?" asks someone unfriendly to Salk. "Naïve, my foot. Whether he believes it or not, Jonas went on the air that night to take a bow and become a public hero. And that's what he became."

Here is what Salk told the people:

"Thank you, Mr. O'Connor. There will appear in the March 28 issue of the *Journal* of the American Medical Association a preliminary report of studies that are in progress in human subjects on vaccination against poliomyelitis. This topic has in recent months been featured prominently in the news and there has been much speculation, varying frcm cautious optimism to definite conclusion. For this reason I welcomed the opportunity, at the time of making our report, to speak to you directly to make clear the facts, so that they *not* be misunderstood nor misconstrued. I know many of the questions that are in your mind, and I shall try to answer some of them in the brief time available.

"I would like first to place before you the fundamentals of the progress that has been made over the years, by many investigators, before it was possible to consider realistically the step that was taken some months ago, when a series of experiments were initiated involving the inoculation of experimental poliomyelitis vaccines into more than 160 children and young adults.

"It is necessary that you understand the basic facts and the historical background of the problem because some twenty years ago several thousand children were vaccinated against this disease in attempts that in retrospect were premature and, for this reason, had to be discontinued. Since those first attempts that were made in the midthirties, progress has been slow because much had to be learned and techniques had to be developed. Later, when progress could be made more rapidly, it was necessary to undo the fear created by the outcome of the first experience and to reestablish confidence that new efforts could be made safely and with reasonable expectation of success.

"Before I am through it will be clear to you that the progress that has been made in recent years, and which will continue into the future, is not merely a collection of haphazard incidents, but rather a series of episodes that fit together in an orderly manner. Although contributed by many investigators in many laboratories, each represents a component part within a logical scheme. In this way a solid foundation has been built, and it is on this foundation that present and future developments will be made.

"I shall begin this brief story with the year 1909, when monkeys were inoculated with material from a patient with infantile paralysis. For the first time this disease was reproduced in an experimental animal. The microbe that caused this paralyzing affliction was so small that it could not be seen under the ordinary microscope, nor could it be made to multiply outside of the living animal. This revealed that the causative agent of poliomyelitis belongs to the group of disease-producing organisms known as viruses.

"It was not until more than twenty years later, in 1931, that evidence was first introduced suggesting that polio could be caused by more than one virus. It required almost another twenty years before substantial evidence was brought forth indicating that three different types of this virus were capable of causing the identical disease. A systematic study, which was completed in 1951, revealed the probability that not more than three types of poliomyelitis virus exist.

"I should like to explain what we mean by three types of poliovirus. First, I should say that all three polioviruses *are* similar, in that they are all able to produce the paralytic disease. The difference between them lies in the fact that each will immunize only against viruses of the same type but not against either of the other two types. For example, it has been shown that monkeys can be paralyzed repeatedly, if the virus inoculated each time is of a *different* type. A person who may have experienced either a paralytic or a nonparalytic infection due to any one of the three virus types will thereafter be immune only to a virus of the same type. But later in life he may become paralyzed when exposed to either of the two remaining types of this virus. This is the reason why two paralytic attacks can occur in the same individual. It is also the reason why poliomyelitis can occur in older persons who may have in the past been exposed to one or two types, but not all three. Therefore, for complete immunity to the paralytic disease, it is necessary that there be immunity to all three types of the virus.

"Along with the elucidation of this very important fact there have emerged several other significant developments, each of which represents a basic prerequisite for the development of an effective means for preventing this disease. One such development was the discovery that the poliovirus, which gains access to the body through the mouth or through the nose, may then be transported to the vital nerve centers by means of the circulating blood. It was soon found that the blood serum of animals or of man, after recovery from an attack of the disease, contains a substance called antibody, which, when injected at the proper time into a susceptible animal, can prevent virus of the same type from reaching the cells of the spinal cord and brain. The prevention of paralysis in this way was first demonstrated in laboratory animals. Then, during this past summer, it was shown that resistance to the naturally occurring disease could be conferred upon children, for a brief period of time, by the injection of protective antibodies contained in the gamma globulin fraction derived from human blood.

"From these observations and many others, it is clear that poliomyelitis is really not different from other diseases which have in the past been controlled by vaccination. Theoretically, a vaccine should be effective for preventing polio if the vaccine can induce the formation of the protective substances that are known as antibodies. It is essential, too, that these protective substances, once developed, will last for a sufficient period of time or be capable of being reinforced at reasonable intervals. But above all, it is necessary that the protective antibodies be induced against each of the three virus types capable of causing the human disease.

"Now, the principle of vaccination is not difficult to understand. A vaccine is made of the virus that causes the disease. Then, when the vaccine is injected, the body reacts with the formation of antibodies. These antibodies are found in the blood and remain to defend against future attacks. It is evident, of course, that the virus contained in the vaccine must be rendered harmless so that when injected it will not cause disease but will result only in the formation of protective antibodies.

"For preparing such a vaccine there must be an adequate supply of the viruses for which the vaccine is to be made. Prior to four years ago, the only source of virus for such purposes was the spinal cord of paralyzed monkeys. Then Dr. John F. Enders and his associates in Boston made the very significant discovery that all three types of poliomyelitis virus could be propagated in test tubes containing living tissue. This may be a new concept to you—that small bits of certain human or other animal tissues can live in a test tube. Such living tissues, like the animals from which they are derived, can be infected with the poliovirus. Upon this principle is based the development of methods for deriving the raw materials for a vaccine. The quantities that now appear to be required can be prepared without practical limitations, using tissues derived from monkeys.

"The next problem was to convert these raw materials, which are themselves potentially hazardous, into a harmless but yet effective immunizing agent. This is possible by chemical treatment of the virus in the fluid derived from the tissue-culture tube. For enhancing the antibody-producing power of the virus another procedure was employed, which involves the mixing of the virus with mineral oil to form a creamy mixture. Before combination with mineral oil could be considered for improving the immunizing effect of an experimental poliomyelitis vaccine, it had to be established that undesirable side-effects would not occur. Fortunately for the poliomyelitis problem this had already been accomplished in connection with studies we had carried out in an effort to develop a more effective vaccine for influenza for the Armed Forces.

"With these prerequisites for a poliomyelitis vaccine available, tests were first made in monkeys. These were then extended and in the studies which are now being reported, it has been shown that an experimental vaccine that appears to be safe is capable of augmenting in human subjects the levels of antibody to all three types of the poliomyelitis virus. It is to be emphasized —there are still many questions that remain to be answered, since these experiments are still in progress and many are quite incomplete. Nevertheless it is possible to say from the one experiment that has been under way longer than any other that antibody formation resulting from vaccination has persisted for at least four and a half months. This is the longest interval observed thus far.

"In the studies that are being reported this week, it has also been shown that the amount of antibody induced by vaccination compares favorably with that which develops after natural infection.

"The results of these studies provide justification for optimism, and it does appear that the approach in these investigations may lead to the desired objective. But this has not yet been accomplished. Although progress has been more rapid than we had any right to expect, there will be no vaccine available for widespread use for the next polio season. We want to reach our goal as quickly as possible and I am certain that you will understand that the actual accomplishment of our purposes cannot be achieved in a day. However, this objective will be achieved if we move cautiously and with understanding, step by step. Certain things cannot be hastened, since each new step cannot be made without establishing first the wisdom of the one before. We are now faced with facts and not merely with theories. With this new enlightenment we can now move forward more rapidly and with more confidence."

He had spoken with quiet assurance, great dignity, and unmistakably genuine warmth. He had spoken the truth and nothing but. He had done the best he could. Anyone who quarreled with what he said, or how he said it, or why he said it, would turn out on closer inspection to be a proponent of live-virus vaccines, incapable of accepting Salk's experimental findings on such short acquaintance. He rose from the table at which he and O'Connor were seated, put on his hat and coat, went to Penn Station, and took the night train to Pittsburgh. On arrival the next morning, he rode directly to his laboratory to see what was going on.

The vaccine was front-page news on March 27. Most of the articles were constructive, emphasizing that the miracle would not be available during the forthcoming polio season. Salk's radio speech was quoted, and so were parts of his report in the AMA *Journal*. One sample from the *Journal* article was particularly objectionable to those of Salk's professional colleagues who did not share his immunologic theories: "The indications from the total experience with mineral-oil emulsified vaccines support the thesis *that with adequate attention to the quantitative factors involved it is possible, with noninfectious material to approximate, and* perhaps to exceed, *the level of antibody induced by infection.*" His restraint in writing "perhaps to exceed" without italics did not diminish the heresy. His theory was unacceptable until proved and, in the view of those on whom the theory had an unsettling effect, he should not have spoken so much about it if he had not yet proved it.

The conclusion of his *Journal* paper was widely quoted and helped modulate public excitement while encouraging public confidence: "Although the results obtained in these studies can be regarded as encouraging, they should *not* be interpreted to indicate that a practical vaccine is now at hand. However, it does appear that at least one course of further investigation is clear. It will now be necessary to establish precisely the limits within which the effects here described can be reproduced with certainty.

"Because of the great importance of safety factors in studies of this kind, it must be remembered that considerable time is required for the preparation and study of each new batch of experimental vaccine before human inoculations can be considered. It is this consideration, above all else, that imposes a limitation on the speed with which this work can be extended. Within these intractable limits every effort is being made to acquire the necessary information that will permit the logical progression of these studies into larger numbers of individuals in specially selected groups."

Scientific advisers to the National Foundation could talk about national field trials, or about tests in twenty-five thousand children, or about getting "the" vaccine into commercial manufacture by 1954 until they turned blue in the face. Here, in the sanctified print of the AMA *Journal,* the scientist was speaking for himself, and plainly. There would be, could be no premature use of his material. There would be no field trials until he had something worth submitting to trial.

The pleasure Salk took from the generally temperate tone of the newspaper reports and from the appearance in print of his own technical paper was obliterated on March 27 by the smart-aleck press-agentry of a pharmaceutical company. He had worked with the Detroit firm of Parke, Davis & Company on development of the mineral-oil adjuvant used first in his flu vaccine and then in some of his polio preparations. In fact, he had been a paid consultant to the company. And now he was appalled to read under a Detroit dateline in his copy of the Pittsburgh *Sun-Telegraph:*

> Parke, Davis & Co. announced today it will begin shipping the new polio vaccine to all parts of the nation once final tests are completed. The drug firm disclosed also that it has closely cooperated with Dr. Jonas E. Salk of the University of Pittsburgh, who announced discovery of the new vaccine yesterday. A Parke, Davis spokesman named Drs. F. D. Stimpert, I. W. McLean, Jr., A. R. Taylor, and Arnold Hook as "assisting" in several phases of Dr. Salk's discovery. Dr. Salk said the vaccine would not be in general use until further tests are completed, but Parke, Davis said once those tests were ended it will begin quantity manufacture of the serum for widespread delivery.

Salk exploded with mortification. To be misrepresented, even by implication, as the consort of a commercial firm was more than he could endure. The news item made a joke of the academic independence that was so important to him. He asked the University of Pittsburgh's public-relations consultant to draft a rejoinder. He phoned Harry Weaver, who was counting on Parke, Davis as the manufacturer most likely to turn out large quantities of adjuvant-fortified vaccine when the need arose for commercial production. He steamed and fumed at Weaver about his absolute refusal to be a promotional pawn. He then wired Harry J. Loynd, president of the drug company:

THE STATEMENT . . . ATTRIBUTED TO PARKE DAVIS IS DISTURBING MISLEADING AND EMBARRASSING TO ME. THE WORKING TOGETHER OF PHARMACEUTICAL AND UNIVERSITY LABORATORIES DOES FUR-THER SCIENTIFIC PROGRESS BUT I DO NOT ADMIRE AND AM PER-SONALLY RESENTFUL OF THE MOTIVATIONS FOR THE ISSUANCE OF YOUR STATEMENT.

The University released a statement to the press later that day: "The developing and testing of a polio vaccine just reported by Dr. Salk of the University of Pittsburgh was not done jointly with any pharmaceutical laboratory nor with financial support from any agency other than the National Foundation for Infantile Paralysis. A vaccine has not yet been fully developed but is in the process of development. There should be no implication that pharmaceutical laboratories are now in a position to deliver such material. In the past, cooperation and assistance of many technical groups has been helpful and will continue to be sought as new problems arise. All commercial laboratories are interested and many are working on this problem but none has any exclusive information about this current research beyond that reported in the *Journal* of the American Medical Association. The statements made by Dr. Salk and issued to the press in New York on 26 March and the paper in the *JAMA* provide all, repeat all, the information for which there is any authority for publication or interpretation."

He got no vaccine work done that day or the next. Or the next. April came before he was able to free himself sufficiently to resume his experiments with human beings. The newspapers and magazines refused to leave him alone. Until he rebelled and uttered threats, various arms of the National Foundation also refused to leave him alone. Nobody would leave him alone. His mind was being trampled by all the interruptions. The only reporter he could trust was John Troan of *The Pittsburgh Press*, a sensitive professional. "Why do they all want to know what I eat for breakfast?" complained Salk to Troan. He later came to respect Robert Coughlan of *Life* and, still later, Edward R. Murrow. But a journalist was a professional viper until proved otherwise, and Salk had neither time nor desire to sit around and await proof. When he could, he fled into his office, closed the door, and had himself represented as busy.

"It was impossible," says Salk. "It was outrageous. No work could be done with those people stumbling all over the place. A request would come from the National Foundation in New York to permit a photographer to take pictures in the lab. Sounds simple, but it meant the loss of a day's work for us. What was more important, the work or the pictures?"

Not that he could get much work done even if he refused the pictures. Albert Q. Maisel remembers a visit to Salk's laboratory in behalf of *Look* magazine. Maisel, an expert on the National Foundation and its research program, bore the highest possible recommendations. "When Jonas heard what we wanted," he says, "he withdrew to his sanctum and didn't reappear for hours. I found out that the proposal of a picture-story was such a trauma to him, coming as it did on top of so many similar traumata, that he coped with it by lying down on his settee and brooding about it. He didn't want to say yes and he wasn't sure he should say no. He was in a dreadful stew. He'd come out and ask a couple of questions and then go back inside and lie down some more. I sympathized with his plight but he gave me a pain in the ass. I wasn't the only one."

Francis Pray, the University's public-relations man, sent some hard-won photographs of Salk's laboratory to Roland Berg, a science writer employed at the time in the public-relations department of the National Foundation. The April 4 issue of the *Journal* of the AMA was due in another day or two. It would contain Tom Rivers' letter and Salk's report on the results of his influenza experiments, a paper he had written when, as he puts it, "the influenza people's noses got out of joint because of all the attention given to the polio work." Pray moaned in his letter to Berg, "We're having trouble today with the influenza story. *The Pitts-*

burgh Press jumped the gun this morning and the roof is falling in with the other papers. However, the University will come out all right.

"The only trouble," he concluded, "is that the whole situation is making Salk extremely nervous and somewhat combative, and I'm sure he'll need some sympathetic treatment during the next week or so if he is not to continue to irritate the newspapers."

The April 4 issue of the *Journal* was another installment of Salk, Salk, Salk. His flu vaccine with adjuvant had induced high levels of antibody, and the antibody had endured for more than two years, so far. Elsewhere in the magazine, an editorial urged the medical fraternity to keep cool about polio vaccines: "With the approach of the poliomyelitis season, there is danger that many will advocate larger and faster steps. Although the laboratory tests and early clinical studies appear to be most encouraging, the degree of safety of the preparations now being tested can be determined only after extensive studies in the field. To this end Dr. Rivers and his committee offer support to the Pittsburgh investigators to expand these studies at a cautious pace. This extension will require the cooperation of the public who will seek advice from the family physician."

Some pages later the *Journal* published Tom Rivers' letter, which listed the experts who had participated in the February conference and said:

> It is evident that any investigator who possesses a promising preparation for the prevention of a human disease is faced with a decision either to conduct innumerable small-scale studies with relatively few subjects, in an effort to develop more effective preparations before widespread application, or to employ the experimental preparation in large numbers of human subjects even though the preparation may not yet possess all of the refinements ultimately desired. The temptation will be great to urge that the experimental vaccine studied by Dr. Salk be prepared for immediate widespread use. Such enthusiasm, however, should be tempered not only by the realization of what we do know but, perhaps even more, by what we do not know. . . .

As a result of . . . critical evaluation . . . this group
recommended that (1) before large-scale field trials are
initiated, additional studies involving increasing numbers of
persons be undertaken to extend the experience already
accumulated; (2) such studies be limited to Allegheny County, Pennsylvania; (3) such studies be stopped for that part
of the summer of 1953 during which poliomyelitis might
be prevalent in order to avoid instances of poliomyelitis
occurring shortly after vaccination being erroneously attributed to the immunization procedure; and (4) these investigations be resumed on an ever-increasing scale after the
poliomyelitis season is passed and that they be conducted
in a sufficient number of communities to permit a controlled evaluation of the effectiveness of this preparation
during the summer of 1954. . . . The opinions herein expressed are conveyed to you in the hope that every assistance will be given to Dr. Salk so that it may be determined whether the preparation that he has developed is the
long-sought practical means for the control of human poliomyelitis. In conclusion I would like to emphasize Dr. Salk's
own statement that, while the results obtained in his studies
"can be regarded as encouraging, they should not be interpreted to indicate that a practical vaccine is now at hand."

Salk had helped draft this. It suited him, all in all. He could
live with it. It did not pin him to any specific number of experimental inoculations. It left him some elbow room. If he could
now contrive to get back into his lab, free of external botheration,
he might perhaps get some work done.

John J. Wydro, the National Foundation's man in western
Pennsylvania and an old acquaintance of Salk, had been trying
without success to get the scientist to help out the local March
of Dimes with a speech here and there and a press conference
or two. He finally wrote to his regional director, Ernest M. Frost,
who replied:

Re: Dr. Salk and press conferences. Your recent memo
dated April 6 . . . was turned over to the public-relations
department for answer. I wish to quote their reply to me.
"Dr. Weaver has requested that Dr. Salk *not* be asked to

talk or give press conferences. National Foundation Headquarters is not handling Dr. Salk's public relations but Mr.
Pray of the University of Pittsburgh is the one assigned to
Dr. Salk in such matters." Under the circumstances, John,
I feel that for all intents and purposes, you had better consider Dr. Salk as being located in New Mexico, Arizona, or
points west. In other words, hands off. . . .

10

SALK'S REFUSAL TO ISSUE BULLETINS, SPIN PERSONAL ANECDOTES,
or coin epigrams had a pacifying effect. So did reminders by the
National Foundation that polio prevention was still in an experimental stage. Salk no longer was big news. The tumult subsided.
By April he had recaptured enough privacy to permit sustained
concentration. New, more potent batches of vaccine were made
ready for human use. Salk inoculated his wife Donna and their
sons, Peter, who was now nine, Darrell, six, and Jonathan, three.
Harry Weaver and Hart Van Riper, medical head of the National
Foundation, brought their own children to Pittsburgh for injections. In May, Salk resumed experiments at the Watson Home,
mainly with local schoolchildren whose blood lacked detectable
antibody. The effects of the various new vaccines would be highly
significant. If the safety record remained unblemished and some
of the vaccines were potent enough to induce antibody in impressive amounts, it might just be possible for Salk to support the
Weaver-Rivers-Smadel demand that a national field trial be held
early in 1954.

Weaver required no such encouragement. On May 18, after
consultation with Basil O'Connor, Rivers, and other individuals
central to his plans, he issued a confidential memorandum outlin-
ing "the conduct of field trials to determine the efficacy of a
poliomyelitis vaccine." Between November 15, 1953, and the
following May 30, nine field teams, directed by Salk, would inject
the material into the 388,800 children expected to volunteer for
the study in 108 counties. Paralytic polio among the vaccinated

[170]

would then be compared mathematically with incidence among approximately 3 million unvaccinated children of like age in the same counties. This study of the vaccine's effect would be carried out independently by prominent virologists such as Charles Evans, Tom Francis, Howard Howe, John Paul, Andrew Rhodes, Albert Sabin, and Herbert Wenner. The whole undertaking would be the responsibility of the National Foundation, guided by an Advisory Committee on Virus Research and Epidemiology, of which Tom Rivers would be chairman. Other members would be Drs. Thomas P. Murdock of the AMA; David E. Price of the United States Public Health Service; Joseph E. Smadel of the Army Medical Center; Ernest L. Stebbins, Director of the Johns Hopkins School of Hygiene and Public Health; Norman H. Topping, who had become Medical Vice-President of the University of Pennsylvania; and Thomas B. Turner, Professor of Microbiology at Johns Hopkins. The first meeting of the special committee took place on May 25.

"I had no inkling of these conferences and plans until sometime in June," says Salk. "Weaver and Rivers had apparently been meeting in Rivers' office at the Rockefeller Institute for weeks, planning field trials of a product that did not exist and planning my duties for me as if I were a staff technician. I think I got my first word of what was going on from a newspaper announcement that field trials were to start in the fall. It was an awful spot to be in. I still react when I think about it. There was only one thing to do. I demanded a meeting with O'Connor to protest what was going on and to insist that I be included in future discussions of plans which affected me and my work."

O'Connor, Salk, and Weaver met in New York on the evening of June 22. If they had not composed their differences at that time, it is inconceivable that the national field trials of the Salk vaccine could have taken place in 1954 or that the polio preventive could have been made available for public use in 1955. Salk got what he wanted from O'Connor. And O'Connor got what he wanted from Salk.

"I had the greatest respect for O'Connor's character and intelligence," says Salk, "but I knew how anxious he was for results and what a hard driver he was. I was not completely sure I could

persuade him that he and Weaver were going overboard with
their plans. I was not even sure that our interview would end
amicably. But I was completely sure that I could not tolerate
the existing situation. I brought a lot of technical material with
me and went through it with O'Connor. I showed him that we
had not even begun to try to develop a vaccine—in the sense
of developing a product—but were still running immunological
tests of fifty or sixty different variables. I showed him that the
inactivation process had not been worked out yet: We had just
begun to discover that we obtained better results if we exposed
the virus to less Formalin but at a temperature approximating
human body heat—somewhere around 37 degrees centigrade. This
seemed to give the widest margin of safety, allowing us to preserve
high levels of antigenicity even when we exposed the virus to the
chemical for days after infectious living virus was no longer
detectable. And we also had just begun to develop the key concept of the inactivation curve, a semilogarithmic graph on which
the inactivation process could be plotted. The idea was that
infectivity diminished at a constant rate. If it was tested at intervals and the results conformed with this declining straight-line
graph, it meant that all the variable relationships involving temperature, time, and ratio of virus to Formalin were under proper
control. If the curve departed from the straight line, we needed
no animal infectivity tests to know that something had gone
wrong. It was really quite simple and immensely convenient, but
it required more investigation before it could be regarded as
established.

"The same was true of the mineral-oil adjuvant. I wanted to
use it and Harry Weaver was committed to it, but a few things
had happened which made me begin to think that an adjuvant
might cause more public-relations difficulty than it was worth. In
April Herald Cox had warned a scientific meeting in New York
that the oil emulsion might produce cancers years after injection.
One contaminated batch of adjuvant had actually caused running
sores in one of our flu experiments, and some scientists were uneasy about the stuff. Fortunately, we had begun to see a way
around the problem. Our vaccines were becoming so much more
potent than they had been that it now seemed possible to get the

same effect with two or three injections of an aqueous preparation as with a shot containing adjuvant. This too was under study,
was important, and needed time."

Having heard all this and more, Basil O'Connor told Salk,
"Now I don't want you to worry about a thing, Jonas. Nobody is
breathing down your neck. It's your work and nothing will be
done with it that you don't want done. You have my word on it.
But just tell me one thing: Do you think it possible—all I mean
is *possible*—that you might come up with something for field trial
by the end of this year or the beginning of next?"

"Yes," said Salk. "It's possible."

He smiles in recollection. "O'Connor may be a driver, but he
is practical, which means he is flexible. All the assurance I needed
was his word that the National Foundation would proceed with
flexibility and would not jeopardize my work and me by usurping
my right to see the work through to a reasonable conclusion. And
all the assurance he needed was my word that I, too, would be
flexible and would not allow some fringe prerogative or academic
ritual to blind me to the social urgency of the work. I was as
anxious as he to prevent polio as quickly as possible, and he was
as anxious as I that the scientific needs of the situation get proper
attention. We understood each other perfectly, as only a couple
of crazy guys like us can. I felt much better when I returned to
Pittsburgh. I could not have worked as I did during the rest of
the year without the security of that understanding."

June 24, 1953
(SALK TO O'CONNOR)

Dear Mr. O'Connor:
  I am sure that you know without my telling you so what
a pleasant experience it was for me to be able to discuss
with you the many questions we did the other evening. It
was very nice of you, indeed, to have made the opportunity
possible—an opportunity which revealed to me so clearly
what Gibran must have meant when he said,

> "It is well to give when asked, but it is better to give
> unasked, through understanding; and to the open-handed

the search for one who shall receive is joy greater than giving."

The only reason for O'Connor's willingness to sheath the spurs with which he had prodded polio research to the threshold of triumph was that Salk had offered scientific reasons for doing so. O'Connor is a doer, a driver, and a demander of the impossible and does not deny it, but he insists with pride that he has never trespassed on the preserves of science. "Scientific work is the responsibility of the scientists," he says. "The responsibility of the layman is to see that they have ample opportunity to do the work." And he adds, with the candor that has unnerved more than one scientific mandarin, "I don't mean that the layman cannot sometimes help the scientists to get the work done more *intelligently* or more *expeditiously,* but the scientific decisions are made by the scientists."

It has been charged that O'Connor's zeal for rapid accomplishment imposed undue haste on Jonas Salk, the pharmaceutical industry, the medical profession, and the vaccine-licensing agency of the federal government, and was primarily responsible for the technical and administrative confusion and the paralytic cases that marred the record of the Salk vaccine after its licensing for general use in 1955. The charge wounds O'Connor. The jocularity with which he discusses it cannot conceal his distress. "Can you imagine a barefoot Wall Street lawyer like me telling a Jonas Salk or a Dave Bodian or a Tom Francis or a Tom Rivers to compromise his scientific standards and renounce his integrity? Can you imagine me being dizzy enough to try? Can you imagine any of them consenting? I wanted a good vaccine as quickly as possible. What good would a bad vaccine have done anybody, quickly or not? If the vaccine had been no good, then it would have been proper to accuse someone of undue haste. But the vaccine was good. The National Foundation discharged its responsibilities well. It could not do the government's job or the pharmaceutical companies' job or the medical profession's job. It owes nobody an apology for the speed with which it made a good vaccine available to the people, saving Lord knows how many thousands of lives."

It had taken more than a century to establish Edward Jenner's smallpox vaccine as medically respectable. O'Connor's advisers assured him that, in the traditional course of events, it might take four to eight years of testing dribs and drabs of Salk's vaccine in clinical trials before its safety and efficacy could be accepted. O'Connor rejected such a delay as a crime against mankind, tradition or no tradition. When he learned that the largest and most elaborate medical experiment in world history could tell the tale about a polio vaccine in one fell swoop, he chose the swoop.

Tom Rivers' special Vaccine Advisory Committee, which convened for the first time in May 1953, met frequently during the ensuing months and in April 1954 awarded its influential medical-scientific endorsement to the launching of national field trials. The committee consisted entirely of men who had identified themselves as cordial to the idea of injecting a polio vaccine into large numbers of volunteers. They needed only to be satisfied that the plans for doing so were appropriate to the situation. In this respect the group differed significantly from the National Foundation's Immunization Committee, where dubiety reigned. Some members of the Immunization Committee, such as Albert Sabin, John Paul, and William Hammon, were unconvinced that a killed-virus vaccine could work effectively. They harbored serious doubts about Salk's theories, to say nothing of his experimental findings. Other members, including even the dispassionate David Bodian, were not entirely satisfied that Salk had selected the most suitable virus strains, a view that Sabin shared with endless vehemence. Still other members, including Sabin himself, were personally engaged in polio vaccine research, the competitive nature of which exposed their scientific objectivity to occasional stress. Some of the members had assumed and others had at least hoped that the inactivated polio vaccine, a mere stopgap, would be developed and tested by the kind of team effort that had proved so satisfactory to them during the virus-typing program. In sum, they wanted to tell Salk and other junior vaccine experimenters what to do and how to do it, and they wanted each man's work to be confirmed in other laboratories. Salk, of course, had had his fill of such procedures while typing viruses. Nor did O'Connor, Weaver, or Rivers see merit in the idea.

"We formed the Vaccine Advisory Committee to break a log-jam," says Harry Weaver. "The Immunization Committee was not able to function with the necessary dispatch. It could get entangled for months in technical debates. Furthermore, its members were virologists and the decisions on which we needed help were not exclusively virological. The Vaccine Advisory Committee, with experienced public-health men like Drs. Price, Stebbins, Topping, and Turner, and Tom Murdock from the AMA Board of Trustees, and virologists like Rivers and Smadel, was a far more efficient group."

Rivers once commented to Saul Benison about the Immunization Committee, "Some members always thought that their responsibilities transcended mere discussion, and when the Vaccine Advisory Committee was formed, they felt that they were being bilked out of making decisions on the Salk vaccine. I tell you this because I want it clearly understood that some members . . . resented the organization of the Vaccine Advisory Committee. They didn't keep their feelings secret, as a matter of fact, and were pretty vocal about it. . . . We didn't think that it would be proper for anybody who had a personal stake in immunization research, whether it was Salk, Sabin, or anybody else for that matter, to be allowed to vote. . . . We thought that such decisions were best arrived at by disinterested people who were not necessarily virologists."

One of the first recommendations of the new Vaccine Advisory Committee was that the design of the projected field trials be altered. Weaver, seeking maximum simplicity and economy, had suggested that school-age volunteers be vaccinated and that the paralytic polio rate among them be compared with the incidence among nonvaccinated children of the same ages. He changed his view after consultation with Dr. Joseph A. Bell, one of the nation's leading epidemiologists, whom he induced to take a leave of absence from the National Institutes of Health and help the National Foundation plan the test. Bell pointed out and Weaver and the committee agreed in principle that if all volunteers were given vaccine, the socioeconomic and medical differences

between those who volunteered and those who did not might
make hash of the field study.

It was well known that families of superior education and
economic standing were most likely to submit their children to
experimentation of this kind. It also was well known that low-
income families, living in inferior neighborhoods, were much less
susceptible to paralytic polio, tending to contract the nonparalytic
form of the disease in infancy and remaining immune for life.
Thus, a project to vaccinate all volunteers would immunize the
most susceptible children. If 1954 turned out to be a year of relatively low incidence, with few real epidemics, the polio rate among
the vaccinated might be unimpressively similar to that among the
unvaccinated. Therefore, the vaccine might be good, but the field
trial might fail to prove it. Furthermore, with everyone knowing
who had been vaccinated and who had not, human bias would
become operative at every step. Polio was difficult enough to
diagnose without people and their doctors deciding in advance
who had it or who did not—decisions that could be affected by
individual preconceptions about the vaccine or about Jonas Salk
or about the March of Dimes.

The only unimpeachable testing method was the so-called
"double-blind," whereby half the volunteers would be injected
with the vaccine and the other half with a preparation that looked
like it but was entirely unrelated. In trials of that kind, neither
the volunteers nor their parents nor their family physicians nor
those who administered the injections would know who was getting
vaccine and who was getting placebo. All such information would
be coded, and the code would be locked in somebody's safe until
time came to compare polio cases in the vaccinated with polio
reported among receivers of placebo.

Weaver recalls, "We were making history with this vaccine.
We had come that far without a serious misstep and it seemed
ridiculous not to finish the job in first-rate style. The results of
a double-blind study would be irreproachable. Any other kind
of a study would invite carping and criticism. If we wanted the
medical profession and the public to accept the vaccine quickly,
the double-blind was the best way. The alternative might have
placed the vaccine in a category similar to that of earlier prepara-

tions which were never tested properly, like the smallpox, whooping cough, and rabies vaccines, doubts about all of which persist to the present day."

When Salk finally heard what was going on and demanded his June interview with O'Connor, one of the prospects that vexed him most was that of being rushed into a double-blind field trial with a product far short of what it should be. "The sensible thing, I thought, was to accept the urgencies of the situation and continue improving the vaccine. I thought the field trial should be designed to permit this, not prevent it," he says. "Precisely because we were in a hurry to conquer polio and also because, as Tom Rivers used to say, 'If we don't act quickly, everybody and his aunt is going to be selling half-baked polio vaccines by 1955,' I thought we should concentrate on polio prevention and be less concerned about making epidemiological history with an elegant double-blind study. I was afraid that, for some people, the *kind* of test had become more important than the kind of protection the vaccine might be able to provide. I frankly feared what this sort of inverse thinking might lead to. I had little confidence that these people would be able to carry out their elaborate plans within the time allotted. I was afraid that they would fall on their faces and drag polio prevention with them.

"I told them over and over again that I wanted a field trial with observed controls not only because it was simpler but because it was suited to the realities. I wanted to know who had been vaccinated so that blood samples could be taken promptly. If tests then showed that a certain batch of vaccine was producing unsatisfactory results, the children could be revaccinated with better material. At the same time, we could be taking steps to improve the manufacturing process and avoid new batches of inferior vaccine. Finally, I was uncomfortable about giving placebo shots to children, depriving them of immunity in what might turn out to be an epidemic year. Many public-health officials agreed with me on this.

"The issue of field-trial design was typical," he goes on. "Here you had someone like myself, trying to adapt to the needs and circumstances, and there you had this rigid insistence that a 'product' be submitted forthwith for ceremonious testing. The emphasis on 'product' and on ritual and on looking good in the eyes of certain elements in the scientific community was being allowed to obscure the real purpose of everyone's work, which was the prevention of polio. For arguing this as often as I did I earned scorn as an eccentric nuisance. My desire to continue my experiments to the last possible moment so that the vaccine might be as close to 100 percent effective as possible was considered intolerably presumptuous. What a dreadful inconvenience to impose on designers of field trials and on pharmaceutical manufacturers and on government officials!"

"Jonas was indeed in an uncomfortable position," says Weaver. "He felt that his baby was premature and was being torn from his arms. He did not like this. Yet it couldn't be any other way. He couldn't take responsibility for the field trials himself. He could not be architect, carpenter, and building inspector—or judge, jury, prosecutor, and defense attorney all at once. Another problem, I think, was that he was already completely satisfied in his own mind about the validity of the killed-vaccine principle but feared the results of a double-blind test might cast unfair doubt on the principle, either because the vaccine used in the trial was not as good as it might be in later years or because of lapses in the manufacturing process. This was understandable. But I and others were reasonably confident that what we finally subjected to field trial would be more than adequate to sustain his principle—always allowing for the possibility that the principle might not be as valid as we thought. In any event, the pitfalls of a field trial that relied on observed controls struck us as more hazardous than those of a double-blind study."

Among the influences that encouraged the Foundation to conduct an irreproachable test of the vaccine were the public razzberries directed at Salk and the Foundation by the authoritatively implacable Albert Sabin. "Since there is an impression that a practicable vaccine for poliomyelitis is either at hand or immediately around the corner," observed Sabin at the annual meeting of the American Medical Association in New York on June 3, 1953, "it may be best to start this discussion with the statement that such a vaccine is not now at hand and that one can only guess as to what is around the corner. The future possibilities of a vaccine for the control of poliomyelitis depend in large measure on what we still must and can learn with the new tools that have become available to poliomyelitis research in the last few years. The objective is clear: to imitate what nature does for 99 to 99.9 percent of the population but without incurring the one in a hundred to one in a thousand risk of paralysis which in many parts of the world is the price for acquiring immunity to poliomyelitis."

It was a stern paper, well reported in the press. "The basic information that one should have about a vaccine before it is tested in human beings is not yet available," Sabin told his audience of physicians, most of whom had read with innocent pleasure about Jonas Salk's tests in human beings and knew that Salk contemplated more. Sabin also said, "The Type I Mahoney virus, used in Salk's preliminary work, is a good example of a virus that should not be used, because in minimal doses it produces paralysis . . . readily. . . ." And: "Unquestionably the ultimate goal for the prevention of poliomyelitis is immunization with 'living' avirulent virus which will confer immunity for many years or for life. In my opinion, more investigators are now needed in the field of poliomyelitis than ever before, because it is more correct to say that we have only just begun to learn than to create the impression that the job is nearly finished."

Sabin had done this kind of thing before and would do it again and again. The National Foundation could not fight him without compromising its position as an even-handed patron of virological science. It had to try to live with him.

Accordingly, Hart Van Riper sent the following message to the National Foundation's public-relations director, Dorothy Ducas, after reading an advance copy of Sabin's AMA paper: ". . . it is the Medical Department's suggestion that there be no attempt on the part of the Foundation publicity personnel to defend Dr. Salk or to attempt to discredit Dr. Sabin. Our only comment is that, in the scientific world, people are entitled to their own opinions. . . ."

The critiques with which Sabin regaled influential audiences were bound to sap medical confidence in the safety and potency of Salk's vaccine, casting doubt on the wisdom of the projected field trial. The Foundation's unwillingness to scuffle with him in public was attractively dignified but could not begin to solve the problems he was creating. And he proved impervious to private appeals. Weaver, Rivers, Van Riper, and others were unable to persuade him that the situation was not nearly as bleak as he insisted. In the end the Foundation coped with his disapproval by deed, not word. If the field trial of 1954 was superbly designed and executed, its scientific bona fides beyond reproach, some credit is due Sabin for nipping at the organization's heels.

"He won't give me the time of day," complained Hart E. Van Riper to O'Connor about his discomfort as Harry Weaver's nominal superior. "I can't find out what's going on in my own research department until he's good and ready to tell me. Even his secretary won't answer my questions." In the summer of 1953, with the vaccine field trial certain to occur within months, Van Riper was annoyed and alarmed by the feeling that he was unwanted at his own table. He was Medical Director of the National Foundation. His responsibilities in the field trial would be numerous and manifest. He would be a spokesman. His neck would be out. It was insane not to be privy to all developments. "Either Weaver goes or I go," Van Riper told Basil O'Connor, registering his protests for one last time.

"I'm leaving for Europe," said O'Connor. "You're in charge of the medical department. Try to salvage the situation but do what you think best." He was playing it by ear. He did not want to lose either Weaver or Van Riper. Each was uniquely valuable. If Weaver went, scientists would suppose, with some warrant, that a dispute about the design of the field trial had been a factor. If Van Riper went, it might unsettle the medical organizations with which he had been dealing and on which the Foundation counted for support during the mass inoculation experiments. Considering the needs of the next months, O'Connor found it impossible to choose between the men. Yet he could not compose their differences. He had tried threats and imprecations, which had not worked. He had tried sweet diplomacy, and it had failed.

He had been having his own problems with Weaver. Most of

these derived from the man's serene belief that the Salk vaccine
was at least as much a Weaver show as a Salk or O'Connor show.
"You could understand why he might feel that way from an
operational point of view," says O'Connor. "He had piloted the
ship, and brilliantly. Now that we were entering the port he gave
the impression that he was the only person who belonged on the
bridge. There was no malice in it. He just was all fired up, apparently convinced that if Salk and I and Van Riper would only
leave him alone things would work out better. I mean it was
getting to be a hell of a situation where even I began to feel
unwelcome at certain meetings, and some of Weaver's assistants
were under orders to report to him only, and poor Jonas was out
in Pittsburgh having plans made for him without his knowledge
and getting all lathered up, and poor Van Riper was in a
similar fix in New York."

"This was the only time Mr. O'Connor ever let me down,"
says Van Riper. "He told me to handle the problem my own
way and took off for Europe. So I handled it."

Within hours of O'Connor's farewell, Van Riper and Weaver
fell into combat over a lengthy field trip Weaver wanted to make,
beginning in the South and working his way north, visiting communities that might take part in the vaccine field trial. Van Riper
objected to various features of the excursion. When Weaver announced that he would resign rather than submit to such nit-
picking supervision, Van Riper accepted the resignation. O'Connor
is still sorry it happened.

"The real reason that relations deteriorated as they did," says
Weaver, "was the design of the field trial. Jonas and O'Connor
never really bought the idea of a double-blind study. It was
thrust on them by me and the vaccine committee and they resisted it endlessly. As the months passed and time pressures
increased and the question of field-trial design remained on the
verge of resolution without ever being resolved, I became more
and more anxious, and more and more dissatisfied. I wanted the
field trial to be *right*. On the day of the big blow-up with Van
Riper, September 1st, I would have had to bet that Jonas would
ultimately have his own way—a field trial designed to his own

specifications and subject to years of criticism in scientific and medical circles."

Jonas would have bet otherwise. Although he and O'Connor had pledged to carry on with complete reasonableness and full flexibility and in tandem, they expected only moderate flexibility from the personalities with whom they were negotiating about the field trial. They were prepared to settle for the best they could get. O'Connor could not tear up all existing plans of the Vaccine Advisory Committee and insist on a fresh start—the nature of which Salk would prescribe—without destroying everybody else's morale, estranging Tom Rivers and his legion of scientific friends, and wrecking the vaccine project. O'Connor's appreciation of these truths was complete. Salk's was less so: He tried several times to talk O'Connor and the committee into reversing previous decisions, but he did it as a supplicant, and without threats, and with every intention of keeping the promise he had made to give O'Connor the fullest cooperation possible —short of undermining his own scientific beliefs.

"On September 9th I attended a meeting of the vaccine committee in New York," says Salk, "and reported some of the results of the May and June inoculations. About six hundred vaccinations had been given, all without ill effect. Half had been vaccine with adjuvant, the rest had been an aqueous preparation. Although the adjuvant had caused no trouble and I was sure it would not, I already was convinced that we would have to abandon it. Joe Bell was at the Foundation by now and was loaded with evidence that tended to support fears about the effects of the stuff. I might have opposed him and the others who felt as he did, but did not have to. The aqueous vaccines seemed to be quite satisfactory. It was beginning to look as if one or two doses of a good aqueous vaccine primed the immunological system of the average individual—conditioning it, you might say—so that, even if the antibody level was not especially high, any subsequent exposure to natural infection produced a recall effect, like a conditioned reflex, and protective antibody was produced at a great rate. This booster effect, or hyperreactivity, as some call it, suggested that a killed-virus vaccine potent enough to prime the immunological system in this way could provide immunity as durable as one got from the disease itself. It was a controversial idea, of course, but terribly exciting and completely plausible. The Vaccine Advisory Committee did not fall in love with it at first sight, naturally, but wanted to get rid of the adjuvant. It voted to have a field trial in which two or three doses of an aqueous vaccine would be given."

On Joe Bell's recommendation, it also was decided that all batches of the commercially produced vaccine used in the field trial would be tested for safety not only in the manufacturer's laboratory but in Salk's and at the Biologics Control Laboratory of the National Institutes of Health at Bethesda, Maryland. The manufacturer in question, Salk discovered, was Parke, Davis, with whom Harry Weaver had negotiated an oral agreement on production of a vaccine with adjuvant. Salk had mixed feelings about being thrown together again with the Detroit firm. "They had capable people there," he acknowledges, "including Fred Stimpert, who had been in polio research before I was even in influenza. This was both an advantage and a disadvantage. The disadvantage was that other polio experts could not be expected to have much enthusiasm for my vaccine, being wed to theories of their own. In normal circumstances this would have been no concern of mine, but an administrative matter for the top executives of Parke, Davis. But these were not normal circumstances. The pressures of time were cruel. We needed adequate commercial production by the end of 1953 and could not achieve it unless I worked closely with the Parke, Davis laboratory, and vice-versa. So this was another ticklish spot. I had still not had time to advance my work to the point of deciding which combination of virus, Formalin, temperature, inactivation time, acidity, and so on would yield a vaccine most suitable for the field trial, yet here I found myself to all intents and purposes committed by Weaver to assist in the manufacturing process. Naturally, the expected took place. The Parke, Davis people were interested in 'product.' Since I had none, but had only a set of principles on which more work was needed, they concluded that they might be able to develop a vaccine of their own before I could develop mine."

As usual, meals, sleep, and recreation were forms of self-indulgence, and were allowed to interfere with work only when they could not be avoided. Salk passed through the family home in Wexford like a visiting relative. He napped when he had to. He ate sandwiches at his desk. He gave inoculations, ran antibody tests on blood samples, improved his inactivation process, ran safety checks in laboratory animals, compiled and studied reams of statistics, completing two or three years of work in less than one. Some of the progress was facilitated by a technical feat for which Salk's principal assistant, Julius Youngner, was largely responsible. John Enders had noticed that when red phenol was dropped into a living tissue-culture it turned yellow, the metabolic acids of the tissue having affected the color. But if virus were multiplying in the tissue and destroying it, less acid was present and the dye remained reddish. Salk suggested that the phenomenon could be put to more refined use. Youngner developed a color test that not only demonstrated the presence of virus but permitted close approximation of their number. Ranging shade by shade from red through orange to yellow, the color scale remains the most accurate method of titrating viruses, enabling workers to do in a few days what formerly required weeks of animal tests. This achievement caused great jubilation in the Salk camp and attracted favorable comment throughout virology.

On September 24, Salk and O'Connor met privately in Syracuse, New York, where O'Connor had gone to make a speech. Again the scientist poured out his heart, this time about the Parke, Davis situation and Joe Bell's approach to a field trial. It seemed that Parke, Davis had been failing to duplicate the results of Salk's inactivation process. Live virus was present in pilot batches of vaccine that should have been noninfectious. Salk, who knew that this was impossible unless the inactivation process was somehow misunderstood or misapplied, had begun to fret about the commercial laboratory's less than reverent attitude toward his ideas. It turned out later that the major reason for the unreliability of the inactivation method at Parke, Davis was an incubator so erratic that its temperature varied by two or three degrees centigrade from the control setting, raising hob with the results. Salk did not yet know that this was the reason, and his nerve ends were twanging. He urged O'Connor not to take the chance of permitting Parke, Davis or any other commercial house a monopoly on production of field-trial vaccine. Too much could go wrong, and for too many reasons. His belief that certain personnel at Parke, Davis might be more interested in developing a vaccine of their own than in learning how to make one of his was heightened, furthermore, by knowledge that the firm was experimenting with an ultraviolet inactivation process as a possible substitute for his Formalin process. O'Connor agreed to inquire. He would canvass other pharmaceutical companies for help in the field trial if the need turned out to be as acute as Salk thought.

As to Joe Bell's design for the most ramified and unassailable medical field trial ever attempted, O'Connor shared Salk's reservations. Apart from Bell's dedication to the principle of a double-blind study, with which it was immensely difficult to quarrel in face of Tom Rivers' own convictions that such a study was essential, Salk and O'Connor were dismayed by the formal punctilio with which Bell, as it seemed to them, approached the task. On September 16, the day after a conversation with Bell, Salk had written the epidemiologist an astringent letter to that effect. As an example Salk mentioned the desire of Bell for preliminary inoculation of several thousand children, by way of establishing that the commercial vaccine was safe for use on a still larger scale. Salk's own view was that no such thing should be done until laboratory tests had indicated that the material was not only noninfectious but capable of inducing the formation of protective antibody. "If it is not antigenic," he wrote about the projected preliminary trial, ". . . then there is little point in determining whether or not it is dangerous."

His tone rose an octave or two when he addressed the next point: Bell's tentative field-trial schedule called for the taking of blood samples to measure antibody increases at specific times. A new recommendation by the Vaccine Advisory Committee that two or three shots be given to each field-trial volunteer at predetermined intervals had aroused objections from Bell. He had

said that he hoped only one would be given during the field trial
so that the blood-sampling schedule would not be interfered with.
"If the choice," wrote Salk, "is between doing something that will
increase the likelihood that the vaccination procedure . . . will
be successful or doing something that will tell us why a partial
procedure may have failed, I would think there is no choice. . . .
If, therefore, the recommendation that a booster dose be given
just before the season will conflict with plans for drawing blood
samples, I would be much in favor of seeing some modification
in the plan for drawing . . . blood samples. . . ."

O'Connor and Salk found themselves in full rapport at Syracuse. Bell was an epidemiologist of the highest standing. He had
contributed a great deal to the National Foundation's knowledge
of how a field trial should be conducted, but his emphasis on
procedure, sometimes at the expense of what Salk and O'Connor
regarded as more urgent questions, made his brief career at the
National Foundation bumpier than he or it could possibly have
enjoyed. "Don't worry about a thing, Jonas," said O'Connor.

The Vaccine Advisory Committee reconvened on October 3
and 4 at the Greenbrier in White Sulphur Springs. To the irrita-
tion of some of its members, O'Connor invited Salk, keeping his
promise that the scientist would not be excluded from matters
affecting his work. "The committee needed to be posted on
Salk's progress and on changes in his approach to polio immunization," recalls a close observer, "but it didn't necessarily want
him interfering in its work. He was supposed to be the developer
of the vaccine, period, and had no especially legitimate claim to
the privilege of deciding how the scientific community should go
about evaluating the stuff. It bothered some of the members of
the committee to have him buttonhole them in the corridors and
try to tell them why one kind of field trial might be better than
another." With Weaver gone and Bell's position becoming more
strained by the day ("He was a fine man," says O'Connor, "but
he wanted to retest everything from the Year One, as if nothing
had yet been tested."), Salk was renewing his efforts to convince
the National Foundation's expert advisers that everyone would
be better off with his kind of field study.

"You couldn't blame a young man in his difficult position

from behaving as he did," says a former Foundation official. "He
was in a worse predicament than even he realized. He probably
knew that if the field trial showed the vaccine up as a dud his
reputation would suffer. But he may not have known what
others knew; as Frank Horsfall once told Tom Rivers, 'If the
vaccine fails it will be a black mark against him but if it suc-
ceeds he'll be ruined. It's affixed to him and he to it.' We could
see that success, if it came, would make a public god of him,
distorting the meaning of his work, crediting him with achievements that belonged to Enders and Bodian and so many others,
and lousing him up with other scientists. We could see it, as I
said, but it was not our headache. Our job was to get a reasonably
promising vaccine and see that it was tested properly. I tell you
true, we used to cringe when we saw Salk coming. When Hart
Van Riper's phone rang at night, his wife used to say, 'Brace
yourself for an hour's chat, dear, it's probably Dr. Salk with
some new ideas.' "

On October 16, after having been rebuffed at Greenbrier,
Salk sent an intensely emotional eleven-page letter to O'Connor.
It was a last-ditch letter, a plea, a prayer, an appeal to reason,
marked by thickets of almost impenetrable prose set aflame
by the scientist's conviction that the National Foundation was
sacrificing itself and him in the ritual of a double-blind field
trial. He wrote to his friend:

> I would like to elaborate for you certain thoughts that
> have occurred to me since our meeting at Greenbrier. If I
> compare my thinking with that of those who have been
> guiding the planning to date, and if it appears that I do so
> in a way that casts doubt on the wisdom and judgment that
> has prevailed, I do so not because I wish to raise ill feel-
> ings but rather to gain perspective and confidence for a
> realistic and strengthened program that will achieve the
> objectives we both seek. . . . As you know, a meeting was
> held, in New York in May, of the Scientific Advisory Com-
> mittee, in relation to vaccination studies, and at that time
> plans were discussed. As you know now, I was not at that
> meeting and therefore had no opportunity to convey directly
> my own thoughts in the matter or to discuss any of the

plans or proposals that were being considered. Approximately
one month later, Dr. Weaver came to Pittsburgh to discuss
with me matters of budget, and on the morning of that day
he announced to me the plan that is now well familiar to us.
I was asked my reaction to this and said it was something
I would have to think about and the immediate reaction was
a negative one, since I had been thinking only in terms of the
earlier plans that Dr. Weaver and I had been considering together. I was told that I would have to give him an answer by the end of the day and that his recommendation
was that my reply be in the affirmative because in effect this
was something that was going to be done anyway. I suggested that we go on talking about other matters, and in
the course of that time I would be thinking about his
suggestions. At the end of the day I told him I would prefer not to give him an immediate decision which would, at
that moment, be that I was opposed to such a plan; I wanted
a chance to talk with you. This, you will remember, was
done at the end of June when I came to New York for
dinner. . . . I think you know from the way I talked in
New York, at the end of June, that I thought it was unwise
for me to be excluded to the extent that was indicated by
Dr Weaver. It seemed to me that an unnecessarily awkward
and cumbersome plan was being formulated for a big job
that could, in spite of its size, be handled much more simply.

I must tell you quite honestly that I was a very unhappy
person for many months and regretted that I could not
talk to you alone rather than through Dr. Weaver or in his
presence. The nature of the relationship was such that I can
see now there was little that I could do, having been bound
by a system and a superstructure that allowed no room for
the expression of individuality. Here, as Nesbitt points out,
is the growth and development of the "big brother" who tells
you what to do. Under such circumstances there is no alternative other than destruction; either the destruction comes from
without, by opposing that which has been superimposed, or
comes from within because you cannot live with yourself
when you are forced to compromise certain fundamental
principles.

I think I now see that my having been kept apart from
the Foundation and from its committees has allowed for

the development of the differences of opinion that now exist;
if not for this, together we could have synthesized and amal-
gamated the best judgment and thinking that could be
brought to bear for the solution of the problem. I know that
two heads are better than one, and I know there are other
ideas in the world that are good—ideas other than my own. I
usually like to test my own thoughts and see how others
react to them, particularly when the thoughts have to do
with action that involves other people. If only I were to be
the victim of the consequences of my actions, then I would
not need to consult anyone but myself; however, it would be
foolish to take steps of the magnitude that we are considering without knowing how those who are involved, or will be
affected by such action, will feel. I think it is equally important, if not more so, to consider *feelings* as well as
thoughts in connection with the problem at hand.

Before continuing with the salient features of this extraordinary document, which became more fervid as its author peeled
off layer after layer of his customary reserve, it should be pointed
out that both O'Connor and Salk now view the letter with com-
posure. "He was properly upset by the way those people were
treating him," says O'Connor. "They could be brutal, you know."
As to his own reaction to the caloric content of the letter at the
time he got it, O'Connor only shrugs. "Jonas was the nicest, sin-
cerest young man you ever met," he says. "There wasn't a mean
or selfish bone in his body. If he wanted a different kind of
field trial than was being planned, it was because he believed
the job could be done better. And his arguments were powerful,
make no mistake about it." When Salk saw the letter, more than
ten years after he had written it, he also shrugged. "Behind all
the emotional slop," he said, "was the need to communicate a
sense of very real danger. I felt that the Foundation had committed itself to a plan that it was not able to implement, at the
expense of a plan that would work." Wrote Salk:

> I was a bit shocked to find that committee people with
> whom I talked before the Greenbrier meeting maintained
> one position in conversation with me and then reversed

themselves completely when faced by other members of the
committee. This kind of social facilitation is hardly to be
admired. . . .

As you know from the background I have given [he
said further on], the pursuit of the problem to its logical end
was taken away from me in spite of my willingness and desire to participate as fully as possible. . . . It would seem to
me that one way of putting things back on the right track
would be to request a reconsideration of plans, not by the
Weaver-selected committee, but by a committee composed
more representatively of people who are to be affected by
the work that is contemplated. I am thinking here of pediatricians who are more practically minded, particularly from
the viewpoint of the clinical diagnosis of paralytic poliomyelitis . . . as well as people representing the public view
—the mothers and fathers and just the ordinary garden
variety of people with common sense. These people could
add measurably to the perspective of the presently constituted committee. I would think that as a sequel to Dr.
Weaver's resignation, it would be quite in order for there to
be a change in the character of the committee that was part
of the original scheme.

Harry Weaver, depicted as the source of so many difficulties,
says he heard about the letter not long after it was written. Unlike
O'Connor and Salk, he now concedes few merits to Salk's valiant
arguments against a double-blind field trial. But he is surprisingly
indulgent about the portrait Salk painted of him. "Perfectly natural," he says evenly. "When you leave a top administrative
post, you expect to be blamed for everything you left behind
that anyone does not like. It happens all the time. It's a law of
life."

In reviewing his attitude toward the use of a placebo in a field
trial, Salk wrote:

. . . if we are aware of the fact that the presence of antibody is effective in preventing the experimental disease in animals and in man, then what moral justification can there be
for intentionally injecting children with salt solution or some
other placebo for the purpose of determining whether or not

a procedure that produces antibody formation is effective. . . . I would feel that every child who is injected with a placebo and becomes paralyzed will do so at my hands. I know this truthfully is not the case, but I know equally well that if this same child were to receive a vaccine that proved to be effective, then he might have been spared. . . . The use of a placebo control, I am afraid, is a fetish of orthodoxy and would serve to create a "beautiful epidemiologic" experiment over which the epidemiologist could become quite ecstatic but would make the humanitarian shudder and would make Hippocrates turn over in his grave. I would prefer not to lay hands on any person and allow him to have the belief that he may be a fortunate one of the 50 percent who will receive something that may have some value, and then have him realize later that while Dame Fortune was at his threshold she did not enter.

You see, Mr. O'Connor, it is not a question of science, or of ethics, or of morality, upon which those who maintain the contrary position make their stand, but rather because of false pride based upon values in which the worship of science involves the sacrifice of humanitarian principles on the altar of rigid methodology. If there is a choice between the use (1) of an approach that respects human life and dignity, and acknowledges personal feelings that are common to us all, and (2) a method that may be regarded as superior, for reasons that are not very convincing, and at the same time does not consider the human values to which I refer, then, in my opinion, there is no choice but to follow a course based upon the principle, "Do unto others as you would have others do unto you."

. . . In talks with many people in our own group, in Pittsburgh, and others as well, I found but one person who rigidly adhered to the idea of a placebo control and he is a biostatistician who, if he did not adhere to this view, would have had to admit his own purposelessness in life. I hope that it will be possible for us to discuss these questions in a way that would help resolve this problem to our mutual satisfaction and in a way that I know your conscience, as well as mine, dictates. If we recognize that a problem exists, I believe that we together can see a way for a solution that would provide the necessary face saving

for those who may have to change the position they now
maintain. If necessary, I am perfectly willing to be the
sacrificial lamb because otherwise something much greater
than myself will be sacrificed.

. . . If vaccine is to be administered to a narrow age
band of the child population, without the use of a placebo
control, the ease with which this can be accomplished will
amaze those who have had no experience of this kind and
will, I am sure, be a source of tremendous gratification to
you personally. I know I tend to be a dreamer at times
but my feet are really solidly on the ground in this respect
because I have had some experience over the past several
years in the conduct of studies of this kind. The expression
"It is easy if you know how" is quite applicable here and I
would like to give you the benefit of what experience I
have.

. . . I know that this year is the year of decision. I am
confident that a study can be carried out easily and in
sufficient time. . . . It is my sincere hope that no state of
nervousness or anxiety will develop within the Foundation
staff and this will be true only if we free ourselves entirely
from the preconceptions and misconceptions that have prevailed to date. Let us separate the wheat from the chaff
and together plan the recipe that will bake the cake that
tastes the way we want it to and not merely one that looks
nice because it is epidemiologically perfect.

Neither Hippocratic conviction nor personal anxiety nor Salk's
sensitivity to the promptings of both can fully explain his huge
effort to convince O'Connor that the Vaccine Advisory Committee, its field-trial recommendations, and Dr. Joseph A. Bell
should follow Harry Weaver out the National Foundation's door.
Salk could not have written so intemperate a letter unless confident that O'Connor would view its excesses with understanding
and sympathy. Also, he had been emboldened by some of the
nation's foremost pediatricians, who shared his attitude toward
the field trial. On October 9, at the annual meeting of the
American Academy of Pediatrics, he had disclosed the results
of 474 successful new inoculations, concluding: "All that should

be inferred now is that studies are progressing satisfactorily; there have been no setbacks nor anything but revelations that shed more light on the course ahead. We must continue to regard the experimental developments to date as providing immunologic markers along the way that tell us whether we are on the right road. That there is more to do now than before indicates that we have not stumbled down a byway but have selected a road, with many lanes, that seems long indeed. Our problem is to select not only the fast lane but the one that is safest and most certain." Afterward, most of the pediatricians with whom he chatted agreed with him that human trials should facilitate vaccine improvement rather than measure vaccine inadequacy. He did not fail to report these sentiments to O'Connor.

On October 31, Joe Bell returned to his post as Medical Director of the United States Public Health Service. His plan for a double-blind field trial had still not been adopted, although the Vaccine Advisory Committee and most members of the National Foundation's medical-scientific staff strongly favored it and were preparing to implement it. Indeed, some staff members, perturbed because so much time had passed without a final decision on field-trial design, began encouraging certain public-health officials to increase the pressure on O'Connor, who had been hearing for some months from various state health departments that the placebo control was essential to medical science.

But O'Connor was engrossed with more immediate questions. It had become apparent that Parke, Davis would be unable to solve its vaccine-production problems by the end of the year and that the field trial could therefore not begin as soon as O'Connor and Weaver had hoped. Furthermore, there were strong suggestions that the company, as Salk had foreseen, might prefer to attempt its own vaccine and abandon Salk's. Before O'Connor could have a field trial, he needed an assured supply of vaccine. And before the supplier could give such assurance, it needed to know exactly what it was supposed to produce. This, of course, was one of the factors that irked Parke, Davis: Salk was reluctant to commit himself to precise vaccine specifications until the last possible minute, implying that Parke,

Davis would not be ready for detailed instructions until it demonstrated an ability to handle tissue-cultures, inactivation, and
other fundamentals.

As if these uncertainties and anxieties were insufficient stimula-
tion for Basil O'Connor during that busy November, Albert
Sabin and John Paul came to a Detroit meeting of the Foundation's Immunization Committee determined that the field trial
should be postponed until a new, safer Type I virus was substituted for the virulent Mahoney strain that Salk was using.
His MEF-1 (Type II) and Saukett (Type III) strains were
accepted with relative equanimity, even by persons who had no
great faith in the inactivation concept, but the Mahoney strain
had a terrifying reputation. It was considered hard to kill and
lethal to monkeys and humans when not completely killed. Sabin
and Paul were by no means alone in their apprehensions. David
Bodian and Tom Francis (who was on sabbatical leave and
absent from the meeting) were no less fearful, even if more
hospitable to Salk's theories.

The discussion about Mahoney was intensified by the Immunization Committee's irate conviction that it had been side-
tracked so that its expert warnings and searching questions
might not delay the Salk project. The atmosphere of the meeting
was heavy with recrimination and intrigue. If minutes were taken
(a matter about which recollections vary), they are no longer
in evidence. Some members still insist that Salk, badgered and
shaken, promised the committee that he would replace the Mahoney strain as soon as he could. They say the promise was
made in a context that seemed to guarantee that the feared
virus absolutely would not be used in a field-trial vaccine.
Others, including Salk, dispute this. "I had been screening and
testing other Type I strains for many months," says Salk, "trying to find a less virulent one that would be more acceptable to
persons who did not appreciate or endorse our inactivation
principles. But I had been unable to find one antigenic enough
for vaccine use. After repeated discussions of the Mahoney
issue, I had come to the point where I tended to answer demands
for a substitute by agreeing in principle that a substitute should
be sought. This was preferable to drawn-out rehashes of all my

previous reports about inactivation, antigenicity, and infectivity. After all, we had now shown beyond doubt that if the inactivation procedures were followed conscientiously and competently, poliovirus was rendered noninfectious, whether it was the Mahoney strain or not. Nevertheless, I agreed, *in principle,* that a less virulent, equally antigenic strain was preferable to a more virulent one."

He remembers feeling like an outcast at the Detroit conference. "I'd walk down a corridor," he says, "and people would stop talking as I approached. By now Sabin and Paul had made several efforts to persuade me to call off the field trial. Sometimes it was done directly and sometimes through mutual acquaintances. I was told that I was going to ruin myself. And I was being used by O'Connor. And I was abandoning my scientific independence. And I would regret it until my dying day. And the whole thing was premature. And an accident—such as deaths caused by the Mahoney strain after a failure of the inactivation process—could disgrace virology. And what was the big hurry? Polio had been with us for centuries. Couldn't we wait another few years? And so forth and so on. I tried to listen politely and to explain that things were not as dire as all that but it was no use. Minds were already made up. What had once been skepticism about attempts to develop an effective killed vaccine was now becoming ideological conflict. It was developing into a war against the killed-vaccine principle waged by persons devoutly unable to reconcile themselves to its heresies, which were my heresies. How dare I persist to the stage of a national field trial with the abominable concept that a killed, noninfectious vaccine could provide immunity as certain and as lasting as the natural disease? How could a killed vaccine contain the magical life force of the natural disease—its *élan vital?* How dare I claim that the world is round, not flat?"

An old friend of Basil O'Connor, a veteran public-health physician named G. Foard McGinnes, had joined the headquarters staff of the National Foundation. His knowledge of polio vaccines and polio workers was impressive. He had presided over the meeting at which Tom Rivers and Jim Leake dismantled Kolmer and Brodie. Later he had worked with O'Connor at the Red Cross. His new job was vaccine procurement, a responsibility which plunged him into the Parke, Davis difficulties. "Besides the technical problems they were having with Jonas' process," he says, "the Parke, Davis scientists were pessimistic about what he was driving at. They had more respect for the ultraviolet inactivation work being done by Albert Milzer at Michael Reese Hospital in Chicago. They thought it a less complicated procedure which could be adapted to commercial production much more rapidly. Also, they didn't think Jonas was far enough advanced in his own research to justify all the tooling-up they were doing. I remember one New York conference at which one of them actually questioned Jonas, got answers which did not satisfy him, and said, straight out, 'Jonas does not have a vaccine.'"

Although McGinnes declines to explore memory beyond this point, there is no doubt that elements in the Detroit pharmaceutical firm were so dubious of the Salk situation and so eager to get into polio vaccine manufacture that an official of the company approached McGinnes with a suggestion that the National Foundation bypass Salk and do its field trial with a Parke, Davis vaccine.

"No question about it," says Salk. "I was upsetting them more than they were upsetting me. They thought I was cuckoo to insist that things be done stepwise—principles first and details second. To them a product was a product. A vaccine was a vaccine. Where were my specifications? Why weren't all the *i*'s dotted and *t*'s crossed? Why did I answer questions ambiguously, saying that inactivation could be done in any of several ways, and yet why did I insist that they adhere scrupulously to whichever way was selected? If we had not been in a hurry to get vaccine for field trial, my attitude would have been different, of course. I would then have been confident that time would bring these people closer to an appreciation of the principles involved. But since we lacked the luxury of time, I felt

that the only viable alternative to a first-rate performance by
our vaccine suppliers was no vaccine at all. Any other alternative
was too dangerous."

After plant investigations by McGinnes and Salk, and several
technical conferences, one of John Enders' associates went to
Detroit at the National Foundation's expense to help improve
the firm's tissue-culture techniques, after which Parke, Davis had
relatively little difficulty with Salk's process. By the time this happened, however, O'Connor had ended Parke, Davis' monopoly.
He held a meeting of pharmaceutical manufacturers, asking if
any were interested in getting into vaccine production. The
spokesman for one company, which had no facilities for such
work, altruistically proposed that the other firms manufacture
the vaccine without profit. Most companies wanted to know
whether there would be any patent problems, and how much
royalty would have to be paid to the National Foundation or
Salk or both, if the vaccine eventually were licensed for commercial sale. O'Connor explained that all National Foundation
research grants forbade patents or royalties: If the Salk vaccine
proved effective, it would belong, without charge, to any manufacturer in the world capable of producing it.

"That was some meeting," says O'Connor. "Jonas had been
talking for months about the probability that the vaccine could
be close to 100 percent effective. But during this meeting I
asked one of the company presidents, just for fun, how effective
the stuff would have to be for him to want to sell it to the
public. He said, 'Oh, maybe 25 percent.' And someone else said,
'Perhaps 15 percent.' I was stupefied. You learn something
every day. Fifteen percent effective means that for every hundred
unvaccinated people who got paralytic polio, eighty-five vaccinated people would get it. But there were some fine people
at that meeting. We couldn't have had our field trial in 1954 if
Eli Lilly and Parke, Davis hadn't come through as they did. And
they didn't get a cent out of the field-trial vaccine, either."

Salk's relations with Lilly, an Indianapolis firm, pleased him
mightily. "They had no polio experts out there," he says, "and
were willing to build their program from the ground up. They
encountered practically no trouble, because they were free of

preconception. Before the field trial, one batch of their vaccine turned up with live virus in it—a human error which was caught in ample time. Otherwise they produced dozens of successive batches of high quality vaccine without a hitch. It was most gratifying to me and most profitable to them later on, when the vaccine was licensed for public sale."

On November 10, while all these negotiations with virologists and manufacturers were in progress, Drs. Albert Milzer, Sidney O. Levinson, and Howard J. Shaughnessy told a meeting of the American Public Health Association in New York that they had tried to duplicate Salk's inactivation process and had found that it did not work. "We followed very rigidly the conditions of Formalin inactivation as outlined by Salk," said Milzer. "For reasons not apparent to us we were not successful in consistently completely inactivating the virus with Formalin, residual infectivity being manifest both in tissue-culture tests and monkey inoculation.

"Before undertaking a field study to evaluate a poliomyelitis vaccine," he announced, "we feel that it would be advisable to proceed cautiously in order to be certain that there are no ill effects and that no risks are taken, for we must avoid the tragic consequences that have accompanied poliomyelitis vaccine research in the past."

Milzer and his associates at Michael Reese Hospital were far more confident of the safety of the ultraviolet inactivation method on which they had been working and in which Parke, Davis was so interested. Their vaccine, said Milzer, "produced a consistent and significant rise in antibody titer to the three types of poliomyelitis virus in most of the human volunteers studied." Furthermore, their inactivation process was "proved by critical safety tests, which included both repeated monkey and tissue-culture inoculation."

The Milzer report was just what O'Connor and Salk needed on top of all their other difficulties. Hart Van Riper commented for the National Foundation in frigid words: "Failure of some scientists to reproduce Dr. Salk's results for making a safe polio vaccine is due to the fact that they have not followed his exact methods. In Dr. Salk's vaccine the virus is killed by the application of a concentration of Formalin at a given temperature and degree of acidity for a sufficient period of time. As an additional safeguard, the treatment with Formalin is carried beyond the minimal time required, as indicated by the laboratory tests, to increase the margin of safety to a point beyond which all doubt disappears. Apart from these considerations is the unquestionable evidence derived not only from extensive laboratory experiments but from more than six hundred volunteer human subjects in studies conducted over a period of more than a year."

Salk had studied ultraviolet irradiation while working under Tom Francis at New York University and had kept in close touch with it to be sure that it was less satisfactory than Formalin. He issued a statement of his own: "Before we touched a human subject, the most stringent safety tests that could be devised by us or anyone else were carried out. As a result, we can state flatly that the vaccine as prepared by us is devoid of any infective virus and that no human being has been, or ever will, in any field trials, be inoculated with any material that has the remotest suspicion attached to it."

It was possible, Salk added, that Milzer had failed to encompass the fact that virus concentration varies from tissue-culture to tissue-culture. Perhaps he had worked with a highly concentrated batch of virus and had not exposed it to the Formalin for a long enough time.

"That may be the reason," responded Milzer, making a concession which got less publicity than his first announcement. "The difference in the concentration of the virus may be the key to the matter. We did not get the impression from Dr. Salk's original report that a higher concentration of virus requires longer treatment with Formalin." He also said, "I did not say that Salk's vaccine was not safe. Absolutely not. We have never had his vaccine to test, and we've never even seen it. All we did was follow his recipe and the cake did not come out right for reasons not apparent to us."

Fair enough. But damage had been done. Milzer, the ultraviolet man, had irritated the medical profession's canker of doubt, already inflamed by the public reflections of Albert Sabin, the live-virus man. On November 12, Salk addressed the National Foundation's annual conference on women's activities and said, "I give every possible assurance I can and that medical science can that the antipolio vaccine will be safe. I will personally be responsible for the vaccine."

This was brave, but more was needed. When Salk had told the Academy of Pediatrics that his problem was "to select not only the fast lane but the one that is safest and most certain," he had refrained from full description of the image that was in his mind. "During this entire period," he now says, "I felt like someone driving a team of wild horses and being whipped at the same time."

On November 13, the Vaccine Advisory Committee met amid echoes of Milzer and Sabin, reviewed its attitudes toward a field trial, and again proclaimed allegiance to the double-blind. Tom Rivers and the others conceded, however, that the difficulties of vaccine procurement and the shortness of the time that remained to organize and mount a national trial might make it necessary for the Foundation to take the simpler route, the one advocated by Salk. Jonas was present and spoke forcefully in behalf of his preference. The committee's respect for O'Connor's integrity, and its confidence that he would respect its beliefs, may be measured in its decision to abide by whatever plan he finally adopted.

Three days later, O'Connor told a press conference that the field trial would start on February 8, 1954. Between five hundred thousand and 1 million schoolchildren of the second grade would be vaccinated before the start of the polio season. The rate at which paralytic polio occurred among them would be compared with the incidence among unvaccinated first and third graders. Salk had won. The field evaluation of his vaccine would rely on observed controls.

The victory did not last. The decision failed to jell. "The trouble we got," remembers a former staff expert of the National Foundation, "from scientists and a few state public-health officers about this kind of field trial was more or less predictable and probably could have been handled. But Tom Rivers and Mr. O'Connor now saw beyond that trouble. They saw that the

real difficulty with this second-choice kind of field trial was that
the National Foundation would be running it. There had been
talk from time to time about the embarrassments that might
arise if the results of the trial were evaluated by us, the sponsor-
ing organization. Salk, for one, had spoken about this rather
early. But not until the date and design of the trial were announced did it become so clear that the study ought to be done
under unmistakably independent supervision. Tom Rivers suggested that we try Francis Schwenkter, who was Professor of
Pediatrics at Johns Hopkins, but Schwenkter turned us down.
Then Tommy Francis' name came up."

"I remember stopping off at the National Foundation office in
New York during the summer of 1953," says Dr. Thomas Francis, Jr. "I was on my way to Rome for the International Congress on Microbiology, after which I was going to take a sabbatical tour of European laboratories. Tom Rivers told me a
big secret—the Foundation was going to announce a polio vaccination study in large numbers of school kids around the country. The next day Harry Weaver asked me what I thought of
it. I was not opposed to it. I also remember spending a day with
Joe Bell, discussing different kinds of controls that might be
used. I was in Rome at the congress when the newspapers reported that a field trial was to be held. You'd have thought somebody exploded a bomb. There was a rump session on the steps
of one of the buildings at the University of Rome, and a tremendous amount of opposition was expressed. 'Too much, too
soon,' someone said, and a lot of the scientists there felt the
same way. 'What is enough and when is soon enough?' I asked.
'How long do you wait to put something to test?' One of the
men finally said to me, 'Well, come what may, I'm glad I'm not
going to be doing it,' and I answered, 'So am I.'
    "I spent that summer touring from one lab to another and
one scientific congress to another. In November my wife and I
got to England from Helsinki and she decided she'd had enough
laboratories and wanted to go home. Just about that time came

a transatlantic call from Hart Van Riper. 'Do you think the University of Michigan would accept a grant for you to evaluate the results of this field trial?' he asked. I told him, 'I don't know, but I'm on sabbatical and I'm not interested.' Well, he wanted to know when I was coming home and when I told him I'd be back early in December he insisted that I come in and see him. Before I left England I spoke to Bradford Hill, a great statistician, and told him about the Foundation's plan to use observed controls. He said, 'I wouldn't touch it with a ten-foot pole.' I agreed."

Francis arrived in New York on Saturday, December 5, and had breakfast with O'Connor and Van Riper. He listened to their description of the field trial and said he thought it was a mistake to use what he called "naked controls."

"You're taking the orthodox approach," said O'Connor.

"That's all very interesting," answered Francis, "but a double-blind study with an injected control is the truest tried method. It's the only way to get reliable data."

"O'Connor got quite annoyed at me," says Francis, "probably because he'd been through this so often. Finally he asked if I'd be willing to think about taking on the job. I told him that I was reluctant even to think about it, because if the field trial was done on a messy basis we might end with false or dubious statistical results, harm medical research, and dampen the confidence of the public. O'Connor's eyes lit up at that. He caught that, all right. But the conference ended without any agreement one way or the other."

On December 6, Francis spoke to Jonas Salk about the advisability of an injected control group and was heartened when Salk agreed with him completely.

"Agreed with you completely?" gasped Hart Van Riper, his senses reeling. "For God's sake, he's been agitating against this for months. Are you sure?"

"Sure I'm sure," said Francis.

Having been dedicated since his tenderest years to avoidance of error, idleness, caprice, and other pollutions of the excellence to which he is committed, Salk is totally unamused that members of the National Foundation staff and the Vaccine Advisory

Committee thought he contradicted himself when he endorsed Francis' views. Such imputations of frailty invariably disturb him, calling his attention once again to the sometimes unbridgeable chasm that separates his values from those of others. Although he does not profess infallibility, he submits plausible, praiseworthy reasons for everything he has done. Some, who know him, including some who love him, think that some of these reasons do not occur to him until after the fact and that his inability to condone his frailties may have generated a protective inability to recognize them. His critics, who do not love him, contend that he simply capitulated to Tom Francis in the interests of expediency, wanting more than anything on earth that the field trial of his vaccine be scientifically respectable and having abandoned any hope of reaching this goal by his own route. Nevertheless, he explains most reasonably why he agreed with Francis after months of propounding a diametrically opposed view. Whether or not the explanation represents what one observer has described as Salk's gift of retroactive infallibility, it shows how his mind works.

"In all previous discussions of the field-trial problem, including my long, emotional letter to O'Connor," Salk says coolly, "the issue had been entirely different. We had been debating how the National Foundation should run a field trial. I knew as well as anyone that a double-blind trial was preferable in many ways. But until it became possible to have a Tom Francis in charge, I had no confidence that the field trial could be conducted properly. Francis, I believed, would do it well or not do it at all. With him in the picture, designing the experiment and evaluating the results independently, my arguments in behalf of a simpler project remained as valid as they had been but no longer outweighed the arguments in favor of the more elaborate plan. Because I respected Francis and was relieved and happy that he might do the job, I told him so."

Francis deliberated for weeks. "I had no stake in the thing. It meant no money to me," he says, "and I knew that ten days after my report came out, my work would be forgotten and the bands would be playing elsewhere." In this he was wrong. The

Francis Report is a permanent classic in the literature of epidemiology. "And the University of Michigan was leery about the level of the work," he goes on. "If it was going to be a mess, they wanted no part of it. But a lot of people were anxious to have me do it. I got phone calls from all over, people saying, 'If you do it, we'll support it.' I'd known that I had a respectable position in this world but I was gratified to discover how respectable. Anyhow, one day at a meeting where I was trying to get advice from public-health officers, epidemiologists, statisticians, and other experts of the sort who would be concerned with the field trial, Hart Van Riper said, 'Whoever directs the study will have full authority to design it, aside from commitments already made.' He obviously was speaking for O'Connor, telling me that I'd get no further argument about an injected control, although some states would have to be done the other way because O'Connor had already made promises to their health officers."

On January 13, Van Riper wrote a memorandum to O'Connor, saying, among other things:

> I am sure that Dr. Francis would not have considered any part of this evaluation had we not indicated to him that there were certain states which were primarily interested in an injected control, and given our assurance to Dr. Francis that we would certainly cooperate in making materials available for such an injected control.
>
> . . . we are still considerably delayed in production, and Dr. Francis, being advised of this, asked me the specific question, "Would the National Foundation consider conserving available vaccine to the end that the greatest proportion of it could be used in those areas where an injected control could be accomplished?" I told him that I could not answer that specifically but would say that you were so interested in the accomplishment of the field trials that you would be willing to abide by his recommendation on any procedure which would give the greatest assurance of an answer to the effectiveness of the vaccine.
>
> . . . Finally, I would think that the Foundation should yield to any reasonable request which Dr. Francis might make which might influence his decision to undertake the

evaluation, since at this late date I would be at a loss as to where to turn to find someone who would be competent to do the evaluation in such manner as would meet the critical eyes of those who we must expect will criticize the results in any event, no matter who may do it.

On January 25, having obtained space for his Evaluation Center in the University of Michigan's former Maternity Hospital, where Jonas Salk's sons Peter and Darrell had been born, Tom Francis reviewed his understanding of the project in a letter to O'Connor. The study was to be conducted under an "open-end" grant from the National Foundation, permitting the University of Michigan to spend more than a million dollars, if necessary. The National Foundation would have no supervisory powers. All raw data from the field studies and the analyses made of them would be in Francis' exclusive possession. The results would be published only when Francis was good and ready (and not before 1955), and "the evaluating group should be free of undue pressures." If the National Foundation had anything to say to Francis during the period of study, it should endeavor to do so through Hart Van Riper. "It is in the effort to ensure an adequate measurement of the vaccine's influence through the collection and analysis of good and, so far as possible, unbiased data that these points are presented," wrote Francis, "for without agreement in understanding and in purpose, fulfillment of the objectives would be quite unlikely. . . ."

Francis was in the driver's seat. He remained there until April 12, 1955, the day on which Basil O'Connor, Jonas Salk, and the people of the world finally heard how well the vaccine had performed during the previous summer.

11

DURING THE EARLY MONTHS OF 1954, JONAS SALK'S USUAL WORK-
ing day began before dawn, ended after midnight, and persecuted
him with a self-replenishing excess of new problems. Most of
the problems were foreign to his field of academic science. But
they demanded his utmost attention: Human lives were at stake;
public confidence in medical research was at stake; Basil O'Connor's crusade against disease was at stake; and Salk's own career was at stake. Having compacted with O'Connor to respond
to human exigency this year and forgo the luxury of waiting
until next, Salk could protect himself and the undertaking only
by engaging in activities that ordinarily would have been none
of his business.

During the Parke, Davis crisis of the previous November, for
example, Tom Rivers, Joe Smadel, and Dr. William G. Workman, of the Laboratory of Biologics Control of the National
Institutes of Health, had insisted that Salk put a vaccine formula
into writing so that manufacturing processes could be perfected
in time for the field trial. "This was entirely out of my line,"
says Salk. "I could state the principles from which my vaccines derived, of course. And I could provide concrete examples
of how we had applied the principles in our laboratory. But I
was not an industrial engineer and had no time in which to
become one. Specifications for large-scale manufacture could not
be my responsibility."

Rivers and Smadel had been hectoring him about this for
months. Rivers was especially annoyed at Salk's evasiveness, sus-

pecting that the younger man was buying time in which to improve his vaccines, deliberately delaying the day when one or
another would be frozen into official print. When Smadel finally
offered to draw up the specifications if Salk would only provide
the necessary information, Salk accepted at once. "Go ahead,"
he said with relief. "It will be a big help to me. I can't write
specifications and do my own work at the same time."

The relief was transient. Merely to commit Salk's laboratory
procedures to English prose was no guarantee that Parke, Davis,
Eli Lilly, Cutter Laboratories, Wyeth Laboratories, and Pitman-
Moore could adapt the document to their own needs and forthwith
make a product of uniform quality. It took many weeks, much
correspondence, several conferences, and numerous changes in
the specifications before the manufacturers pronounced them intelligible and practical. Each amendment required deep consideration by Salk, lest the practicalities of commercial manufacture
collide—as they sometimes did—with the demands of his science.

Nor did all questions about the specifications originate among
the manufacturers. The government man, Bill Workman, raised
many of his own. His natural caution, which was plentiful, had
been exacerbated to the brink of dread by the rapidity of events.
One of his former associates explains, "Anyone in Workman's
job would have felt the same. He was a public servant who woke
up one day in the kind of spot which few public servants enjoy,
fraught with potential danger to the public and therefore threatening disaster to his bureau, the National Institutes of Health,
the Public Health Service, the Department of Health, Education,
and Welfare, and the Eisenhower Administration. He knew the
hazards of viral vaccines and the difficulties of converting the
procedures of a small laboratory into those of large-scale manufacture. He had been burned once, when an encephalitis vaccine
that was supposed to be inactivated turned out to be virulent. His
guard was up. So here come Salk and O'Connor and Rivers,
proposing to give half a million injections in the spring of 1954
when no manufacturer had as yet produced even one shot
of vaccine.

"Now, in normal circumstances this would not have been

Workman's problem; his bureau was concerned only with the licensing of manufacturers and their commercial products. The law required no license for a field trial. But the National Foundation had put us into a box from which we couldn't escape. We were damned if we helped with the field trial and damned if we didn't. If we helped and the vaccine killed some of the kids in the field trial, we'd be ruined. But if we did *not* help and the vaccine turned out to be a killer of children, we wouldn't really be off the hook either. Congress and the public would demand to know why an arm of the Public Health Service had not been protecting the public's health. So far so bad. Let us now suppose that we avoided the field trial, but the vaccine turned out to be safe and effective. We'd then have been in the soup for fair. We wouldn't know enough about the vaccine and the ins and outs of its manufacture. We would not be able to act on license applications for months. But the public would want action in hours. After all the publicity about the polio menace, they'd want polio shots immediately. So, the way things were developing we needed to be in on the field trial and learn all we could about the vaccine as quickly as we could. Why didn't we know much about it to begin with? Simple. Polio research had been exclusively a National Foundation show up to that point. The government had been completely out of it."

For all these reasons, relations between the National Foundation contingent and most functionaries with whom they dealt at the National Institutes of Health fell somewhat short of the idyllic. The NIH people may have been only casual acquaintances of polio but knew full well that Salk's theories were disputed in his own field. His assurances that poliovirus died at a reliably constant rate when exposed to Formalin under properly controlled conditions were granted small credence in Bethesda. His semilogarithmic, straight-line graph, similar to those that depict the half-life of radium or the progress of a first-order chemical reaction, left Bethesda cold. His contention that nine days of inactivation in accordance with the graph would permit the survival of poliovirus at the rate of not more than one infectious particle for every million tons of vaccine (enough to immunize the world with absolute safety), was dismissed as unproved and unprovable. The NIH people, like Salk's critics in virology, felt that his theories could apply only to unvaryingly homogeneous mixtures of virus and Formalin, in which the chemical had full access to each virus particle. But such homogeneity was hard to come by, and the slightest deviation from it could permit lethal viruses to survive. Governmental trepidation increased when, as happened several times, the commercial laboratories encountered difficulty in duplicating Salk's results. Each company had the experience of discovering millions of live viruses where all were supposed to be killed. From reading the work records—known as "protocols"—on which the laboratories logged the production of every batch of vaccine, Salk and Tom Rivers usually were able to show why the failure had occurred. It was a failure to filter the virus fluid at the right time, or a failure to maintain the proper temperature, or a failure to clean a pipe before pumping vaccine through it. Rivers, whose normal boiling point was only slightly higher than room temperature, lived at a simmer during these months, his patriarchal ego offended beyond calculation by the refusal of the NIH people to accept expert assurances about technical matters of this kind. But the NIH dared take nothing on faith. One of the officials recalls, "As administrators in the executive branch of the federal government, we were concerned only with results. Either the field-trial vaccine was safe or it wasn't. Jonas could explain everything that went wrong in the commercial laboratories on grounds of failure to conform with the spirit of his principles, and Rivers could offer his own arguments, but we needed to be satisfied that Salk's recipe could be applied successfully by industry before we could rest easily with this thing."

They also needed to be reassured that children inoculated with field-trial vaccine would not contract allergic kidney disease from the monkey tissue used in its preparation, and that the vaccine would be free of contamination. To eliminate vagrant bacteria, the NIH insisted that an antiseptic, Merthiolate, be added to each batch of vaccine. "I fought this," says Salk. "In the first place, the field trial was to be a short-term affair in which vaccine would be used as soon as it had been manufactured. There

was no need for a preservative like Merthiolate—no danger that
bacteria which accidentally found their way into the preparation
could multiply dangerously. Secondly, and more important, none
of our work had been done with Merthiolate and we did not
know what effect it might have on the vaccine itself. Obviously,
nobody else knew either. But the NIH was obdurate and so was
Joe Smadel, who insisted that every vaccine had to contain a
preservative. It was a complete impasse. The NIH would not go
ahead without the Merthiolate. Here was another example of the
tendency so many people had to make assumptions of a cookbook nature—'Toss some Merthiolate in.' And when I would
beseech them to stick to demonstrable facts and not make
changes that had not yet been studied, I faced a blank wall.
Rather than call off the field trial, I finally submitted. I still
regret it. It still hurts. The Merthiolate spoiled the vaccine. It
reduced the effectiveness of the Type I component. The field-
trial vaccine would have been close to 100 percent effective if
the Merthiolate had not been rammed down my throat. I remember trying some of the commercially produced vaccine with Merthiolate at the Watson Home and realizing before the field trial
even started that the results would be far below 100 percent
effectiveness. In areas where the placebo was being used, there
would be no opportunity to revaccinate with a more potent preparation. Do you see how cancerous matters of form can be? Do
you see how emphasis on matters of form can squeeze the essence out of something?"

Thus did questions, proposals, demands, and demurrers from
Bethesda and from the various manufacturers occupy much of
Salk's time. So did his own tests of the safety and potency of
the samples of vaccine that the manufacturers sent to him at
each stage of production. So did his plans for inoculating five
thousand schoolchildren in the Pittsburgh area prior to the field
trials. So did the growth and purification of sixty liters of poliovirus in his own laboratory, for shipment to Eli Lilly. The intellectual excitement of basic science, so briefly enjoyed, had
given way to the nervous tension, luncheon diplomacy, and power
ploys of vaccine production.

"It was a factory," says someone who worked with Salk during
that period. "It was unlike any university laboratory I or anyone else had ever seen. Salk now resembled the front-office man
for a successful commercial outfit. He was all efficiency and
dispatch. Communication was minimal. He would appear in
the morning with slips of paper that told each of his adoring
technicians which batches of virus to titrate that day and which
monkeys to bleed and so forth and then he would materialize
again at ten at night to see what had been done. It could have
been a paradise for those of us who were above the technician level, because the work required attentiveness rather than
creativity and plenty of energy remained for more stimulating
pursuits. But there were no seminars, no discussions of any
kind. People with scientific ideas of their own had to conspire
to try them out—something almost unheard of in a normal,
academic atmosphere, which not only permits but requires experimentation and an exchange of information. If someone wrote
a paper of his own, it gathered dust on Salk's desk before it was
approved and sent off for publication—he had too many other
things to do. Val Bazeley, Major Bennett, Julie Youngner, Elsie
Ward, and others close to Salk were still suffused with the excitement of being part of his life-saving enterprise, but even
some of them showed the strain. The cards were never on the
table, you see, and each person had to provide his own morale."

Salk sighs, "It's true that the lab people didn't get as much
time as they should have. Things were very active. It was different from an academic situation. We were dealing with real
life, and the needs were therefore different. Besides, I think it
fair to say that I am a very poor teacher other than by example,
and there aren't too many people who would care to follow my
example. I remember one chap who came from the East and
went back there after a year or two. He tried in every way possible to prevent me from extending the vaccinations into the
public schools. He was terribly nervous. What would happen if
by some chance a child should develop meningitis and it was
erroneously attributed to the polio vaccine? When his neighbors
asked whether they should volunteer their children for this preliminary field trial in Pittsburgh, he advised against it. And he

was the person who was supposed to help me with that phase of the work! So once again I had to do something myself. The position I took was that I'd give every one of those five thousand vaccinations myself and would put the responsibility in nobody else's hands."

Dr. Dankward Kodlin, who worked with Salk for a while and remained at the University of Pittsburgh after Salk's departure, had been conscripted into the German Army long enough to take part in the invasion of Poland. He then was released to continue his medical education. Drafted again, he accompanied General Rommel to defeat in North Africa, was mustered out, got his medical degree, and, after the war, emigrated to a job in a Bronx hospital. When he heard of an opening on Salk's staff, he applied, was accepted, and, because of his background, went to Pittsburgh with great apprehensions. "I fully expected that Salk would confront me sooner or later with my history. He had every right to ask me, for example, what the devil I, as a German medical officer, had done about the inhuman experimentation in the concentration camps. He had every right to ask how many Jews I had mistreated. It would have relieved me to tell him the truth, that I had mistreated nobody and, unbelievable though it might seem, had been unaware of the camp experimentation until long after the war. It would have relieved me and I should have thought it would have relieved him to some degree, too. But he never said a word to me. At first I wondered if he were bashful, or just being unreasonably considerate of me, but in time I decided that he didn't have the slightest curiosity. It made my blood run cold to see a man so engrossed that he would not even care to find out whether or not he had employed a Nazi."

If a seriocomic predicament like Kodlin's failed to engage Salk's interest, so did problems more heavily burdensome to staff morale. Salk was indeed engrossed. To prevent any given day from ending in an irreparable shambles, he had to put first things first. The first things were work. He let morale take care of itself. When occasion required, he offered counsel and encouragement to the emotion-ridden drinker, Major Bennett, but he seldom peered into the souls of his other associates. It is scarcely surprising that disenchantment took root. A few members of his staff now began to differentiate Salk the celebrity from Salk the polio worker, reposing little faith in the former but counting on the other to bring a great scientific-humanitarian enterprise to a fruition so rich that it would reward one and all with honor for the rest of their lives. Three or four were no longer so sure that there would even be enough honor to go around, a feeling that arose after Salk and Julius Youngner differed over which of the two deserved major credit for development of the laboratory's famous color scale for titrating viruses. There was similar unease about Salk's propensity for signing some of his scientific papers, "By Jonas E. Salk, M.D., with the collaboration of . . ." They would have preferred him to share the credit outright, with a multiple by-line, "By Dr. Jonas E. Salk, Dr. Soandso, Dr. Soandso, and Dr. Soandso." They felt that the phrase, "with the collaboration of," placed them below the salt. Members of this dissident group began referring to Salk as "Jonas E. Christ," but not to his face. Meanwhile, the work got done, most of the staff continued to worship its leader, some of the staff even understood him and his problems, and personnel turnover was low. Even for the embittered or dubious, the prospect of success was a powerful inducement to remain aboard.

The term "Salk vaccine" was beginning to appear in headlines and was becoming household language. It drove Salk wild. The rabies vaccine was rarely called the Pasteur vaccine. The yellow-fever vaccine was never called the Theiler vaccine. Nobody outside the scientific community could name the men who had developed whooping cough, diphtheria, influenza, tetanus, typhoid, or encephalitis vaccines. One obtained a smallpox vaccination without hearing the name of Edward Jenner.

"It's *not* the Salk vaccine," he protested to Basil O'Connor again and again, especially when some exuberant spokesman for the National Foundation said "Salk vaccine" in public. "It embarrasses me with my colleagues to have it called 'Salk vaccine.'

I'm not entitled to that kind of credit and everyone knows it.
When the National Foundation uses the term, my scientific colleagues assume that it does so with my approval. They think me
a self-seeker. This is intolerable."
    O'Connor instructed his own people to depersonalize the vac-
cine publicity as much as possible. "But what could I do?" he
asks. "What could anyone do? We are living in an age of communications and here was a vaccine produced by popular demand. The whole world was waiting for it and everyone wanted
to know who developed it. The scientist turned out to be a nice
fellow named Salk, whose name fit conveniently into headlines.
That vaccine was going to be called the Salk vaccine whether
he liked it or not or I liked it or not. Jonas would come to me
about it and I'd say, 'I understand your position but you're
just wasting your time. Now for God's sake, stop wasting your
time and stop wasting mine. Skip it. Forget it. Go home.' I
knew he meant it seriously when he said he was only one worker
in a long line of them and that all this was getting him in trouble.
But it was out of our hands. Finally I got so tired of the subject
that I just forgot it."
    Salk's friend John Troan tried vainly to popularize the prepa-
ration as the "Pitt vaccine," in celebration of the University of
Pittsburgh. He used the term at every opportunity in the *Press,*
but nobody was buying. The age of communications is most
emphatically an age of heroes and Salk had qualified. His polio
preventive was the Salk vaccine and the Salk vaccine it remained.
He has now become philosophical about it. In his cheerlessly
sophisticated awareness that names make news and news makes
box office, he has even allowed the dream of his life, his cherished
research institute, to be named the Salk Institute for Biological
Studies, hoping that the fund-raisers are correct when they claim
that the name will attract some badly needed financial support
from the public. In 1963, with the same hope in mind, he relaxed
his previously impenetrable embargo on journalistic vaudeville
and allowed *Life* to publish pictures of him barbecuing a steak,
sailing a boat, peering thoughtfully at the Institute's site, and, in
one full-page display, smiling broadly while taking a swim.
Every magazine in the country had courted such intimacies in

1954 and 1955, without success. He was too busy and too fearful
during those years, although at one point he submitted to interviews with Robert Coughlan of *Life*, after being persuaded
that Coughlan was concerned with the imminent conquest of
polio and entirely uninterested in personal matters. On the
other hand, and more typically, Salk gave only the most grudg-
ing, uncordial, and fundamentally unhelpful assistance to Gilbert
Cant when the astute medical writer of *Time* was preparing an
article about him and his work and the field trial. The article
appeared in March 1954, complete with Salk's portrait on the
magazine's cover. When Salk's mother saw the picture, she
noticed a flaw: "Why couldn't they show you smiling?"

In January 1954 Basil O'Connor announced that the national
trial of the vaccine would be delayed until March or April. "We
have been confronted with some of the usual production problems that have to be expected in the manufacture of any new
product," he said. "Added to these has been the length of time
required to check and recheck the many processes involved in
converting the results of any laboratory research into commercial production on a large scale. None of the problems encountered is insuperable and all are being rapidly solved."

A scientist employed at Cutter Laboratories in Berkeley, California, wrote to an old friend back East: "The name Salk is a
dirty word out here." The reason was elucidated by another scientist: "Every batch of vaccine is a damned research project."
Salk was acutely aware that his theories of virus inactivation and
safety control aroused no happiness among persons accustomed
to, as he puts it, "preparing vaccine as one bakes a pudding,
adding a little here, taking a little away there, sticking it back in
the oven if it doesn't look done." The tradition was to simplify
production processes to the maximum, relying on routine safety
tests to disclose any errors that might jeopardize the consumer.
If monkeys dropped dead as a result of inoculation, something
was wrong with the vaccine and it went back into the incubator.
The proof of the pudding. But Salk was asking that such improvisation be abolished. If his procedure were followed, tests

at various stages of production would show that viral activity was declining at the prescribed, constant rate. The traditional monkey-safety tests would then be formal verifications of a success assured by the production process itself. Wasteful surprises would be fewer. In an effort to popularize this concept in science, medicine, and the pharmaceutical industry, he published several technical papers about it. In one of these he pointed out, "Although the procedures here described for virus inactivation and for safety testing may seem complicated and to some may seem unnecessary, they do provide a means for knowing when the last virus particle in a particular preparation was converted to the noninfectious form and they provide a means for limiting the amount of overinactivation, to guard the antigen against unnecessarily excessive destruction."

Having had a head start in the field and time to experience the benefits of Salk's doctrine, Parke, Davis was now beginning to prepare vaccine of good quality. So was Eli Lilly and Company, which had accepted Salk's dicta from the start. Although Wyeth and Pitman-Moore were having no unusual difficulties in mastering the process, the National Foundation decided to use only Parke, Davis and Lilly vaccine in the field trial, to reduce the possibility "of variability from multiple manufacturers." Cutter Laboratories was ruled out of the field trial when two of its batches proved to be devoid of the Type II component. Somebody had simply omitted the Type II, substituting an extra helping of Type III. The Foundation reimbursed Cutter, Wyeth, and Pitman-Moore for their efforts and made clear that they would be counted on to produce vaccine for public distribution, if the field trial was successful.

On February 23, Salk went with his secretary, Lorraine Friedman, and Dr. Mary Lynch Bailey and Francis Yurochko of his laboratory staff and four nurses to the Arsenal Elementary School in Pittsburgh to inoculate the first 137 of five thousand schoolchildren who had volunteered to try the vaccine. The preparation he injected had been produced in his own laboratory in accordance with the formula being followed by the commercial houses. The children marched to the gymnasium in the school basement, where Dr. Bailey took samples of their blood, Miss Friedman made sure that each sample was labeled with the right name, and Yurochko prepared the syringes. Salk gave every shot himself. "Once the injections started," wrote John Troan in the *Press,* "Dr. Salk gave them at the rate of one a minute. Yet he appeared unhurried and confident. Though usually serious looking, he was grinning broadly today and frequently joking with the youngsters. The whole thing went off with clocklike precision, despite the hubbub created by reporters and cameramen witnessing the start of the biggest tests yet to be conducted with the Pitt vaccine."

Inoculation of twenty-five hundred other Pittsburgh children with Parke, Davis vaccine was to have begun at approximately the same time. Dr. Robert F. Korns, Chief Epidemiologist of the New York State Department of Health, who had become Tom Francis' deputy director of the field trial, and Morton Boisen, assistant chief of the study's statistical operations, were to be on hand to study the reactions of the vaccinated, with special alertness to the possibility of kidney allergies. The test had to be postponed, however, when Parke, Davis reported that the vaccine seemed to be contaminated with tuberculosis. Nobody could imagine how such a thing was possible, but there it was: Fred Stimpert said that guinea pigs were reacting to the vaccine exactly as they would to purified tuberculin. Basil O'Connor remembers being annoyed but not disturbed. "Here was an example of how the education I'd been getting from Tom Rivers and Jonas paid off," he says. "I was sure the vaccine was free of tuberculosis, even if somebody had spat in the vat. The Formalin would have killed the germ, I figured. I asked Tom how we could get rid of this problem quickly and he said we should give samples of the vaccine to Merrill Chase, who worked with him at the Rockefeller Institute. Chase put it into guinea pigs and showed that it wasn't tuberculin at all but a harmless reaction to Merthiolate and of no consequence to the field trial." It was March 22, however, before Salk could get the commercial vaccine for the kidney-allergy study. There no longer was any hope of beginning the national trial before April.

On March 11 Salk had to go to New Orleans to tell a group known as the New Orleans Graduate Medical Assembly what he had been doing lately. It was essential to keep the worlds of science and medicine posted on developments. However, the selection of the March 11 date had been made, to all practical purposes, by Albert Sabin, who was scheduled to undermine the Salk vaccine on the very same day in an address before the Michigan Clinical Institute, a prestigious annual gathering of physicians to which the Michigan Medical Society customarily invited leading scientific speakers. Edward F. Stegen, the National Foundation's specialist in publicity to the medical profession, found that the New Orleans group was meeting on that day and would enjoy hearing Salk. The National Foundation, of course, would enjoy neutralizing Sabin by getting Salk into print in the same issues of the nation's newspapers.

Sabin's speech ran true to form. Too little was known about inactivated polio vaccine to justify confidence in the Salk preparation. On the other hand, he, Sabin, was making significant progress toward isolation of living but tame strains of poliovirus which, by causing harmless infection, might provide lasting immunity. He made a joke. "I felt certain that after you all had read the *Life* magazine story of the conquest of polio, no one would be here." And he uttered a warning: "Let us not confuse optimism with achievement." In a press conference he said he believed that the field trial should be deferred as "premature."

Salk's New Orleans paper reported the vaccination of seven thousand children without harm to any but with results that warranted hope that an inactivated vaccine, by priming the human immunologic mechanism, could provide immunity as durable as that which resulted from natural infection. "Still to be established," he said, "is the optimal interval between injections for the most effective primary immunization schedule, and the optimal interval for whatever reinoculations may be required for long-term immunization." He had obtained his best results when seven months elapsed before he gave the booster shot. Perhaps, he said, that much time was necessary "to allow adequate development of the state of immunologic hypersensitivity which is a prerequisite for the booster effect." The field trial, of course,

could not take seven months. All shots had to be given before
the polio season started. But Salk did not seem to mind. "It will
be of interest," he said, "to know whether or not the course of
immunization being employed, without sufficient time for the full
booster response, induces full or partial resistance; it will be of
further interest to determine whether or not . . . natural exposure
[to the disease] will provide the booster stimulus to reinforce any
basic immunity that is provided by so-called primary immunization effect.

"One might question the justification for the conduct of a
study such as the one under way," he continued, "when it is
known from the immunologic evidence here presented that a
different schedule of immunization is capable of producing a more
substantial effect. The answer to this question might well be,
'What justification is there for *not* proceeding with test of a
procedure that, on theoretical immunologic grounds, and thorough
laboratory studies in experimental animals, as well as observations in man, indicates that the presence of antibody . . . even in
low levels, may be capable of preventing paralysis—at least in
some individuals?' Since the final answer to the question of efficacy of any procedure can be had only by direct test, it would
seem that only by proceeding in the manner currently under
way can any progress whatever be made in gaining the ultimate
objective—the prevention of paralysis in children.

"No experiment, well conceived, ever fails," he concluded.
"We must keep an open mind and, based upon whatever findings
are made, plan for the next step ahead."

On Sunday, March 21, Foard McGinnes was in Detroit,
awaiting word from Bill Workman that the government had approved a batch of Parke, Davis vaccine for Salk's use in schoolchildren. The word came. "I went to the plant, signed for the
vaccine, and flew to Pittsburgh with the two cartons on the seat
next to me," he says. "I gave it to Salk and then I flew to Washington with a vial. Mr. O'Connor got a shot from it and so did
my daughter. It was a great day."

The next day was not. Salk had taken some of the commercial
vaccine to the Colfax School, where he did some inoculations and
supervised the taking of blood samples. A surprise awaited him

at his office. It was a letter from Workman, demanding that the
field trial be postponed. Five of the first six batches of commercial vaccine checked at Bethesda were unsafe for use, Workman wrote. The material had caused polio in monkeys, either at
NIH or in the manufacturers' laboratories. "We have reviewed
manufacturers' protocols on Lots 501, 502, and 503," he went
on, "indicating that these lots were manufactured in accordance
with the specifications and minimum requirements. Although we
have not seen the protocols, we believe that Lots 504 and 506
were likewise manufactured in accordance with these requirements. Needless to say, I am much disappointed in these results.
I again come to the conclusion that the specifications and minimum requirements . . . are inadequate to assure the reasonable
regularity of production of a vaccine of acceptable safety to be
used in the field study. Under these circumstances, I cannot
escape the feeling that an occasional lot, such as 503, which
does pass the test, may actually contain living virus and be unsafe for use. My recommendation is that the proposed field
studies be postponed until—

"(1) specifications and minimum requirements can be revised
to give greater assurance of the safety of the final product;

"(2) it has been shown that the vaccine prepared in accordance
with such specifications meets acceptable criteria for safety."

By May the polio season would be on. Vaccine used in the
field trial might be blamed for paralytic infections already incubating when the children were vaccinated. If the field trial
could not begin in April, it would have to be put off until 1955.
Salk, McGinnes, and David Bodian hurried to Bethesda to see
what Workman's latest anxieties were about. Bodian, the country's leading expert in the pathology of polio, examined the monkey brains and spinal cords that NIH laboratory people thought
showed polio lesions induced by unsafe vaccine. "That's not
polio," he said, "and that's not polio. And that's not polio. And
that *may* be polio. We'd better do additional tests."

The situation was tolerable. Two batches of vaccine, one
produced by Eli Lilly and the other by Parke, Davis, had clearly
infected monkeys. In each instance, the explanation was obvious
in the manufacturer's own protocols. Lilly had neglected to filter

the virus fluid before exposing it to Formalin—an error that Lilly did not plan to repeat. The Parke, Davis lot had been treated with Formalin too briefly to inactivate all the virus, an error that Parke, Davis did not plan to repeat. The other batches of vaccine that had aroused Workman's apprehensions seemed to Salk to be perfectly all right. The protocols were in good order and the overwhelming majority of monkeys that were supposed to have suffered polio after inoculation with samples had not suffered polio at all. Indeed, none had displayed any signs of illness before being sacrificed for spinal and cerebral study. Bodian almost agreed with Salk, but not quite. Of fifty-four monkeys vaccinated with one suspect batch, the tissue of one animal had lesions that might possibly have been brought about by a nonparalytic polio infection. In another batch, there were two such monkeys. Without testing additional monkeys and subjecting their central nervous systems to fully competent postmortem examination, one could not be absolutely certain that these two lots of vaccine were devoid of infective virus. Better play it safe.

Accordingly, two of the lots would be discarded for reasons apparent in the protocols, and two others would be withheld for retesting.* The other two lots were entirely acceptable. With drug-company operations proceeding more smoothly each day, there seemed to be little likelihood of further confusion about inactivation and safety testing.

On Thursday night, March 25, Basil O'Connor and Tom Rivers arrived at Bethesda for a meeting with the director of the NIH, Dr. W. H. Sebrell, Jr. "We expected that everything was going to be fine and that they were going to tell us to proceed with the field trial," remembers O'Connor. "Instead they almost blew us out of the water." The conference started smoothly enough. Dave Bodian had been at Bethesda all week, and the NIH people now knew a great deal more than they had about examinations of monkey-nerve tissue. Sebrell and his chief assistant, Dr. James A. Shannon, agreed that there was no reason to delay the field trials so long as the vaccine manufacturers

---

* A later study showed that the monkeys in question had not suffered polio infections. The batches of vaccine were perfectly all right.

displayed ability to produce safe material with consistency. But Shannon had some additional points to make. They flowed from his substantial disbelief in Jonas Salk's inactivation theories and his adamant conviction that security against public disaster could be had only with more elaborate and demanding safety tests than were being required.

The minutes of the meeting are under governmental lock and key, pursuant to laws, regulations, and customs that forbid government agencies to publicize the secret ordeals and triumphs of private industry—in this case, the pharmaceutical industry. However, several persons who attended the session remember vividly that Shannon was appalled by the failure of four of the first six batches of commercial vaccine to pass the monkey tests. This meant that only one-third of the vaccine was safe for use, assuming that the safety tests were precise enough to permit such assurance. He was not ready to make that assumption—quite the contrary. For instance, the present regulations required that only fifty-four monkeys be inoculated with samples of each batch of vaccine. Perhaps if 350 monkeys were inoculated, the safety findings would be more valid from a statistical point of view. Perhaps some of the batches now considered safe would turn out to be unsafe when larger samples were tested.

"Three hundred and fifty monkeys?" said O'Connor. "For every batch? Nobody in the country will have the money to buy a shot of the stuff."

This was a mild comment. Tom Rivers' were more lively. He knew more about statistics than O'Connor did and more about polio than Shannon did. Neck scarlet and jowls aquiver, he challenged Shannon's right to evaluate the present safety tests on the basis of two vaccine failures that were so clearly attributable to a neglect of manufacturing specifications and two other failures that probably were not failures at all. Shannon was comparing apples and pears. What kind of statistics were these? But Shannon would not be budged: If it were true that every batch of vaccine produced according to the specifications was safe for use, then nothing remained but to design safety tests certain to demonstrate this. The present safety tests were statistically inadequate.

"Old Tom was getting madder and madder," says O'Connor. "I kept kicking him under the table and telling him to shut up and take it easy, but he was beyond help. I finally told him to get out of there, catch a train back to New York, and return on Saturday."

Rivers did, but before he left, he directed an indignant eye at Jim Shannon and his sheets of statistical formulations and barked, "I've been making vaccines all my life. As far as I'm concerned, you can take your pencil and paper and shove them up your ass." He, too, thought that there probably was residual live virus in Salk's vaccine, but he was confident that there was not enough to cause harm. "When it's made right it doesn't hurt anybody," he used to say, "so what's the difference whether every virus particle is really killed or not?"

The meeting continued into the small hours, with much elaboration of statistical principles. "They were arguing about this statistical 'universe' and that statistical 'universe,'" says O'Connor, "and that you couldn't mix this 'universe' with the other, or that you had to mix the two. I didn't know what they were talking about, although I thought Shannon and some of the other NIH people were being unreasonable about the so-called failures of the vaccine and about trying to substitute safety tests for properly controlled production and about refusing to concede that one of the worst headaches was their own unfamiliarity with monkey lesions. Anyhow, I got to a phone as soon as I could and called Ruth Freeman, who used to work with me at the Red Cross, and had her rush me some books on statistics, so I could get into the next fight. I also called the members of the Vaccine Advisory Committee and said, 'This is General O'Connor. I have been attacked from all sides and need reinforcements.' They were all in Washington by Saturday morning. Meanwhile, I studied up on statistics."

If the NIH clung to Shannon's belief that every batch of vaccine should be tested in significantly larger numbers of monkeys than had been used so far, the field trial would be off for a year, if not forever. All previous tests would have to be repeated. The National Foundation, Salk, O'Connor, and Rivers would suffer disastrous embarrassment, their project having been terminated because of allegedly inadequate safety precautions.

When the NIH and National Foundation groups faced each other for the final showdown in a conference room at the Hotel Statler on Sunday, O'Connor said, "Gentlemen, we are at the crossroads of whether we will put on the field trials or not. I'm not concerned about anything and I'm not worried. We can call off the field trials just as easily as we can put them on. Just give me the facts."

Henry Sebrell remembers that O'Connor was very much in command of the occasion. The former chief of NIH once told Victor Cohn, the Minneapolis science writer, "O'Connor wanted to do the safe thing. He wanted to do the right thing. The thing he wouldn't take was any dillydallying around. He held our noses to the grindstone until we made our decisions."

"I was all primed with statistical knowledge," says O'Connor, "but I didn't have to use it. The NIH people had changed their minds after talking to us and each other over the weekend." The conference agreed that Salk should resume vaccinating Pittsburgh children with Parke, Davis vaccine. The two lots about which Bodian was not yet fully certain should be withheld for retesting. The testing methods would be unchanged. The statistical worries of Shannon, Workman, and other government officials would be dealt with not by increasing the number of monkeys injected with samples of each lot of vaccine but by application of a principle that had Salk's full approval: Before the vaccine of any manufacturer could be accepted for use in the field trial, his laboratory would have to demonstrate its ability to produce safe vaccine *consistently*. Eleven successive batches of safe vaccine would be ample evidence that the manufacturer's production methods were secure. For example, if samples of every fifth or seventh or eighth batch proved harmful to laboratory animals, serious doubts would be cast on batches that the monkeys had happened to survive: Possibly live virus had actually been present but had escaped the sampling process. Thus, instead of evaluating each batch separately by trusting monkey tests based on relatively small samples, Salk and the NIH (and therefore the manufacturers) would now demand consistently unblemished performance in an entire series of batches. If batch No. 1 passed all tests but batch No. 5 did not, batch No. 1 would be rejected, and for excellent statistical and scientific reasons. Salk was immensely relieved. He knew that no laboratory could hope to turn out eleven consecutive batches of safe vaccine by relying on "cookbook" improvisation and the results of isolated monkey tests. Quality control of the kind now required would compel assiduous attention to the step-by-step checking that was the basis of Salk's inactivation method. At last the elusiveness of living poliovirus would be acknowledged in practice as well as in conversation. At last every batch of vaccine would be "a damned research project" in fact as well as in the official specifications. At last there was assurance that the field-trial vaccine would be as safe as the material Salk produced in his own laboratory.

From now on, consistency would be the watchword. The groups would reconvene in four weeks—on April 24—and make their final decision about the feasibility of the field trial.

When Basil O'Connor had come to the Red Cross in 1944, a smart sociologist named Melvin A. Glasser was the organization's chief of field operations for foreign-war relief. They liked each other. Later, when Glasser was Director of the White House Conference on Children and Youth and Assistant Chief of the United States Children's Bureau, the men kept in touch. One day early in 1953 they were at lunch and O'Connor said, "If you were the president of General Motors and one of your top vice-presidents came to you and said, 'We've come up with a new device that will make automobiles as obsolete as the horse and buggy,' what would you do?"

"I'd start worrying," said Glasser.

"How would you like to come to the National Foundation and be in charge of worrying?" answered O'Connor.

"What do you mean?"

"We're now certain we have a vaccine. Maybe not this year, but within five or eight years it will be ready. If I had my way I'd give every member of my board a bronze plaque and say go home for keeps. But I can't make a decision like that so quickly. It needs study. You come and study it. Help decide what we do after the vaccine is accepted and polio is on its way out."

Glasser came to the Foundation in the spring of 1953 and began his study. "On August 29 I had twelve people to the house for dinner," he reminisces, "and at ten o'clock when we were sitting around having a drink I got a phone call from O'Connor. 'I don't know how much you know about the plans for the field trial but we're having serious problems,' he said. 'Some are personality problems, but the main problem is a bunch of doctors and scientists trying to administer it and messing it up. We might miss the greatest opportunity in medical history. We need someone to administer this so that it will work. I want you to take a year or so off and run this field trial. Take as much time as you want to think about it. I'm leaving for Europe at seven in the morning. Let me know by then.'

"I showed up at the National Foundation on August 31, 1953, as administrative director of the field trial," continues Glasser, "and a few hours later some guy came and asked me how many monkeys I wanted per month and whether I wanted rhesus or cynomolgus. I told him I didn't know I wanted any monkeys and didn't know the difference between a rhesus and a cynomolgus. But I learned. I had to, and not just about monkeys. The basic problem, of course, was to get three shots of either trial vaccine or placebo into upwards of a million children in communities representing a cross section of the country. Also, blood samples had to be taken from about one of every fifty. So we had to begin educating the half million or million children who were going to be injected, and we had to remember the additional children —perhaps three-quarters of a million—who would have to be observed as *uninjected* controls. Therefore we had to consider not only about 2 million children but more than 3 million parents and had to do whatever was necessary to help them know what the field trial was about, so that the parents would request the children's participation.

"We also had to take into account the recruitment, instruction, and education of the professional and nonprofessional volunteers required for the program. Eventually twenty thousand physicians and public-health officers, forty thousand registered nurses, fourteen thousand school principals, fifty thousand teachers, and 220 thousand nonprofessional volunteers were involved. I remember at one point there was discussion about hiring people to do the clerical chores with the literally millions of printed forms on which the community programs would record what was being done. O'Connor wouldn't hear of it. 'What makes you think our volunteers can't do it better?' he said. 'You can't hire ten thousand clerks with that kind of ability. But our people will do it free and do it better.' He was right. The three thousand chapters of the Foundation had more than a quarter of a million year-around volunteers with considerable know-how in community service and community education. Sure enough, they staffed the vaccination centers, provided transportation, collected the so-called 'request' forms from parents, performed public-information chores, and so forth."

O'Connor was absolutely confident that the public would cooperate in the validity study, just as he was sure that his own volunteer membership would rise to the occasion. As he expected, the General Federation of Women's Clubs, the National Congress of Parents and Teachers, the National Council of Catholic Women, and the American Legion Auxiliary all favored the project, influenced public and parochial school systems to participate, and contributed thousands of volunteers to the work itself. Except in times of war, the mobilization has never been equaled in the history of the United States.

"It was O'Connor's sense of the vitality and power of his voluntary movement that kept the project going at times when there were forgivable reasons to abandon or postpone it," says Glasser. "I'll never forget a meeting in the fall of '53, when we were having problems about vaccine procurement and the design of the field trial and whether the Foundation should have any voice in the evaluation of results and whether the vaccine would cause kidney damage. O'Connor sat there writing figures on a yellow pad and listening to the scientists go around in circles. Suddenly he said, 'I have just figured out that during this coming summer thirty or forty thousand children will get polio. About fifteen thousand of them will be paralyzed and more than a thousand will die. If we have the capacity to prevent this, we have a social responsibility here that none of you have been talking about. Let me remind you that we are supported by the people and it is our duty to save lives, no matter how many difficulties may be involved.' This stopped the debate in its tracks. It was one of the most impressive things I've seen O'Connor do. It dramatized the strength of a people's voluntary agency."

Dorothy Ducas, a prominent newspaperwoman before she became public-relations director of the National Foundation, was responsible for the printed and broadcast material which explained the field study to the public. "The world of research, to most people," she has written in a review of the work she did, "is a Never-Never land where a strange language is spoken. Scientific procedures are accepted, in the main, on faith rather than knowledge. Yet in an undertaking involving one's *own children,* faith is not enough. *Facts* are needed. Our problem was one of translation of scientific facts into laymen's language, without sacrificing either accuracy or intelligibility . . .

"The selection of counties in which to hold the trials was one of our first public-relations problems. The choice had to be made on strictly statistical grounds. Only areas that had shown high incidence of polio over the years could be considered. In the beginning, many areas clamored for inclusion. Enthusiastic March of Dimes workers were disappointed because top fund-raising counties were not selected; the statistical criteria allowed of no deviation. But our 'pitch' prevailed: This was a completely scientific operation, even though engaged in by lay people in partnership with medical and health authorities.

"The word 'experiment' was barred from all publicity because of its erroneous connotation that human beings were being used as 'guinea pigs. . . .' This particular problem was met by unfailing reference in all our copy to a 'trial' vaccine, rather than an experimental vaccine, which did not have the same harsh connotations. . . .

"How to tell the story of a practical experiment-that-couldn't-be-called-an-experiment in understandable terms, particularly to about 25 million people inhabiting the 217 areas chosen for the trials. That was our task.

"Complicating it were two facts: One, the trials were under the direction of 217 local health officers, with widely varying facilities for telling the story themselves; and two, our spokesmen in these communities, the information chairmen of our county chapters, were volunteers, mostly nonprofessionals who leaned heavily on suggestions, advice, and actual copy from national headquarters, yet who had to tailor every item to conditions in their own particular communities.

"Looking back today, it seems as if a veritable sea of mimeographed material poured into the 217 areas. But it was *two* seas, not one—literally, a blue sea and a yellow."

Blue paper was used for the material distributed in thirty-three states where children in the second grade of school were to be injected with vaccine and children in the first and third grades were to act as observed controls. The first and third graders were not to be injected, but blood samples would be taken from some, and their health records would be used for comparison purposes. In eleven other states, yellow paper was used, containing quite different information. In these areas, children in the first three grades of school were to be injected, half with the trial vaccine and half with an inert fluid that looked like vaccine. "To avoid confusion," says Miss Ducas, "only one procedure was mentioned on the radio and in the newspapers of the localities where that procedure was to be used. . . . An information guide with two supplements, a series of mats and cartoons, educational leaflets, teachers' guides, radio and TV scripts, and 'spot' announcements, all were produced with the two color markings. The information guide and supplements had to be rather comprehensive, since they were for use by volunteers. Thirty-five different stories were provided for fill-ins and servicing in the localities. These included announcements of dates for the three injections over a period of five weeks, suggested editorials, and statements from local health and medical authorities, civic leaders, school authorities, and chapter leaders."

There was also material of a third color. A purple kit was for use in case of accident. Miss Ducas' colleague Ed Stegen explains,

"We realized that you couldn't march three and a half million kids past a given point without anticipating trouble of some kind. We were prepared."

For years the March of Dimes had counted the swashbuckling Broadway columnist Walter Winchell among its friends. He helped the cause in his writings and in the radio and television broadcasts with which he excited an enormous national audience every Sunday night. From time to time he contributed substantial amounts of money. It therefore came as a surprise to the shockproof Basil O'Connor to learn on Saturday, April 3, that Winchell was planning to announce on the following evening that the Salk vaccine was unsafe. Word of the columnist's intentions had been spreading in Michigan medical circles, where the skepticism recommended by Albert Sabin had gained many adherents. One was the renowned science journalist Paul de Kruif, mastermind of polio science's Stone Age, who now lived near Holland, Michigan, his zest for adventure largely undiminished. Through absolutely no coincidence, the Ottawa County, Michigan, Medical Society (whose constituency included the town of Holland and de Kruif) had resolved on April 1 to ask the State Medical Society to disapprove the field trial, for reasons of safety.

A few physicians who disagreed with the Sabin-de Kruif school of thought phoned Foard McGinnes of the National Foundation after learning that Walter Winchell had now been enlisted in the antivaccine crusade. McGinnes asked O'Connor whether anything could be done to stop the threatened broadcast. "The last thing I'd do is try," said O'Connor, wondering why Winchell had not bothered to check with him or Salk or Tom Francis or Rivers. "I'm not going to do a thing," said O'Connor. "I'd just be accused of trying to cover up."

"Attention everyone!" exclaimed Winchell during his simultaneous radio and television program of April 4. "In a few moments I will report on a new polio vaccine—it may be a killer!" And then: "Attention all doctors and families: The National Foundation for Infantile Paralysis plans to inoculate one million children . . . with a new vaccine this month. . . . The U. S. Public

Health Service tested ten batches of this new vaccine. . . . They found (I am told) that seven of the ten contained live (not dead) polio virus . . . that it killed several monkeys. The name of the vaccine is the Salk vaccine, named for Dr. Jonas Salk of the University of Pittsburgh.

"The Michigan State Medical Society has refused approval— the first state to do so. . . . The polio Foundation is trying to kill this story. . . . But the U. S. Public Health Service will confirm it in about ten days. . . . Why wait ten days?"

The National Foundation was ready with a rejoinder. Hart Van Riper told the press, "Any product that contains live polio virus is not the vaccine developed by Dr. Jonas E. Salk. . . . Dr. Salk has inoculated three thousand children with commercially produced vaccine which was found to contain no live virus in the triple tests by the manufacturer, Dr. Salk's laboratory, and the National Institutes of Health. . . . The purpose of these triple tests is to prevent the use of any product not manufactured pursuant to Dr. Salk's specifications. Four batches which have failed to pass the required tests were not manufactured in that manner and were therefore eliminated by the testing. This demonstrates the validity of these tests and the safety they assure to the public."

The Public Health Service acknowledged that live virus had been found in some lots of commercial vaccine, but promised that no such material would be released for the field trial. Salk released a statement in the third person: "Dr. Jonas E. Salk has reassured parents of children who have received polio vaccine that 'there is no possibility that live virus could have been contained in any inoculations given.' As recently as last Friday his own children received booster shots of commercially prepared vaccine. The process of commercial manufacture is being undertaken with care. . . . All vaccine used by Dr. Salk has been tested and found to be completely safe, and he plans to continue with his program. . . ."

Albert Sabin took a statesmanly position. Winchell's broadcast had been "irresponsible," he said, "but on the other hand, the field study was premature." And Tom Rivers said, but not for publication, "It's too bad that scientists have to be human beings,

but they are." The Michigan State Medical Society acknowledged
that Winchell had been correct: It would not endorse use of the
field-trial vaccine until it was assured that the material was safe.
Two weeks later, it reversed itself and allowed the field trial to proceed in the twelve Michigan counties that had scheduled inoculations. By this time, Winchell had identified Paul de Kruif as his
informant about the supposed hazards of the vaccine. The National
Foundation estimated that Winchell frightened the parents of
about 150,000 schoolchildren into withdrawing them from the
experiment. Minnesota also withdrew, along with scattered counties elsewhere.

"If all went well from here on," recalls Melvin Glasser, "the
program would begin on April 26. Unfortunately, all did not go
well. We still were awaiting delivery of 2 million hypodermic
needles. A week before the vaccinations were to start, the only
factory in the country able to produce the needles was shut down
by a strike. This was the date of my first psychogenic illness.
After I heard about the strike, I found I couldn't move my head.
My neck was as stiff as a statue's. My wife kept urging me to
go to the doctor but I knew better. As soon as the union resumed
making the needles, my neck improved miraculously. We got
the needles in the nick of time."

"My Vaccine Advisory Committee was a wonderful group,"
says Basil O'Connor. "They had all put their scientific heads on
the block, and knew it. Old Tom Rivers sat up there in his office
at the Rockefeller Institute and approved the manufacturing protocols on every bit of field-trial vaccine, which meant he was on
the hot seat if anything went wrong. But he didn't waver, once
his mind was made up that we should have the field trial. The
other members of the committee had less direct responsibilities,
but would have to affix their names to a document advising us to
go ahead with the trial, and would have to do so in a public
way, and would be accountable for the rest of their days. Naturally, some of them were nervous once in a while, and you couldn't
blame them. Each time we'd meet, some new question would
come up: 'How about vaccinating another fifty thousand before

we go ahead with the full-scale study?' Or something like that.
And I'd ask what another fifty thousand would tell us that we
didn't already know and there'd be no answer. And then somebody would get back on the business of extraneous viruses in the
vaccine, or the safety tests, or whether the trial was starting dangerously late and might run afoul of the polio season, and that
kind of thing. It was like when you think you have come to the
end of a court case but the judge brings up another question and
another and another. Here we were approaching zero hour, but
questions already answered about the vaccine were coming up in
new form, one by one. So I told the committee, 'Let's do this as
if we were trying a case. You fellows just adjourn. Go home.
Each of you write me a list of every question you want answered,
every doubt that's on your mind. I'll consolidate all the questions
and we'll have Jonas answer them all at once.' We did it that way
and it cleared the air. Made everyone feel better."

On Saturday, April 24, O'Connor, Salk, the Vaccine Advisory
Committee, and David Bodian returned to Bethesda to see if
there was going to be a field trial or not. Salk reported that he
had now injected commercial vaccine into seventy-five hundred
children. The preparation was entirely safe. The search for kidney
damage had revealed none. The manufacturers were producing
acceptable vaccine consistently. The government people acknowledged that all this was most reassuring. However, Bill Workman
and a colleague, Dr. Roderick Murray, had something to show
the group: mice that had become paralyzed after injection with
recent batches of the vaccine.

"One of the NIH people looked at Dave Bodian and asked him
what he thought of *that*," says O'Connor. "Dave studied a while
and said, 'I don't know.' If he had stopped there, we'd have
been ruined. But he waited a moment. Then he said, 'But I know
it's not polio.' It was what they call Theiler's disease, a mouse
paralysis unconnected with human polio. Don't think it didn't take
guts for Dave to do that. He would have been well within his
rights if he had hedged and asked for a few days on the one
chance in a thousand that one of those mice actually had polio.
But he's a man. He had been close to this thing from the beginning and had come to the end of the line and was fully satisfied

that the field-trial vaccine was safe for use. He was not the kind to wreck the program because of some cases of mouse paralysis, scientific caution and personal jeopardy to the contrary notwithstanding. When he said, 'But it's not polio,' the meeting ended. Nobody was prepared to argue with him. It was still the middle of the day and the vaccine committee was not supposed to meet and make its final decision until ten o'clock the next morning. On the way out of the NIH, Norm Topping said to me, 'Why don't you hold your committee meeting now? You know what the decision is going to be.' But I said, 'Now wait a minute. Take it easy. Let's follow schedule. Schedule is for tomorrow morning. We'll wait.' "

Dorothy Ducas had dinner that evening with a member of the committee, who told her he did not know how he would vote. "The man was in agony," she says. "I remember him sitting at that table and saying, 'I *think* the vaccine is okay, but I don't *know*. What if a dozen children are paralyzed by it? It will be our responsibility. It will be on our conscience.' "

The next day he told her that he had not slept. Neither had some of his colleagues. "It was a cruel ordeal for those men," says Jonas Salk. "They were now going through an experience similar to what I'd gone through two years earlier when I gave the first injections of vaccine and had to wait to see if anyone were harmed. I, at least, was the party of the first part, had developed the vaccine and tested it in the laboratory, and was as certain as I possibly could be that it was safe. But these men were not involved at that level. All evidence strongly suggested to them that the vaccine would not hurt anyone. It had not hurt anyone so far. But until more injections were done, there was no absolute *proof*."

No proof. There could be no proof, as Salk says, without mass injections. Yet the scientific world was not unanimously ready for proof. Respected colleagues of the committee members were uneasy about the trials, and resentful. If the program could be deferred for a year, proof of the vaccine's invariable safety would still be lacking, but perhaps by then something—such as the conservative forbearance of delay itself—might have won the confidence of scientists. Something to make them less vengeful

against the National Foundation and its advisers if children should
die. . . .

On Sunday morning the committee entered a conference room
at the Hotel Carlton in Washington and faced O'Connor. Dr.
Thomas P. Murdock, a practicing physician and a member of
the Board of Trustees of the American Medical Association, was
ill and absent, but later concurred with the committee's decision.
Everyone else was there: Tom Rivers, and Assistant Surgeon
General Dave Price, and Joe Smadel of Walter Reed, and Ernest
L. Stebbins and Tom Turner of Johns Hopkins, and Norm
Topping of the University of Pennsylvania. The committee was
a sea of gray faces. O'Connor offered no advice. It was up to them.
He would abide by their decision.

Newspapermen were infiltrating the Carlton from their press
headquarters at the Statler. Dorothy Ducas came over to retrieve
some of them and found Jonas Salk biting his fingernails on a
bench in the corridor outside the meeting room. He was all alone.
"What are you doing out here?" she asked.

"It's not my decision to make," he said. "It's best that I just
be available to give them my views."

The committee voted quickly, and without dissent, to recommend that the field trial begin. For men of pride who had come
so far together, no other decision was possible. There had been
meetings at which Tom Rivers had bellowed contempt for their
caution: "Goddam it, I have more at stake in this than any of
you." There were no tirades today. The only surviving reasons
for caution were now personal, irrelevant to science. And so they
voted. And Rivers presented them with a resolution that O'Connor
had drafted, a summary of their reasons for voting as they had.
"They had no complaint with the content," says O'Connor,
"but it wasn't formal enough for them. They missed the 'whereases.' This was funny, because I had written it with 'whereases'
and had then edited them out, thinking that scientists wouldn't
like such jargon. But now I could see why they would prefer
the feeling of parchment, sealing wax, and ribbon. You don't risk
your reputation and your career every day. When you do, you
want to solemnify the event. So they took the draft and added
some of the trappings of a formal resolution. Then we went to

lunch while it was being typed, and when we got back they read it through carefully again. They not only signed it but demanded duplicate originals so that each could have one as a memento. Then Henry Sebrell arrived with a written statement from the Public Health Service, approving the trials, and don't think that wasn't a relief. And Len [Dr. Leonard A.] Scheele, the Surgeon General, came along and wanted to know if the PHS statement was satisfactory and I said, 'Well, you can make it a little better.' He asked me how and I said, 'Pin a thousand-dollar bill on it.' "

At nine the next morning, one Randy Kerr, six, of Fairfax Country, Virginia, accepted an injection of Salk vaccine and a button that proclaimed him a "Polio Pioneer." The biggest clinical experiment in the history of medicine had begun.

12

"WE WILL MATCH OUR PERSONAL INTEGRITY AND THE INTEGRITY of the University of Michigan against anyone who might even suspect the possibility of bias," said Dr. Thomas Francis, Jr., in tones of annoyance. Someone had committed the faux pas of wondering aloud if the public might view Francis' field-trial evaluation skeptically, considering how heavily the National Foundation and various drug manufacturers were committed to the Salk vaccine.

To discourage public doubt and to thwart members of his own profession who might be tempted to encourage doubt and, above all, to guarantee that his own time would not be dissipated on a project susceptible to doubt, Francis had driven a hard bargain with Basil O'Connor. The field study was pure Francis. He designed the double-blind section of the study exactly to his tastes and required that the other, lesser, observed-control section be conducted with meticulous attention to rules of his devising. As he had remarked and as O'Connor had agreed during their negotiations, the paramount requirement was that the evaluation be entirely independent of external influence. A subsidiary requirement was that no word or deed of the National Foundation mislead the scientific community on this score. Francis' independence had to be conspicuous and authentic.

"O'Connor understood this perfectly well," says Francis, "and did not try to tamper with it, although it took a while before his organization grasped every subtlety. I remember when one of his publicity people came to visit me in Ann Arbor and said, 'It's necessary for the public to know who you are so that your report will be given the respect it deserves.' I was as uncommunicative as possible. For God's sake, that man had some cartoons of me on the order of Ripley's 'Believe It or Not' which he was going to distribute to newspapers. I froze him out. When he left he said, 'I'll be seeing you,' and I answered, 'Not too soon, I hope.' Naturally, I had the publicity squelched. The big danger was in having the work spoiled by a circus atmosphere which could only result in us being seen as an appendage of the National Foundation instead of what we were—an evaluation center."

Neither Francis nor any other individual working in the old red maternity hospital on Catherine Street in Ann Arbor had more than an inkling of the results of the study until shortly before he made his announcement in April 1955. All data were carefully fragmented and coded, and nobody's job gave access to an overview until the time came to assemble and analyze the fragments. Once in a while, of course, there were glimmerings, but Francis brooked no intraoffice discussion of them. And gossip with outsiders was unthinkable.

The core of the evaluation problem was comparison. The vital information was polio incidence among the vaccinated, polio incidence among receivers of placebo, and polio incidence among the entirely uninjected. The information had to be reliable. No diagnosis of polio was accepted without verification, including laboratory attempts to isolate and identify the infecting virus. If paralytic damage occurred, its severity was evaluated by experts. Cases that arose not in members of the study group but in their families were studied in the same way. Perhaps a vaccinated child had contracted an inapparent infection from the vaccine and had passed it, in more virulent form, to other members of his household. Or perhaps the vaccine had protected the child against paralytic polio brought into the house by a member of the family. Twenty-seven laboratories in all parts of the country were employed in these studies and in antibody assays of the blood samples taken from forty thousand children before vaccination, seven weeks later, and at the end of the polio season.

All relevant data about the children and their health were recorded on IBM cards—144 million items of information. The evaluation center's daily mail delivery often filled an entire elevator. The National Foundation volunteers whose clerical work in the field accounted for most of the mail were remarkably efficient, but mistakes were inevitable. Thousands were made. Even an infinitesimal percentage of error loaded an abundance of trouble on the evaluation group. A child's name would appear on one record sheet and be omitted from all other pertinent records. Or two complete but conflicting reports would arrive, showing that a child had been vaccinated and not vaccinated. Names, ages, places of residence, the lot numbers of vaccine, individual reactions to vaccination—all such items of vital information were botched from time to time. The forms sent by one city were so badly confused that Francis decided to eliminate them from the final evaluation. The National Foundation volunteers reacted as if the honor of the town were at stake. They repeated their work, repaired the errors, and restored clerical order in time to qualify the community for inclusion. In another town, whoever was in charge of the records scratched out the names of children whose parents had declined to request that they be vaccinated, thus editing out part of the control group. The volunteer explained righteously that these people had been uncooperative and should not enjoy the distinction of a listing in Francis' files. To guarantee the completeness of local studies, many volunteers, including practicing physicians, spent days tracking down vacationing or otherwise absent children so that blood samples could be taken on the prescribed dates. One physician overdid it. When a vaccinated child who had been living in one of the observed-control areas moved to a town where placebos were being used, this zealous physician in the new place gave the youngster his scheduled second injection from several vials, to make sure that he got at least some vaccine. The doctor, of course, could not tell which vials were vaccine and which were placebo.

Margaret Hickey wrote about the Lexington, Kentucky, vaccinations in *The Ladies' Home Journal:* "When you have 949 first, second, and third graders as at Picadome, the city's largest public elementary school, things don't go so smoothly. Mrs. T. C. Walker, PTA health chairman, counted anxiously every time a teacher turned in a batch of parent-request slips, giving permis-

sion for the inoculations. The day before spring vacation, nearly
one hundred were missing. These request slips had to be signed
—or else! Ignoring the rainstorms that blew up, Mrs. Walker and
three other mothers put on overshoes and raincoats, tramped over
hills and back roads calling on parents until every single child
had been accounted for." The Kentucky counties of Fayette and
Jefferson, where the vaccinations were given, suffered a polio
outbreak that summer—thirty-four cases, none among the vaccinated. It was an outbreak of Type III polio, which was lucky
for the vaccinated children. The Type III component of the
batches of vaccine used in Kentucky was excellent, but the Type
I had been destroyed by the preservative Merthiolate. If the area
had been attacked by a Type I virus, the vaccine would have
been useless.

Jonas Salk knew that the Merthiolate was depleting the Type I
potency of the vaccine and, in extreme cases such as that of
Kentucky, actually ruining it. If it had been his experiment, and
not Tommy Francis', he would have been free to rush to the
rescue with vials of fully potent Type I vaccine and immunize
the youngsters with supplementary injections. But it was Tommy
Francis' experiment. Extra injections were impermissible. When
Salk's laboratory tests showed that a batch of vaccine was suffering from the Merthiolate, he could do nothing but telephone
Ann Arbor and report the damage. On a few occasions Francis
got the information in time to replace spoiled batches with potent
vaccine for subsequent inoculations. This relieved Salk to some
extent but not entirely. He hoped that Francis would take due
judicial notice of the effects of Merthiolate when he wrote his
report. He hoped that the report would differentiate cases of
Type I polio among children inoculated with spoiled vaccine
from cases among children who had been given good vaccine.
If the potent batches were close to 100 percent effective, as Salk
had reason to expect, he hoped the report would emphasize this.
The effects of Merthiolate were not, after all, any fault of the
killed-vaccine principle but were the result of an ill-considered
addition to the manufacturing formula. Because of his uncertainty
about the immunizing effects of the many batches of vaccine that
had been partially spoiled by Merthiolate, and because of his

equal uncertainty about how Francis would deal with the matter in his report, Salk lived on pins and needles until April 12, 1955. "Most people assumed that I knew exactly what was going on," he says, "but I was in the dark as much as anyone else. Perhaps not quite. Actually I had that information about the Merthiolate, which few others had, but the information did not relieve suspense —it increased it."

Basil O'Connor was also in suspense. During the summer of 1954, he dearly wished he knew how the vaccine was performing in the field. One reason was his personal desire for the quick conquest of polio. Disappointment would be hard to swallow. If failure was in the cards, it would be nice to know now and prepare for it. And there were other reasons. The National Foundation was essentially penniless, as usual, but had greater financial obligations than usual. Francis was on his way to spending over three-quarters of a million dollars in 1954; the services of the twenty-seven field-trial laboratories were going to cost another six hundred thousand; the field-trial vaccine was costing seven and a half million; gamma globulin costs were also in the millions; the research program was expanding (more millions), and patient-aid costs were at an all-time high, after recent epidemics. An emergency fund-raising campaign was unavoidable. It would be helpful to know what was happening in the field trial. Also, something had to be done to ensure a supply of vaccine for public distribution immediately after Francis made public the results of his study. Unless the manufacturers began work soon, there would be no vaccine available in the spring of 1955, and thousands of new cases would occur before mass vaccination could begin. In June and July 1954, O'Connor took a calculated risk, a $9 million one. He arranged to pay that sum to Cutter Laboratories, Eli Lilly, Pitman-Moore, Parke, Davis, Wyeth Laboratories, and Sharp & Dohme for a total of 27 million cubic centimeters of vaccine, which he proposed to distribute, free of charge, to the public during 1955. First priority would be given to children who had been injected with placebo during the field trial. The manufacturing specifications for the vaccine would depend to a great extent on the field-trial findings and would be the responsibility of the federal licensing agency, the Laboratory of Biologics Control.

In announcing this arrangement with the manufacturers, O'Connor acknowledged that he was "purchasing vaccine before it has been found effective." On the other hand, he said, "we have every reason to hope and believe that the vaccine will be effective." This was the whole truth. He hoped and believed, with good reason, but he actually knew nothing. His staff biostatistician, Gabriel Stickle, had for years been compiling and maintaining the country's only reliable records of polio incidence, working with hospitals, public-health officers, and National Foundation workers involved in aid to patients. Stickle's figures indicated that polio cases were falling below the ordinarily expected level this season, but expectations were unreliable where polio was concerned—it might simply be a mild year. Without the kind of information Tommy Francis' organization was getting, it was impossible to be sure how the vaccine was faring. And Francis would not talk. He would not even listen. When one of his own statistical experts came to him waving a piece of paper and asking if he wanted to know what was on it, he would answer, "No."

O'Connor asked Francis and the evaluation center's chief statistician, Robert B. Voight, who was on leave from the United States Bureau of the Census, to meet him in Chicago. Francis recollects, "O'Connor had learned that some newspapers were going to conduct a straw poll among public-health officers to see how the trial was going. One of the terms of the experiment had been a ban on straw polls. All health officers were obligated to profess ignorance when questioned by newspaper people or anyone else. O'Connor had more need of knowing what was happening than the newspapers did and was naturally aroused. He was afraid the papers might find out something and upset some apple carts. He asked me what we were going to do about the straw poll. I answered, 'Nothing, I hope. The health officers won't talk.' Then he said, 'But what about your own people? How can you be sure all of them will keep silent?' Perhaps he was fishing. I don't know. If he was, he caught that day exactly what I hoped he would catch. I told him, 'No fear of that. No single person knows enough to be any help to anyone. Please believe me. Nobody will know the results until we put all the data together. People might just as well stop trying to get advance hints. There are none and there will be none.' O'Connor gave me the long look and then said, 'I'm going to instruct everybody at my office to call you only if they have useful information for you, or if you want something from them.' He kept his word, and I know how hard it must have been, considering his position."

In June, as soon as the field-trial inoculations were completed, the American Medical Association's House of Delegates approved "in principle" a mindless resolution introduced by its Texas delegation. After one patently false assertion ("The United States holds acknowledged leadership in scientific achievement and health standards. . . ."), and a presumptuous one (". . . all true physicians are sincere scientific investigators. . . ."), the document lurched on square-wheeled prose toward its central complaint:

> WHEREAS, therefore, the American medical profession was surprised and put in a difficult situation, so far as public relations were concerned, in recent months when a national health organization, without any official consultation with any qualified council or group of the American Medical Association, launched a nationwide comprehensive program for the use of a new vaccine which gives great theoretical promise of success in combating a dread disease and yet which admittedly had been used a few months, without sufficient time to evaluate the safety as well as the efficacy of the vaccine, and with practically no published data in the scientific literature on the use of the vaccine. Earnest attempts of a few medical societies to secure advance information on the proposal, so as to be ready for it, were fruitless until, practically overnight, the national group requested local medical societies to approve and be responsible for the administration of the new vaccine. . . .

Although the resolution came too late to affect the field vaccinations, it was a storm warning. In the best of circumstances, the AMA was certain to dislike the mass distribution and cut-rate injection of vaccine which would be necessary for a sensibly concerted attack on paralytic polio. Public-health officials and the National Foundation had hoped that, in the event the vaccine was licensed for sale in 1955, the AMA might at least restrain itself in peeved neutrality when people began queuing up for free inoculations. It now seemed probable that the medical organization would be more peeved than neutral. Its view, of course, was that any health service that could be rendered by private physicians in exchange for fees should be rendered in that way. To lure patients to government health stations and other dispensaries for free or nominally priced polio injections could be denounced as socialism of the worst sort, if the AMA was in a denunciatory mood. In face of the Texas resolution, a sign that organized medicine's gorge was rising, hope diminished that the AMA could be persuaded to accept rapid, mass immunization against polio as compatible with the security of private medicine.

The resolution could not be ignored. It had to be knocked on the head. Few physicians could afford to risk professional reprisals by flouting the wishes of their medical societies. Lest the uninformed opinions of the AMA House of Delegates infect state and local societies, and doctors begin to shy away from the polio vaccine, Hart Van Riper took up his cudgel. "Every step in the development and trial of the polio vaccine," he observed to the press, "was submitted to, supervised, and approved by a committee of distinguished scientists, all of whom are members of the American Medical Association. This Vaccine Advisory Committee is headed by Dr. Thomas M. Rivers, Director of the Rockefeller Institute for Medical Research, and includes a member of the Board of Trustees of the AMA.

". . . The AMA is apparently confused in thinking this vaccine is one for immediate use. It is being tested at this time to determine its usefulness through trials that have proceeded with great success, with doctors participating willingly and voluntarily in 217 communities. Prior to utilization in any single community, the trial was approved by the local county medical society, a constituent member of the AMA.

"The AMA has no facilities for testing a vaccine on the scale this one had to be tested. Furthermore, the testing of this vaccine was discussed on various occasions with appropriate committees of the Association of State and Territorial Health Officers, under whose supervision and direction all the vaccine used was administered.

". . . In a speech made on April 17, 1954, Dr. Walter B. Martin of Norfolk, Virginia, the present President of the AMA, in endorsing the field trials, said:

" 'There are enough safeguards around the production and use of the vaccine so that there is no real danger in giving it to large numbers of children. And if the experiment is successful, as we have great reason to hope, it will be of tremendous value when it is used in a more widespread way to check and control polio.' "

Van Riper mercifully refrained from listing the numerous scientific publications, including the AMA *Journal,* in which Salk had reported his work and in which the work had been evaluated by experts.

In September Salk, O'Connor, Rivers, Francis, Bodian, Sabin, Hammon, Paul, and Enders joined a distinguished assortment of European and American experts at the Third International Poliomyelitis Conference in Rome. Warfare between proponents of live-virus vaccines, led by Sabin, and the corporal's guard, led by Salk, had long since moved beyond any possibility of armistice. In Rome every panel discussion was a skirmish, every meal a reconnaissance. Rivers, Francis, and Bodian, who respected Salk's work and were entirely willing to let events determine its validity, stood out oddly among their countrymen, many of whom had not yet abandoned hope that Albert Sabin could produce a safe infectious vaccine in time to fend off the Salkite deviation.

Salk's paper, "Studies with Noninfectious Poliomyelitis Vaccines," was a laborious effort to explain his principles to anybody who cared to pay heed. After asserting that antibody represented immunity and that his killed vaccines produced ample antibody, he paid his respects to his adversaries:

> Those who believe that living-virus vaccines present the only satisfactory means for immunization say that there is

no immunity like convalescent immunity. We faced this issue for ourselves several years ago and proceeded to go both ways at once until such time as we could determine whether or not the immunizing effect of the living virus might possibly be simulated by a nonviable preparation. . . . Work in our laboratory on the development of an attenuated living virus was continued up to the time it was shown in human subjects that serologic responses that accompany recovery from natural infection could be simulated by the injection of a noninfectious virus preparation. Even though the actual determination that a noninfectious vaccine could prevent paralysis in children has yet to be made, further studies in our laboratory on the development of an attenuated virus vaccine have been postponed.

Which was as close to a horselaugh as he cared to go at that time.

He then described his inactivation principles, carefully explaining that they applied only to preparations adequately filtered and protected from contamination. The process would go wrong if "virus is protected within tissue particles," he said, anticipating the commercial laboratory failure which, overlooked by a supine, undermanned federal regulatory agency, would cause paralysis and death for some American children in 1955. He explained what he meant by his famous, controversial phrase, "margin of safety": One could expose adequately prepared poliovirus to Formalin for days beyond the stage at which live virus was no longer demonstrable and then for additional days beyond the point at which live virus was no longer mathematically likely to have survived in significant amounts. But the fluid would remain antigenic, because, as he had demonstrated years earlier, infectivity and antigenicity do not go hand in hand.

He explained immunologic hyperreactivity, the effect of priming the system with one or two shots of potent antigen so that it would respond with a flood of protective antibody whenever exposed to new infection.

Now [he concluded] there is much to be learned about the persistence of antibody following artificial immunization. This is equally true for the question of persistence of immunity following *infection*. . . . Nevertheless, it does appear from the data presented, as well as from additional studies under way, that by suitable manipulation of the doses of vaccine and the intervals between inoculations, it should be possible with relatively few injections, properly spaced, to provide long-term immunity. This suggestion will have validity, of course, only if the hypothesis is correct that low levels of antibody, or merely a suitably sensitized immunologic mechanism, are sufficient to immunize against the paralytic consequences of the infection. . . . The ultimate objective, of course, is not merely a reduction in the amount of crippling and death from poliomyelitis but also the elimination of these as a cause of fear. It should be clear, therefore, that the problem of poliomyelitis will not have been fully solved until a means is available that will, with certainty and for life, make this possible.

Albert Sabin was next on the agenda: "Avirulent Viruses for Immunization Against Poliomyelitis." He was able to report immensely promising work. Through use of a dilution technique which Tom Rivers and other well-wishers would shortly persuade him to abandon in favor of a more expeditious method developed by the talented Renato Dulbecco, he had managed to segregate variant strains of virus that seemed harmless to chimpanzees, even when injected into their spinal cords. Unfortunately, these strains paralyzed monkeys when administered by that route, although they had no effect on the animals when injected into the brain. A Type I variant developed by C. P. Li and Morris Schaefer, of the United States Public Health Service, seemed less dangerous to monkeys than Sabin's own and less than one that had been developed by John Enders. Sabin was now testing it in chimpanzees, to see if it would immunize. The consensus was that Sabin was only a hop and a skip from human experimentation.

During the discussion period, Dr. Sven Gard of Stockholm,

resolutely unconvinced that Salk's margin of safety was safe, declared that in his own laboratory the inactivation process was not at all like a first-order chemical reaction. The straight line of Salk was actually a diminishing curve: Long before all the virus died, their antigenicity was destroyed completely. If Salk's vaccine was antigenic, there was live virus in it.

Next came the ebullient Hilary Koprowski, limited to five minutes by the conference ground rules, a severe handicap to impose on one of his forensic gifts, but time enough to report that persons fed his pioneering live vaccine were still producing antibody four years later. "I would like, Mr. Chairman," he said to Tommy Francis, "to make one closing remark—that we are living in the era of live-virus vaccine. What we want is to elicit as nearly as possible all the latent capacities of human talent to apply principles, established by Jenner, Pasteur, and Theiler, to the field of poliomyelitis."

He happens to be a nice man, albeit a formidable alley-fighter. He regrets some of the darts he blew at Salk. "This is not the era of live-virus vaccine," he now says. "Now that it is becoming possible to isolate and purify the antigenic component of a virus, infectious vaccines are going the way of the dodo. To the extent that Salk realized this and attempted with his inactivation process to implement it, he was right and the rest of us were wrong."

Tommy Francis suggested that very possibility in responding to Koprowski's peroration. "I think it is fine that you called forth the principles," said Francis in softly abrasive tones, "but I think that we can also look forward in immunology to the idea that perhaps we can work through the lines of Avery, Heidelberger, and others in terms of purified antigens. At least it is a point of view for discussion." Francis then asked Salk if he wanted a minute to comment on Sven Gard's criticisms.

"I can do it in less," said Salk perkily. There was nothing wrong with Gard's experiments, he said, except that the Swedish scientist had used too much Formalin and too low a temperature. "We have attempted to extract every bit that we could from the available information," he went on, "and it seems not to be a matter about which we need to have any concern." Anyone who applied properly calculated chemical and thermal energy to polio-virus would find himself with a more than adequate margin of safety.

A few minutes later Francis asked Salk and Sabin, "Do you not fear the allergic effect of the injection of tissue-culture?" Salk said no. Repeated experiments had turned up no reason for such fears. But Sabin disagreed. "I think that the question that has been asked is one that must receive careful consideration," he declared, "and perhaps cannot be answered completely at this moment, because of the allergic effects of the product of any organ—and there is a great deal of decomposed kidney tissue in kidney-tissue cultures." He was now in overdrive. The allergic reaction to monkey kidney might not matter after only one or two or three inoculations of vaccine, he said, "but if one has to go on giving inoculations many times repeatedly, we know that the larger the number of injections, the larger the number of allergic reactions that might occur." Here, garnished with threats of kidney disease, was one of the fundamental assumptions of orthodox virology: Whatever immunity was provided by a killed, noninfectious vaccine would be so transitory that new injections would be required every season. But, as Sabin observed, neither the inconvenience of repeated inoculation nor the cumulative danger of kidney damage would be problems with an orally administered, infectious polio vaccine, lasting benefits from which could be expected after only one or two doses. He admonished his audience to recognize that the entire question of kidney damage was "something to study and observe, rather than to form premature conclusions [about]."

Salk could not let that pass. He cited experiments in his own laboratory which failed to substantiate fears of kidney damage. And he questioned the logic of persisting in worry about a side-effect of that kind, considering that far more concentrated organic materials, such as liver extract, had been used in medicine for years. Then came Dave Bodian, challenging Sabin's "implica-tion . . . that it might be necessary to vaccinate repeatedly over a long period of time with many doses." He reminded the gather-ing that Salk's vaccine provoked enough antibody to assure durable immunity. Bodian and Salk won the skirmish, but it was obvious

that Sabin was winning the Third International Poliomyelitis Conference. "I felt like Semmelweiss," Salk recalls. "I was telling
obstetricians to wash their hands. But they had never washed
their hands and resented me telling them to do so. And Albert,
in effect, was legitimizing their attitude by assuring them that he
shortly would provide a means of delivering babies safely without
washing the hands."

A few months later, while embroiled in maddening negotiations
with the Laboratory of Biologics Control about protecting the
potency of the vaccine by removing the Merthiolate from it, Salk
found time for a repeat performance in the role of a modern
Semmelweiss. He read a blistering paper called, innocuously
enough, "Present Status of the Problem of Poliomyelitis," at a
meeting of the Association for Research in Nervous and Mental
Disease.

> In selecting a particular point from which to begin a dis-
> cussion of the present status of the poliomyelitis prob-
> lem . . . [he began] it seemed to me that a consideration
> of certain of the peripheral questions that bear directly upon
> the work in which we have been engaged would be of in-
> terest. This choice was made as a result, in part, of ex-
> periences I had during the recent International Poliomyelitis
> Conference, in Rome, where I was able to sense the feeling
> of and to discuss different points of view with many and
> diverse people. . . . A rather large number of those with
> whom I discussed our mutual problems hold the view that
> an effective means for preventing paralytic poliomyelitis will
> come with the development of a live-virus vaccine. The point
> that was of particular interest to me was that many are of
> the opinion that even if a vaccine that contains nonliving
> virus is found to be effective, a live-virus vaccine would still
> be more desirable; and, if such could be developed, that it
> should be used either alone or in conjunction with a killed-
> virus vaccine.

> I have consistently and assiduously avoided discussing the
> question of a live-virus vaccine for poliomyelitis, since there
> has been not much to discuss other than the idea. I see
> such obvious reasons for retreating from this idea, except as
> a last resort, that I have felt nothing could be gained by

debate. I find, however, that the *idea* of a live-virus vaccine has exerted and still does exert a very powerful influence, and one that seems to determine not only attitudes and opinions but policy for action as well. It is for this reason that the time has come for me to speak about this question.

Perhaps I should introduce this discussion by saying that the work in which I have been engaged for some time, both in influenza and poliomyelitis, has had as one of its objectives the determination of the validity of the hypothesis that it may be possible to create, with a noninfectious vaccine, an immunologic response that might surpass that which results from those mechanisms that normally operate to prevent the recurrence of disease. . . . I know that the hypothesis . . . is contrary to a view held almost universally. The more widely expressed viewpoint is expressed by the statement, "There is no immunity like convalescent immunity." This is merely another way of saying that it is not possible to reproduce the degree or the quality of the immunity resulting from either natural infection or . . . the infection induced by a living-virus vaccine.

I would like to illustrate the many factors, both qualitative and quantitative, that enter into the immune reaction and to show that the response observed in the convalescent state can be simulated by the *proper use* of a *properly constituted noninfectious* poliomyelitis virus vaccine. I want to stress this view, which is the result of experience gained in the course of studies . . . and its corollary, that the limitations that are usually attributed to . . . killed vaccines are not limitations inherent in such vaccines, per se, but have to do either with the way in which such vaccines are constituted or the way in which they are used, or due to errors of both kinds.

I am approaching the central theme in a roundabout way in order to provide a somewhat broader background against which the narrower problem of poliomyelitis should be viewed. It seemed helpful to me to do this, and perhaps even necessary, in spite of the fact that the principles that apply to immunization against poliomyelitis should be the same as those that apply to, for example, immunization against the agents that cause diphtheria or tetanus. . . . There seems to be a firmly fixed notion in the minds of many that the laws of immunology that apply to other microbial diseases do not apply to poliomyelitis nor, in fact, to other virus diseases.

He then called attention to the numerous experiments in which inactivated vaccine induced antibody formation in animals and in which the antibody was a sign of immunity. And he showed that children injected with some of his earliest, least potent vaccines, maintained satisfactory levels of antibody for a year. And he emphasized the booster effect achievable when a supplementary injection was given seven months after primary immunization.

We have now shown, in a variety of ways [he went on], that the level of antibody induced by the use of a killed vaccine can be similar to the levels observed in persons who have had a prior natural infection. We have shown, also, that the antibody so produced is not evanescent and can be easily recalled. . . . If what has just been said is true, then why should one be desirous of taking the risk of using a live virus vaccine to attempt to immunize man, albeit at the moment of injection the virus inoculated is nonpathogenic for experimental animals? I believe that the answer to this question might be that one would want to do so only if it were not possible to accomplish the desired objectives with a killed vaccine.

But then there are other answers which are less satisfactory—namely, that a live-virus vaccine has been found to be so highly effective against smallpox and yellow fever and, therefore, would be the kind of vaccine of choice for poliomyelitis. It is true, of course, that effective live-virus vaccines are available for the control of smallpox and yellow fever; but there are some who see, in a live-virus vaccine for poliomyelitis, the risks involved in putting live poliomyelitis viruses into man, and in this respect there is sufficient difference from smallpox and yellow fever to make one hesitate to attempt to pattern a solution for poliomyelitis along similar lines.

His allusion was to the well-known capacity of attenuated poliovirus to revert to virulence without warning—and to the difficulty, as yet insurmounted, of being sure that a colony of supposedly tame poliovirus did not include particles virulent enough to paralyze. He now turned to the assumption by live-virus advocates that their vaccines, when available, would provide long-term immunity. What about the smallpox vaccine? It was a live vaccine but offered no such immunity. Most countries barred entry to persons who had not been revaccinated against smallpox within three years.

Salk had now taken his first comprehensive, public thwack at Sabin. In doing so, he had implored his peers to look at the record, appreciate the truths and probabilities documented there, and reconcile themselves to the likelihood that his theories, even if blasphemous, were valid. In the years that lay immediately ahead, the record would enlarge. Vaccines prepared according to his principles would virtually eradicate paralytic polio as a public-health menace. But he would not win forgiveness. He would still be the upstart, his vaccine belittled as a stopgap. A live-virus vaccine of Sabin's would finally be pronounced safe enough for use in the United States. It would have virtually unanimous suport in virology, medicine, and government. It would retain that support even after it was shown to be associated with cases of paralysis in human beings, year in and year out. And Salk, removed by now from those arenas of the absurd in which polio experts chanted their archaic liturgy, would sit in his office in the splendid new Salk Institute, a monument to the future of man. And he would shake his head and shrug his shoulder when told of the latest absurdity, and would pick up the phone to call O'Connor, closer to tears than to a smile.

The Vaccine Advisory Committee agreed with Salk that Merthiolate should no longer be included in the vaccine. It destroyed the antigenicity of the Type I virus. Dr. William G. Workman, speaking for his Laboratory of Biologics Control and for other functionaries of the National Institutes of Health, said that it would be impossible to license a vaccine without Merthiolate unless the safety of such a preparation were demonstrated. When they received this intelligence, Tom Rivers, Basil O'Connor, and Jonas Salk went up like Krakatoa. All safety tests on field-

trial vaccine had been performed before Merthiolate was added
to each batch. How, then, could safety be at issue if Merthiolate
were left out? Tom Rivers wrote Workman, "The National Institutes of Health and the National Foundation for Infantile Paralysis accumulated a considerable body of scientific information as
to the safety of the vaccine that was utilized in the field trials
in the spring of 1954. We would be happy to discuss with you
modifications of the currently accepted minimum specifications
upon your presenting to the committee scientific evidence that
would warrant such discussions."

Workman replied, ". . . All of the vaccine used in the field
trials . . . did contain Merthiolate. . . . It is proposed now that
we consider for license essentially the same vaccine, except that
no Merthiolate is to be added. None of this vaccine without
Merthiolate prepared by the manufacturers . . . has been administered to human beings. There is enough time to secure
clinical data on at least representative lots of this vaccine and
I think we would be open to criticism if a reasonable attempt
were not made to do so. . . ."

The issue had to be resolved in favor of the government, which
held the power of licensure in its whip hand. Salk and the
manufacturers therefore inoculated thousands of new children
with a non-Merthiolate vaccine early in 1955. It proved entirely
safe, as everyone expected.

The staff of the evaluation center at the University of Michigan
would finish tabulating its 144 million items of raw data by late
February or early March. Tommy Francis would then analyze
the figures and write his report. "It ought to be ready sometime
during the last two weeks of March or the first two weeks of
April," he told O'Connor. He could name no firmer date before
studying the statistics and their complications. O'Connor foresaw
another cliff-hanger. To get vaccine into the arms of children
before the onset of the 1955 polio season, it would be necessary
to implement the Francis report almost as soon as it was released.
There would be no time for scholarly rumination by the medical
profession or virologists or epidemiologists or the National Insti-

tutes of Health. If Francis' conclusions were unfavorable to the vaccine in any respect, casting even the slightest doubt on its safety or suggesting that its effectiveness was unimpressive or uneven (Merthiolate!), the resultant debate would consume months. Polio prevention would be impossible this year. On the other hand, if (as O'Connor assumed would be the case) the field-trial results proved decisively favorable to the vaccine, debate would be a felonious waste of time. Had the vaccine prevented paralytic polio? If so, to what extent? Should people have their children inoculated? Francis could answer these questions in a few unimpeachably authoritative sentences.

The primary purpose of the field trial had been to test the immunizing powers of the vaccine under natural conditions on a scale large enough to provide an unequivocal answer in one year. A secondary but strategic purpose had been to subdue virological and medical skepticism not only with the weight and substance of the study but with its manner. Never in history had the formalities of scientific inquiry been celebrated with an observance more reverential than Tommy Francis' disciplined performance as field-trial designer and evaluator. The question now before O'Connor and Francis was how to act promptly on the field-trial report (if it demanded action), without offending the very traditions they had been at such pains to honor. It was an impossible assignment.

Tradition required that the medical profession and Francis' scientific peers have time to mull over his report before anything more be done with it. Considering the magnitude of the work, to say nothing of the interest it had attracted in science and medicine, the first disclosure of his findings would be offered, traditionally, at one of the more important medical conventions of the year. One possibility was the meeting of the American Medical Association in June. Another was the meeting of the American Public Health Association in November. The very dates of these assemblages ruled them out, tradition or no tradition. Neither O'Connor nor Francis was *that* anxious to please. If the report was to be read for the first time at a scientific meeting, with pomp, the meeting would have to occur before the polio season, as soon as the ink was dry on Francis' manuscript. A special meeting would be convened. The nation's leading virologists, epidemiologists, pediatricians, and public-health officers would be invited.

Yet tradition called not merely for a meeting but for publication of the report in a learned journal, so that scientists and physicians could become acquainted with it at first hand before committing themselves to its implementation. This, too, was impossible. No journal could print the report in time for the polio season. The *American Journal of Public Health* agreed to publish an abridgment in a supplement to its May issue. Good. But mass vaccination could not await such publication. What to do without seeming entirely indifferent to the rights and prerogatives of the medical profession? Eli Lilly offered to spend a quarter of a million dollars on a closed-circuit telecast. Francis could talk about his findings to fifty-four thousand physicians seated in theaters in sixty-one cities. Not bad. Much better than nothing.

Francis summarily rejected an alternative proposed by the American Medical Association. Would he allow an AMA committee of experts to go over his material in advance, so that an authoritative article could appear in an April issue of the AMA *Journal?* He most certainly would not. No previews. No peep shows. No breach of secrecy. "Tommy was annoyed," says Hart Van Riper, "that the AMA thought it necessary to prejudge his work or, as I once said, evaluate the evaluator. He felt that if he violated his rules of secrecy, he would create more problems than he would solve. Also, one member of the AMA committee was to be Albert Sabin, and Tommy saw no reason to invite more controversy than we'd already had. His report would stand on its own, he felt. Anyone who understood epidemiology would absorb it easily. The findings and conclusions would be stated in simple language."

Thus, there would be a special scientific meeting and a closed-circuit telecast, and journalism would attend to the rest. Jonas Salk remembers, "I was keen on having the meeting at the National Academy of Sciences in Washington." No setting in the world seemed more appropriate for disclosure of the results of a scientific undertaking in which millions of Americans had taken part. When Dr. Detlev W. Bronk, President of the Academy, agreed that the idea merited consideration, Salk was jubilant. "He ran around the lab like a little boy," says a former associate, "smiling from ear to ear and telling us, 'It looks like we may get the Academy.' He was awfully disappointed when Bronk's board turned O'Connor down." But O'Connor says he turned the Academy down. "Didn't have adequate facilities," he says.

The University of Pittsburgh was more than willing to accommodate the meeting, but Tommy Francis and the University of Michigan balked. The Francis report was a Michigan project. It was not the Salk report or a Pittsburgh project. O'Connor had to agree. He also had to accept the dictum of Dr. Harlan H. Hatcher, President of the University of Michigan, that the meeting would be a Michigan show, planned and administered by the University. The date would be April 5 or April 12, Tuesdays. A Monday might be better from the standpoint of the national news magazines, which had deadlines to meet, but Tuesday would be preferable for the University's public-relations staff, allowing them all day Monday in which to gear up after their customary weekend off. Facilities would be made available for radio and television crews. This was to be the University's day, and it would be done up brown.

Radio and television crews! "We were flabbergasted," says Melvin Glasser, who had gone to Ann Arbor to check the arrangements. "We had wanted the meeting at the National Academy of Sciences so the occasion would be as grave and solemn as any scientist could wish—and here the Michigan people were building a platform for television cameras right in the meeting room. We never thought Tommy Francis would permit it, but he was unperturbed. The University administration had assured him that the situation could be controlled and that decorum would be maintained at the highest level. One thing is certain, I suppose: Even if the cameramen had been barred from the hall, they would have been stampeding around outside it. As O'Connor used to say, 'If Tommy were to announce his findings in a men's room, the reporters and cameramen would be there. This thing is bigger than us all.' "

Considering the exigencies that influenced these arrangements for the delivery of Francis' report to an anxious world, they seem unobjectionable enough. The main exigency, after all, was the human need for immediate vaccination. Other factors were less pressing. For example, the disgruntlement in the upper echelons of organized medicine could not be ignored but could not be allowed to delay vaccination. While physicians should know as much as possible about the products they prescribe and should not be pressed by time or human suffering to prescribe a medicine about the safety or value of which they may be dubious, the truth was that better information, more expertly analyzed, would be available about the Salk vaccine than about most new medical products. The clinical evidence that Francis would present was distinctly superior—as the leaders of organized medicine knew quite well—to the evidence on which drug manufacturers usually based their expensive campaigns of new-product promotion.

The customary method of introducing a new drug is with comparatively skimpy research testimonials at meetings that few physicians attend and in journals that few of them read. These ritualistic amenities attended to, and the formalistic ethics of the enterprise assured thereby, the companies then spend millions on advertisements in professional periodicals and on promotional material mailed directly to physicians. Additional millions support traveling representatives (known as detail men), who explain to individual physicians why the new drug is better than old ones. But the most potent promotion of all is the news story. A break in *Time, Newsweek,* or the *Reader's Digest* is the publicist's grail. If popular demand for the drug can be generated in this way, the item becomes profitable that much more quickly. Sometimes it becomes profitable months and years before scientific investigation reveals its dangers or its lack of efficacy. The AMA has never applauded this routine, but neither does it put a stop to it. Hence, there was a tinge of inconsistency in the belief of the AMA that Tom Francis' report on the most extensive clinical trial in the history of the world should be previewed by an AMA committee. One may guess that the AMA's pique arose from practical rather than from purely scientific considerations. The Salk vaccine was the most spectacular new medical product since penicillin. The AMA wanted a voice, not just a ringside seat.

Among virologists, immunologists, and other denizens of the

scientific community who knew more about the Salk vaccine than
the AMA's strategists did, the attitude toward the plans for announcing Tom Francis' findings was even less favorable. To these
scientists, the Ann Arbor meeting was a promotional charade.
They regarded the outcome of the field trial as a foregone conclusion. Nobody worthy of attention doubted Francis' talent or
integrity, but many assumed that he had simply been swept off
his feet by Basil O'Connor. "Do you think O'Connor would have
had a to-do in Ann Arbor if he didn't know in advance that the
vaccine was a success?" inquires one veteran cynic, ascribing
infallibility to O'Connor, as so many scientists manage to do,
and refusing to believe that the Ann Arbor meeting was not an
O'Connor production.

John Enders, who did not regard O'Connor as infallible,
declined an invitation to Ann Arbor to hear Francis. But he was
there a short time earlier and said in a lecture that, even if the
vaccine had prevented paralysis during the summer of 1954 (a
strong probability in light of news that had begun to leak out of
various public-health departments), important questions would
remain unanswered by Francis. "For a long time," he said,
"researchers will be concerned with such matters as the duration
of immunity, the determination of whether dissemination of the
virus is reduced in the community, and whether resistance established as the result of vaccination will be reinforced and maintained, as Dr. Salk believes, through repeated inapparent infection
of natural origin."

Any virologist or immunologist in whom suspense about the
field trial had perished would agree that Enders had outlined the
remaining issues of greatest concern. Suspense persisted, however,
in those few who knew how nervous Salk was about the deleterious
effects of Merthiolate on the potency of the field-trial vaccine.
Like Salk, they expected to learn from Francis that numerous
cases of paralysis had occurred among vaccinated children. But
these scientists, too, agreed with Enders that, regardless of the
outcome of the Francis study, the matters Enders had mentioned in his lecture required investigation before anyone could
rest easily. To say whether the vaccine had worked in the field
trial or not—which was Francis' assignment—would punctuate

the story of polio prevention, not end it. It bothered the virological brotherhood to realize that the significance of the field study would be exaggerated by the world at large and that the plans for reporting the study could only encourage exaggeration. The prevailing mood among virologists who accepted invitations to the Ann Arbor ceremony was amused resentment, as when rejected suitors attend a wedding in hope that the bride may have sprouted a pimple on her nose. And, of course, to enjoy the buffet and the music and the dancing.

Would Tom Francis make due allowances for the adventitious ill effects of Merthiolate? Salk did not know and could not find out, but his guesses were unenjoyable. In December, at a two-day joint meeting of the National Foundation's Vaccine Advisory Committee and the jilted Immunization Committee, Francis had referred to some of the batches of vaccine in which Merthiolate had virtually destroyed the antigenicity of the Type I component. "Suppose," Francis said, "they were used in areas where there was a fair amount of polio and the better lots were used in areas where there essentially was no polio anyhow?" The prospect was unnerving. It could have happened. Francis had put his finger on the sore. Salk vaccine ruined by Merthiolate might turn out to have been of zero effectiveness in areas where there were many cases of paralytic polio. Salk vaccine affected less drastically by Merthiolate might have been 100 percent effective in areas where there was too little polio for statistically valid interpretation. What would Francis do then? Combine both kinds of areas and both kinds of vaccine? Salk shuddered. Francis did not discuss his plans for coping with such an eventuality, nor could anyone ask him.

It had been a difficult meeting altogether, called mainly to placate John Paul and Albert Sabin, who were still smoldering because their Immunization Committee had been bypassed by Basil O'Connor. On the first day, Sabin reported that, with the approval of the Vaccine Advisory Committee, he was about to give experimental doses of a live-virus vaccine to federal prisoners at Chillicothe, Ohio. Some of his modified viruses were showing signs of reverting to virulence after passage through the alimentary tracts of monkeys. What would happen after passage through a

human and after subsequent passage through other humans accidentally infected by the first? David Bodian and others were
uneasy; but Sabin planned only the most conservative experiments, the prisoners knew what they were volunteering for, and
the findings would be instructive.

Salk was not present at this session. He was in Pittsburgh
giving booster shots at the Watson Home. But he arrived the next
day, and listened to John Paul's suggestion that the role of the
Immunization Committee be clearly defined and that the National
Foundation consider handling its vaccine research program as the
virus-typing had been handled—enlisting the cooperation of various investigators in a joint effort supervised, or at least subject
to discussion, by an expert committee. A polite brawl developed.
Salk was riled at the implication, no longer new, that vaccine
research had somehow suffered because he had not been required
to submit his experimental plans, procedures, and findings to a
committee of other National Foundation grantees. The secondary
implication, that he had turned his back on scientific advice and
assistance, was no less infuriating to him. He was jangled with
fatigue. He was unhappy at having to justify his existence to
men who disapproved of him. Tom Rivers was saying, "Perhaps
Dr. Salk won't object to some people helping him carry out some
of his program. He has been doing it all now. It is a terrific
burden. There are certain segments . . . that could be appor-
tioned. . . . I don't know how you feel about it, though, Jonas."
Salk recognized that Rivers was more on his side of the debate
than Paul's or Sabin's, but he could not let this pass. He tried
to control his anger, but it showed: "I would like to amplify the
wording that you used," he said to Rivers, "and perhaps correct
any misinterpretation that might result therefrom as to whether
I would object to help. I would want to say, first off, that what I
have done has been by default, by virtue of the fact that this is
something that needed to be done. At no time along the way, I
hope, has anyone felt I objected to anyone else working on this
problem. If you would read the first paper that was published in
the *Journal* of the AMA, the specific request was made for specific
investigators to come forth to either corroborate or refute the
data that were presented. I have carried an enormous burden,

an unjustifiable one, one that continues to be unjustified. I will not go into that. That is a personal matter. I surely would like to leave for the sake of the record the very obvious fact that this is not the private activity of any one individual, but this is something in the field of science. . . .

"I don't see," he said tensely, "why I should be the one that should have to stand and hold the fort against the NIH and against the pharmaceutical houses. These are unreasonable things for one individual to have to do, and I say right here and now that I am perfectly prepared at this point to withdraw completely because I think I have done enough. . . . I am tired."

In his few public statements during the months that preceded the Ann Arbor report, Salk was a study in ambivalence. For his own sake as an aspirant to full acceptance in the scientific world and for the sake of public sanity, he could not encourage premature optimism about the vaccine. He had to represent himself as scrupulously detached, awaiting with full equanimity the outcome of Tom Francis' study. But there stormed within him the equal need to keep the record straight about his immunological principles. Perhaps inevitably, he contributed more than once to the widespread feeling that the vaccine was proving effective and that the Ann Arbor meeting would be a theatrical anticlimax.

In June 1954 he modestly refused an award from the Albert Einstein College of Medicine, observing that the honor would imply "a foregone conclusion" about the vaccine. Shortly thereafter he gave similar reasons for declining an award from the Newspaper Guild of Pittsburgh. But the aggressive defense of the killed-virus principle contained in the paper he read before the Association for Research in Nervous and Mental Diseases was reported by William L. Laurence on page 1 of *The New York Times* and was noted with comparable emphasis elsewhere. Laurence's report naturally included Salk's informed conjecture—outrageous to most virologists—that the vaccine, if properly prepared and administered, could produce an immunity considerably more potent than that which resulted from the natural infection. On January 1, 1955, Salk announced that nine thousand Pittsburgh schoolchildren had received booster shots and that not a single member of the vaccinated group had as yet contracted polio. The Associated Press dispatch added, "It is hoped, Dr. Salk said, that the additional shots will ensure permanent immunity from polio."

In an interview on the *See It Now* program, Edward R. Murrow asked Jonas Salk whether he expected the Francis report to be "conclusive and favorable." Salk answered, "Well, the evidence —depends on what kind of evidence you want. Different people require or demand different kinds of proof, but let us say that the evidence that we are all awaiting is the evidence in terms of the occurrence or nonoccurrence of paralytic poliomyelitis in vaccinated children . . . in the proper areas where observations were made, and since I've had no access to such information, then I can't answer the question other than to say that . . . the results should be a conclusive indication of trend."

"When you read criticism in the newspapers or heard it on the air," asked Murrow, "did it cause you to be disturbed or doubtful?"

"I wondered what all the fuss was about," Salk answered. "What all the shouting was about. It seemed to me that perhaps I had an advantage over those who made the criticisms or repeated the criticisms. . . . I knew something more than they knew, and perhaps if they knew what I knew they wouldn't have had the questions or the doubts that they seemed to have expressed."

Later in the program: "I'd like to say, Mr. Murrow, that this is not the Salk vaccine. This is a poliomyelitis vaccine. It's come about as a result of contributions made one upon the other not only by men working in the field of polio but by others working in related fields. There are not only the virologists and microbiologists but then there are the biochemists, the biophysicists, and then persons who work exclusively in the field of tissue-culture. Perhaps the most noteworthy of these most recent contributions was that of Dr. John Enders and his associates in Boston, who first found that it was possible to grow the poliovirus in tissue-culture. Now, it is true that Enders threw a long forward pass and we happened to be at the place where the ball could be caught. You must remember that nothing happens quite by chance. It's a question of an accretion of information and experience.

You must see—it should be obvious that there is an enormous heritage into which I was born, so to speak, and it's just chance that I happen to be here at this particular time when there was available and at my disposal the great experience of all the investigators who plodded along for a number of years. And essentially that's what we have been doing ourselves, but acknowledging fully that which has been contributed by everyone else. It should be clear that without the development of the hypodermic needle, as silly as that may sound, it would not have been possible to proceed. The booster phenomenon, for example, that you hear spoken of . . . was first observed in 1903. So, what I am saying really is that the . . . science of immunology is not a new one, and it's one that has been contributed to by many investigators ever since the time of Pasteur."

These modest declarations, which he repeated with complete sincerity whenever occasion warranted, left the public more hopeful than ever about the Salk vaccine and more disinclined than ever to call it "inactivated polio vaccine" or "Pitt vaccine." The boyish slenderness, the scholarly intentness leavened by a charming smile, the sensitive hands, the eagerness to communicate with nonscientists in their own tongue without patronizing them, the obvious discomfort when the conversation turned to Salk himself—all were most endearing to Murrow's huge audience. When the public read the next day that Salk had reported to a New York gathering that some children still displayed signs of immunity two years after vaccination, could persons who had seen him on television doubt that all was well? And, when noting such claims by the new public figure, could those of his fellow scientists who doubted him and his ideas do more than writhe in their chairs and mutter in their beards and bide their time?

Humpty Dumpty sat on a wall. The optimism that Salk generated was enhanced by others who knew a bit about the field trial and could not resist publicity. A county health officer in South Carolina announced that of twenty-seven polio cases in his area, not one had occurred in a vaccinated child. The National Foundation's chairman in New Jersey issued similar news about the sixteen thousand youngsters who had been vaccinated there. Humpty Dumpty's wall grew higher with each new story of this kind. If the double-blind part of Francis' study proved the vaccine mediocre or worse, unmanageable disappointment and confusion would result. Francis and Hart Van Riper tried to silence health authorities and National Foundation volunteers and wished once or twice that it were possible to muzzle the beleaguered Salk. Rumors continued.

On Thursday, March 30, 1955, the *New York World Telegram and The Sun* featured a copyrighted story to the effect that "not one child who received the Salk vaccine during last spring's nationwide tests contracted the disease." The information had come from "an unimpeachable medical source." Unfortunately, several cases of polio had already turned up among vaccinated children in observed-control areas of the field trial. When reporters questioned Francis, he replied coldly, "There is no basis for the story. No information has been released from the evaluation center. The official report has not yet been written." A reporter protested, "But there must be *some* basis for the story." Francis disemboweled him: "You better go to the same 'unimpeachable source' from which the alleged information came." He then returned to his manuscript, on which he had been at work since March 8.

The report could not be ready by April 5. The meeting would be held on April 12. "Do any of you know the significance of that day?" asked Basil O'Connor at a meeting of National Foundation executives. Nobody did. "It will be the tenth anniversary of Roosevelt's death," he said. Life was full of coincidences. "Someday," he remarks, "I hope to run across a coincidence that will not be blamed on me. I had no more to do with holding that meeting on Roosevelt's anniversary than you did. But nobody believes me."

On Saturday, April 9, Jonas Salk consented to hold a press conference in Pittsburgh. Its purpose was to brief reporters on what they might expect of the Francis report. Television cameramen and interviewers turned the session into an orgy. "Dr. Salk, I notice some beautiful paintings in your office. Does this mean that painting is a sort of hobby with you?" asked a network representative. Salk shriveled. "My work provides me with a very satisfactory hobby," he said, as pleasantly as he could. "Does Mrs. Salk have any objection to your working such late hours in your laboratory?" inquired someone else from videoland. Salk replied, tightly, "I don't consider that subject material to this discussion." John Troan finally rescued him by protesting that a scientist's press conference should not become a soap opera.

A few days earlier Salk had come home and said to Donna, "The kids and you better come to Ann Arbor."

"I was high in the eyebrows," she recalls. "I never went to scientific meetings. Our children were small and I didn't feel comfortable leaving them at home. So I just never went. But now Jonas said that this was likely to be a special thing and we all should go. Well, having known him ever since medical school, I had no doubt that the results of the field trial would be what he wanted. So it *was* likely to be a special occasion. We arranged to go, expecting to return the day after the meeting."

"Can you imagine that?" says Salk. "I actually thought I'd go to that meeting, hear the report, read a paper of my own, talk to a few newsmen, and return to Pittsburgh and my laboratory the next day. I was totally unprepared for what happened at Ann Arbor."

In Greek tragedy the gods and the chorus and the audience know what is going to happen before the protagonist does. And by the time he finds out, it is too late. Ann Arbor was like that for Jonas Salk.

13

In May 1954, a Gallup poll disclosed that more Americans were aware of the polio field trial than knew the full name of the President of the United States. The situation had embarrassing aspects but was wholesome. It showed what could happen to the national consciousness when large numbers of people actually became involved in something. The arithmetic was impregnable: More Americans had participated in the development and testing of the Salk vaccine than in the discovery, nomination, and election of Dwight D. Eisenhower. Not less than 100 million Americans had a proprietary interest in the vaccine, having financed it with contributions to the March of Dimes. At least 7 million had collaborated still more closely as National Foundation fund-raisers and committee workers, as Polio Pioneers in the field experiments, as parents or classroom teachers or health workers responsible for the well-being of the Pioneers, and as volunteers at field-trial clinics and record centers. Each of all these individuals was entitled to look upon himself as a colleague of Jonas Salk. Few were indifferent to the honor.

Accordingly, the announcement by Dr. Thomas Francis, Jr., that the Salk vaccine had been effective against paralytic poliomyelitis made April 12, 1955, a day of uniquely proud jubilation for the American people. It also was a great day in the history of medical science and a great day for the world. It was a great day for Basil O'Connor, whose concept of active partnership between the laity and its scientists had been vindicated by results. It was

[268]

a great day for Tommy Francis, whose report was immediately recognizable as a permanent classic in epidemiology. It was a great day for Tom Rivers, the stern eminence of virology, who had committed his prestige to the Salk undertaking long before most other virologists conceded even doubtful promise to killed-virus vaccines. It was a great day for Harry Weaver, architect of the National Foundation's research program. It was a ghastly day for Jonas Salk.

The pride and pleasure he might have derived from Tommy Francis' partial substantiation of his immunological theories were crushed for Salk by the hundred offenses, slights, misunderstandings, indignities, and vulgarities of that incredible day. Before the day's end, the gulf between him and his colleagues in polio research had widened impassably. From their side they beheld a synthetic godling in custom-fitted halo, a smoothly ambitious operator who had maneuvered his way to a kind of stardom that no true scientist would accept, much less seek, and—worst of all—they saw a wordmonger, a vendor of heterodox claims unsupported by present knowledge. From his side he saw the stone face of orthodoxy, the curled lip of academic snobbery, the green eye of envy. The instant divinity awarded him by a world better attuned than his peers to the social significance of his achievement should have given him joy. But in the circumstances it fell on him like a curse. "I was not unscathed by Ann Arbor," he says in melancholy understatement.

The 150 press, radio, and television reporters and commentators who came to Ann Arbor from all over the Western world arrived with premonitions of an epochal story. Among the five hundred luminaries of medicine, biological science, and public health who came as invited guests, premonitions were diverse. The bleakest forebodings were those of the National Foundation staff, which was in the ticklish position of knowing a great deal about the University of Michigan's plan for the big day without, however, having the right to impose plans of its own. "I wish," said Hart Van Riper to an associate on April 11, "I could get a case of influenza and not get out of bed until this thing has blown over."

Dorothy Ducas asked University officials to remove the Foundation's name from the release that was to be issued to reporters on the morning of April 12. The release, summarizing Francis' conclusions, was prepared by the University press office under conditions of secrecy so total that National Foundation personnel were barred. "We're not signing any blank checks," said Miss Ducas with some emotion. The plans called for Tom Francis to begin reading his report to the meeting at 10:20 on Tuesday morning, April 12. Secrecy would be maintained and news embargoed until that moment. The reporters would be given the official press release and a copy of Francis' report only an hour earlier. One hour in which to read, attempt to comprehend, and try to phrase news bulletins about one of the most complicated projects in medical history. The release had better be a gem of unflawed accuracy. One of Miss Ducas' associates, David R. Preston, an expert science writer, was in Ann Arbor to help, but no help was wanted. "Do you know what one of those people told me?" said Preston to Miss Ducas after a visit to the University News and Information Service. "He told me, 'If we play our cards right this may turn out to be the Michigan story of the year.' The *Michigan* story of the year!"

From *The New York Times,* April 13, 1955:

FANFARE USHERS
VERDICT ON TESTS

———

Medical History Is Written
in Hollywood Atmosphere

———

Special to *The New York Times*

ANN ARBOR, Mich., April 12—The formal verdict on the Salk vaccine was disclosed today amid fanfare and drama far more typical of a Hollywood premiere than a medical meeting.

The event that made medical history took place in one of the University of Michigan's most glamorous structures— Rackham Building. Television cameras and radio microphones were set up outside the huge lecture hall. Inside the salmon-colored hall a battery of sixteen television and newsreel cameras were lined up across a long wooden platform especially built at the rear.

At 10:20 A.M. Dr. Thomas Francis, Jr., Director of the Poliomyelitis Vaccine Evaluation Center and the man of the hour, was introduced. A short, chunky man with a closecropped mustache, he was wearing a black suit, white shirt, and striped gray tie.

He stepped behind a lectern decorated with a blue and gold banner bearing the seal of the University. He appeared small, hidden up to his breast pocket by the lectern, as he looked out toward his audience of 500 scientists and physicians. Cameras ground and spotlights played upon him.

Then Dr. Francis adjusted his horn-rimmed glasses and began to read his long-awaited report in a slow, conversational tone. It was the report of a meticulous and dedicated scientist, presented without dramatics.

The audience was quiet and respectful. There were no bursts of applause. Even at the end of Dr. Francis' address, after he had made it clear that the Salk vaccine had been proved an effective weapon, the applause sounded restrained.

Outside the hall, however, the Hollywood atmosphere prevailed. Students and the curious crowded close behind television cameras set up for interviews with medical celebrities. In a pressroom three floors above, more than 150 newspaper, radio, and television reporters were sending out details. . . .

"I don't know how it could have been stopped," said Tom Rivers years later. "But it was a madhouse all over the place, created by newspaper people and photographers. God, it was just a madhouse, it really was! I don't know when I've seen such wild people!"

"Science writers were sizzling Tuesday," wrote Cathy Covert in *Editor and Publisher,* "after what they called a colossal foul-up in the release of the Salk polio vaccine story at the University of Michigan.

"There was wholesale chaos as some 150 newsmen struggled and fought for copies of the report on the success of 1954 field trials of the vaccine."

"Seeing the messengers get off the elevator," wrote Greer Williams in his book *Virus Hunters,** "some of the best-educated persons in American journalism surged through the pressroom door into the hall, shouldering, jamming, and clutching for vaccine news. One of the smartest had the foresight to meet the messengers at the elevator, seize his handout, and then run back to his telephone and typewriter in the pressroom through another door. Appalled, the messengers backed off, pitching packets into the crowd like oceanarium keepers throwing fish to leaping porpoises."

"Released at 9:17 Tuesday morning," Miss Covert continued, "the report caught many reporters up against early deadlines, forced them to rely largely on a press release and an abstract prepared by one of the scientists attached to the Evaluation Center's staff.

"Writers called the release not only inadequate but misleading. The atmosphere of the release, declared AP-man Alton Blakeslee, was 'circuslike, ill befitting a story of such importance.'

"Members of the National Association of Science Writers covering the Salk story were set to protest the manner of announcement to the National Foundation for Infantile Paralysis.

"Only comment immediately available from University of Michigan officials came from Cleland Wyllie, editor of the University News Service, who said the release was written in only twenty-four hours' time. 'Our science writer went through six drafts of the release before he produced one that was okayed by Dr. Francis. If there is optimism in the release it has been approved by the source of the Evaluation Center's report.'

"Most sizzling indictment came from William Laurence of *The New York Times,* who called the release a 'pretty inexcusable

* Alfred A. Knopf, New York, 1959.

performance. . . . The Polio Foundation should have given us a
better chance to prepare and write a story of this kind. . . .'

" 'We don't like being put in the position of hungry dogs at a
garbage pail,' declared Jack Geiger, of International News Service."

The indignation of the press was as nothing compared with the
disgust of scientists. "The bedlam was revolting," says one who
was there. "It was as if four supermarkets were having their
premieres on the same day in the same parking lot. Those of us
who expected egregious corruption of scientific procedures by the
National Foundation naturally attributed the bedlam to O'Connor.
One had to be calloused indeed not to regret one's own presence
there. One felt like a stage prop, an item of window dressing.
It was a souring experience and a black eye for us all."

The day started rather pleasantly for Jonas Salk. He break-
fasted with the great humanist philosopher of American medicine,
Dr. Alan Gregg, Vice-President of the Rockefeller Foundation,
who was to preside at the medical meeting in place of the ailing
Detlev Bronk. O'Connor, Rivers, and Van Riper were at another
table at Inglis House, the campus mansion for visiting dignitaries.
Tom Francis arrived and told everyone that his report was
favorable to the vaccine. There was handshaking all around. Salk
was somewhat relieved. Apparently the Merthiolate had not done
too much damage. So far so good.

"I've been thinking a great deal about you, Jonas," said Gregg.
"In the next thirty days you are going to be at the crossroads of
your life."

"Oh? Why?"

"You must make a conscious decision. You must decide whether to spend the rest of your days enjoying your fame or working. You will be unable to do both. You can spend your life
traveling, reading papers, accepting awards, and being comfortable. Or you can have the courage to turn aside publicity, the
courage to resume your work, the courage to face the possibility

that you may never again be able to do a piece of work as important as the work which brings us here today."

The thought had crossed Salk's mind but had not taken root until now. "I want to follow through on polio, of course," he told Gregg. "But after some of the remaining questions are answered, I'm not sure what I'll want to do. Pittsburgh has asked me to head a new department of microbiology and preventive medicine and I have agreed, but I'm not happy about it. I'm just not sure what I should do."

"Jonas," said Gregg, "do only that which makes your heart leap."

By digging deeply into Tom Francis' 128-page report, Salk found that his theories had been upheld to the letter. Some of the geographical tabulations of polio incidence revealed that, in several communities that had used vaccine relatively undamaged by Merthiolate, not one vaccinated child had contracted paralysis. The vaccine had been 100 percent effective in such places. And, even though Francis lumped the poor lots of vaccine with the good before making the statistical computations that concluded his study, he showed that the material had been 94 percent effective in preventing bulbospinal paralysis, one of the gravest forms of disease—"an extremely successful effect," as Francis wrote. Furthermore, when considering paralytic cases that had occurred in the double-blind experiments, Francis pronounced the mixed bag of vaccine 100 percent effective against Type II virus and 92 percent effective against Type III. To be sure, it had been only 68 percent effective against Type I, but Salk understood that Merthiolate was the culprit. He could see, with greater assurance than ever before, that properly manufactured vaccine would wipe out paralytic polio in a few years.

Some of Francis' other statistics were unimpressive, unless one knew why. Nor had Francis felt constrained to emphasize the reason. The word "Merthiolate" appeared nowhere in his text, although he showed that vaccine antigenicity had varied from lot to lot and observed, "It is evident that the results obtained represent the influence of a number of vaccines and the summary data are a composite of those effects." His study had been designed to evaluate the performance of a product, not the vagaries of its manufacture. He therefore presented valid statistics that represented the vaccine's effectiveness against all paralysis in the placebo-controlled areas (72 percent) and in the observed-control areas (62 percent). And he broke the figures down to show effectiveness against spinal and bulbospinal paralysis in the two different types of experiments. And then he calculated effectiveness when the diagnosis of paralysis rested not only on clinical observation but also on laboratory studies. The more demanding he was of accurate diagnosis, the more cases of paralytic polio turned out to be something else, and the more effective the field-trial vaccine proved to have been. A breakdown showing the effectiveness of the good lots, as contrasted with the poor ones, was not made, largely because the statistical significance of such figures would have been susceptible to attack on technical grounds.

Francis said at the end of the report:

> From these data, it is not possible to select a single value giving numerical expression in a complete sense to the effectiveness of vaccine as a total experience. If the results from the observed study areas are employed, the vaccine could be considered to have been 60 to 80 percent effective against paralytic poliomyelitis, 60 percent against Type I poliomyelitis, and 70 to 80 percent effective against disease caused by Types II and III. There is, however, greater confidence in the results obtained from the strictly controlled and almost identical test populations of the placebo study areas. On this basis it may be suggested that vaccination was 80 to 90 percent effective against paralytic poliomyelitis, that it was 60 to 70 percent effective against disease caused by Type I virus, and 90 percent or more effective against that of Type II and Type III virus. . . .

The first news bulletins from Ann Arbor repeated the opening sentence of the University's press release: "The vaccine works. It is safe, effective, and potent." And the first statistic to reach the public was that contained in the second sentence of the release: "Dr. Thomas Francis, Jr., . . . Director of the Poliomyelitis Vaccine Evaluation Center, told an anxious world of parents that the Salk vaccine has proved to be up to 80 to 90 percent effective in preventing paralytic polio." When the reporters had time to study the statistical conclusions on which these assertions were based, they were infuriated by what they found. As Greer Williams complains in *Virus Hunters,* "A 60 to 70 percent effectiveness against Type I, the cause of most paralytic polio, promises no great cure-all; turned around, it means 30 to 40 percent ineffectiveness." Several writers wrote follow-up articles in which they hedged their bets on the vaccine, pointing out that, while it was an unquestionable blessing, it was not infallible. These stories reached the public too late to dampen the joy that prevailed. This was just as well. There was small sense in trying to persuade the public that the early bulletins had overstated Francis' statistics, unless this revelation were accompanied by the compensatory disclosure that the statistics themselves had understated the obvious potentialities of the vaccine.

One of the extremely few journalists intimate with the history of the vaccine and conversant with the theories of its developer was John Troan. He looked into the Francis report for the same information that Salk sought there. Troan wrote in *The Pittsburgh Press* that "a detailed study of the Francis report shows that the 'good' batches of vaccine . . . were more than 94 percent effective against Type I crippling.

"For instance," he continued, "in the 'placebo areas,' where half of the children got dummy shots, 84,000 youngsters were given 'good' vaccine.

"As a result, only two cases of Type I paralysis occurred among them. In contrast, twenty-six of the 84,000 nonvaccinated children were crippled by this same virus.

"In the other areas, where no dummy injections were given, the 'good' vaccine batted a perfect 100 percent against the Type I virus. . . . Thus, only if Dr. Francis had counted the 'good' vaccine and had ruled out the stuff whose strength was listed as moderate, low moderate, or poor, the Salk antipolio weapon

would have rated even better than '80 to 90 percent effective'
in preventing paralysis."

Although the scientist in him was heartened by the presence
of such nuggets in Francis' tabulation, Salk's principal emotion
while reading the report was one of terrible loneliness. Who in
virology but he would seek out the nuggets? Who but he would
interpret them as he did? The form of the report was above
reproach. Its mathematics were unassailable. Its orientation was
flawlessly objective. To urge that its ponderous orthodoxy had
obscured the most significant truths about the killed-vaccine
principle would be graceless and futile. Nobody in virology but
Salk accepted these truths as truths. Nobody in virology was
prepared to concede that the Salk vaccine—or any other—
could actually approach 100 percent effectiveness. Salk pru-
dently refrained from quarreling with the report. Even now he
does not criticize Francis. He says almost blandly, "I was alone
in seeing the field trial as an opportunity to discover what was
possible in the given scientific situation. To everyone else it was
a product test and had to be treated as such. If it had been
my study—which it could not be—I might have taken trends
into account rather than simply evaluating one point in the
process. I might have emphasized that the vaccine was capable
of controlling polio essentially completely and that the value of
the procedure had been indicated not only by its success but by
its failures, the causes of which were understood and could be
overcome without difficulty. But this would have been a highly
unconventional approach."

The paper that Salk read at the Ann Arbor meeting supplied
some of the emphases that were lacking in the Francis document. The title was "Vaccination Against Paralytic Poliomyelitis:
Performance and Prospects." A lengthy review of Salk's latest
findings and theories and a detailed analysis of the field-trial vaccines and their limitations, the paper nettled Francis so severely
that he upbraided Salk later. It offended Tom Rivers so much
that he never forgave Salk and never again trusted him. For
other reasons, it wounded certain members of Salk's own staff.
Yet the paper seems to have been a useful piece of work, aside

from its devastating effects on various members of the audience. When Salk approached the lectern to read this paper, Harry F. Stambaugh, President of the Watson Home, rose from his chair, applauding. The rest of the audience joined the standing ovation. Salk smiled uncertainly and then with greater assurance, looking thin and paler than usual under the lights. He had prepared his report without knowledge of Francis' findings or how they would be presented. "Great progress had been made in the months since the field trial," he recalls. "I felt that I should report on what had been learned. Whether the Francis paper were favorable or not, the new knowledge was significant."

Salk acknowledged the ovation with some introductory remarks before getting to his scientific text. "While many like to listen to music," he said, "those who know how a musical score is put together can appreciate the creation of a theme from notes that to others are merely disconnected sounds. The unification of the diverse elements that have just emerged in a simple score, and yet so rich in overtones, could have been accomplished only by one of the great masters." He was paying homage to Francis. He went on at some length, graciously, communicating no hint of his disappointment. "Many have been surprised when they heard me reply, repeatedly, this past year that I did not know what answers were being formulated in Ann Arbor. I felt no impatience whatever since I would learn in due course what was to be learned this morning.

"It is said that you can know people only when you live or work with them. Perhaps it was for this reason that I could feel comfortable in spite of not knowing.

"For Dr. Francis, whatever is worth doing is worth doing well. He could not do otherwise. His kind of objectivity is rare, even among scientists—and it is that kind that in human terms is called honesty. . . ."

He then hailed Harry Weaver, the Connaught Laboratories, the pharmaceutical manufacturers, the virologists and physicians who had assisted in the field study, Tom Rivers and the Vaccine Advisory Committee, Foard McGinnes, Hart Van Riper, Henry Kumm, Theo Boyd, Basil O'Connor.

"Then," he continued, "there is the group, the role of which seems to be taken so for granted that I may, for the sake of emphasis, seem to exaggerate. But they gave so much more than they received that I cannot find analogies with which to portray what I mean—no less say it directly." His staff associates of the Virus Research Laboratory at the University of Pittsburgh perked up their ears. "Imagine the pride and excitement," one of them says. "Most of us who had done the work were there in that hall. The world is listening to Salk, along with us. The *whole world* is listening. He seems about to give us credit for our work. But it never comes. The other shoe never drops!"

By "group," Salk meant not his own but "the early volunteers and then the larger groups who joined the ranks when the call went out and without coercion lent themselves and their bodies to a cause that might, if not now, then sometime soon, bring to each the protection and freedom from fear that each of us seek."

He then awarded credit to the Watson Home, and Dr. Jessie Wright, its medical director, and Stambaugh, and Lucile Cochran, its administrator, who "was to us the Minister of Confidence, the Florence Nightingale and more besides." He mentioned the Polk State School and Chancellor Fitzgerald, Dean McEllroy, and the trustees of the University of Pittsburgh, and ended with praise for the nation's news reporters. "The potential of their medium for good and for evil is clear," he said, "but that it has been utilized far more for good is a tribute to those who made this choice."

His introductory remarks were over. His staff had not been mentioned. That night his senior associate, Julius Youngner, rode an airplane to California with Joseph Melnick, the talented Yale scientist whose own vaccine investigations had not kept pace with Salk's. They got plastered en route. Major Byron Bennett took a train back to Pittsburgh with his co-worker L. James Lewis and wept most of the way.

On an occasion that demanded his self-effacement, Salk had attempted to spread honor as far and wide as he could. He chose an overly subtle means of honoring his laboratory staff.

Instead of affixing his own name to the paper he read that day, he signed it, "From Virus Research Laboratory, School of Medicine, University of Pittsburgh." In a preface he wrote, "The studies upon which this report is based represent the joint efforts of many. That the produce of their labors is greater than the sum of the individual contributions is the measure of the extra devotion for which there is no compensation save the satisfaction of doing what each enjoys most and can do best." By neglecting to mention their names in the moment of victory, he convinced some of his more sensitive colleagues that he was no longer one of them. He seemed to have forgotten that, in the academic world, self-effacement is a luxury but enforced anonymity a hardship. Which is why the faithful Major Bennett wept.

Salk started his scientific report with a haughty swat at the live-vaccine partisans who had been heckling him for so many months. "During the course of our work," he said, "it has become quite clear that commonly accepted opinions that are not founded on quantitative observations cannot be supported for long. Having conducted a number of exploratory experiments, it became evident that destruction of viral infectivity with retention of antigenicity and the reaction involved in the immunologic response were both governed by certain definable and unalterable laws. While in some respects the existence of such rigid laws imposed restrictions and limitations, they also helped define the degrees of freedom within which certain effects could be produced consistently. I shall dwell lightly upon these considerations merely to emphasize that it is not gambling in which we have been engaged, but rather . . . pursuits in a field of science."

He turned to the inactivation principle: "With a margin of safety of this magnitude, both for destruction of infectivity and retention of antigenicity, it might be said that this aspect of the problem demands little, if any, further attention."

And now the affront to Tom Rivers: Salk had discovered before the field trial—and had reported in other papers—that a booster injection given seven months after primary immunization produced a state of hyperreactivity in which the fully sensitized patient apparently could be relied on to produce ample amounts of protective antibody when exposed to natural infection. He now pointed out that, in the field trial, "it was not possible to put this knowledge into practice, because there was barely sufficient time, before the onset of the seasonal upsurge, to begin the studies then initiated. We might say, therefore, that the study conducted in the field in the spring and summer of 1954 was a test of the question as to whether or not *primary vaccination alone* could prevent paralytic poliomyelitis, and not a test of the question of the effectiveness of *full immunization,* which could be achieved only if the course of inoculation could have been extended over a number of months." Later in the paper he proposed that "for the year 1955 vaccine be administered in two doses, separated by an interval of two to four weeks and that this should be followed by a third dose, not earlier than seven months later, but before the 1956 poliomyelitis season."

Tom Rivers remained angry about this for the rest of his life. "This was supposed to be Tommy Francis' day," he used to complain. "Salk should have kept his mouth shut. Tommy had reported on the results of three shots a few weeks apart and Salk just *had* to get off his behind and make a speech about how that was the wrong way to do it. He just *had* to get into the picture. He couldn't keep still and let Tommy have his day. The dosage schedule didn't have to be changed on that day, dammit."

Much of Salk's paper was devoted to the effects of Merthiolate on the field-trial vaccine. He showed that vaccine being manufactured for use in 1955 was more potent than the material used in the field trial. "Theoretically," he said, "the new 1955 vaccines and vaccination procedures may lead to 100 percent protection from paralysis of all those vaccinated."

Now it was Tommy Francis' turn to boil over. "After Jonas was through talking," says Francis, "I went over to him, sore. 'What the hell did you have to say that for?' I said. 'You're in no position to claim 100 percent effectiveness. What's the matter with you?' Jonas was a good worker, but he was sometimes in too much of a hurry."

On orders from Surgeon General Leonard A. Scheele, Bill Workman had gone to Ann Arbor to make sure that no need existed to delay issuance of product licenses to the vaccine manufacturers. As soon as Salk finished his address, Workman collected Albert Sabin, Bill Hammon, Joe Smadel, and several other prominent virologists in a hotel room to discuss licensing. Mrs. Oveta Culp Hobby, Secretary of Health, Education, and Welfare, was sitting by in Washington, waiting to sign the licenses. Was there any reason for her to refrain? Ten and a half million shots of vaccine were ready for official clearance and distribution. Versions vary as to how much opposition to licensing arose in that hotel room. The meeting lasted two hours, by which time Scheele had canceled the press conference that had been arranged for Mrs. Hobby. "The press was baying at our heels all day," he remembers, "and I had to keep apologizing because things were running late at Ann Arbor." Shortly after five o'clock in the afternoon, Workman told Scheele by telephone that his group had voted unanimously to recommend licensing. Mrs. Hobby signed the official documents and issued an official statement: "It's a great day. It's a wonderful day for the whole world. It's a history-making day."

The bells pealed and the whistles blew and voices rose in a crescendo of praise. A world hungering for gentleness found it in Jonas Salk, the living saint who had conquered a plague.

Because of the hurly-burly at the Rackham Building and the demands made on him there, Salk was unable to perceive at first what was happening in the world outside. The schedule permitted him little news and less reflection. The thoughts he had were not of glory but of serious trouble. Indeed, as the day wore on, there began to accumulate in him a feeling that something was terribly awry. Before nightfall he knew from a montage of impressions that he was, as he puts it, "cast out" by his peers. The anger of Tommy Francis was, of course, more than an impression. It was official notification that Salk's paper had been adjudged a major affront. And the ceremonial handclasps offered to Salk by his colleagues and acquaintances included several that were more perfunctory than usual. Salk sensed the reservations of many, the displeasure of others, and the envy of still others and knew before long that these men implicated him in responsibility for the excesses of the day. And he knew that the spotlights shining on him and the flashbulbs flashing at him and the microphones thrust at his face and the anxious deference being paid him by the nonscientists who cluttered up the place had combined with the controversial substance of his paper to seal an indictment against him. The name of the crime was impropriety.

That evening he and Francis and Alan Gregg joined Ed Murrow in the Evaluation Center for a *See It Now* telecast. The debate about 100 percent effectiveness resumed before Murrow's national audience, with Salk and Francis each standing firm, politely. "Your figures," said Murrow to Francis, "go from 60 to 90 percent in effectiveness, depending upon the type of polio. What about going to 95 or 100 percent? What are the prospects?"

Francis replied, "I think we must say we are limited in this study by the fact that [it was] done under certain conditions with certain preparations of vaccine and that these results apply only to this particular study. Dr. Salk indicated today that . . . the preparations of vaccine that are being made at the present time . . . are far superior . . . but when you talk about 95 to 100 percent, there is no vaccine that really . . . even reaches that point except under very ideal conditions. . . . The future depends upon the future."

"What do you think of the chance of total immunity?" Murrow asked Salk.

"As you were talking to Dr. Francis about this," answered Salk, "it reminded me of our conversation of several weeks ago when we discussed the question of Is this a year of victory, and I believe I said then I preferred to regard whatever the findings were as indicating a trend. Well, I think what Dr. Francis has provided today is a very substantial indication of trend, and the mere fact that there were differences in the degree of immunity, with respect to Types I, II, and III, is part of the indication of the trend. Now, as you were speaking together, I felt a bit excited with respect to the challenge. Dr. Francis said that no vaccine is better than 95 to 100 percent effective. Well, this may be so and I think that this is one of the things that would be very interesting to try to do something about. . . ."

Later in the program Murrow asked Salk, "Who holds the

patent on this vaccine?" Salk replied happily, "Well, the people, I would say. There is no patent. Could you patent the sun?"

The outcast was bearing up, indomitable, an element of nature, the logic of his existence ordained by nature, his gifts as natural as the sun. He would survive.

14

"After the television program there was a reception at Inglis House," Salk recalls. "The phone rang constantly. The pressure was on. Offers and invitations of all kinds were coming in. People were milling around the room, arguing about my future as if I were beef on the hoof or had just swum the English Channel or something. It all seemed unreal, the sort of thing that would surely end and be forgotten as suddenly as it had begun. But Ed Murrow knew better. When we found ourselves alone for a moment he said, 'Young man, a great tragedy has just befallen you.' When I asked what he meant, he answered, 'You've just lost your anonymity.'"

An affable publicist named Thomas J. Coleman, press representative of the University of Pittsburgh School of Medicine, spent most of that night and all of the next day answering Salk's telephone at Inglis House and then was obliged to stop, having lost his voice. "Jonas was slow to catch on to what was happening," he says. "With all the build-up during the field trial and all the excitement about the Ann Arbor meeting, I'd been sure that he knew he was on his way to becoming a god, but now he was behaving as if the situation would blow over in a few hours. He told me to go back to Pittsburgh on the twelfth. If he needed me, he'd call. So I left and when I got to the Pittsburgh airport, I was paged and had to turn around and go back to Ann Arbor. By this time, Jonas was swamped. I took over the phone and fed messages to him, and when I lost my voice we put a secretary on the phone and I worked through her. It never stopped. It went on all day and all night for the entire week at Ann Arbor and for months afterward."

Salk discusses this phase of his career in terms that combine the objective and the personal, like an anthropologist describing cannibal rites at which one of his own ears was served as an hors d'oeuvre. "It was almost in the more-than-anyone-could-bear category," Salk shrugs. "I remember right at the beginning there was a call from Governor Knight of California, who wanted me there as a mental-health consultant, because something favorable had been said about mental health on the *See It Now* program. And then the Mayor of New York asked me to go there for a ticker-tape parade. A public-relations official of the University of Michigan urged me to do it. That woke me up a little. I remember thinking to myself that if this was the kind of advice I was going to get, I had better attend to the decisions myself. So I isolated myself in a room and took the messages from Tom and made the decisions. One of the first decisions was that there was no point in transferring all the tumult to Pittsburgh. We could see it through in Ann Arbor and then leave it behind us when we went home. Little did I know."

Donna Salk was appalled by the adulation. When it and her embarrassment began, she gave a dusty answer to someone who asked about her plans for the future: "The first thing I'm going to do is change my name to Smith." She and Jonas were in entire accord about life in the public eye. The sooner the eye turned elsewhere and the noise subsided, the happier they would be. "We had no stated policy toward all the offers, not at first," she says, "but we recognized that Jonas had to choose between remaining a scientist and becoming a public figure. It was obvious that if he yielded an inch, the nation's children would be wearing Jonas Salk sweatshirts and playing with Jonas Salk doctor kits."

He decided to accept awards from institutions with which he had been affiliated, but he would avoid the banquet circuit, would make no appearances irrelevant to his science, would rebuff all efforts to commercialize his name. Tom Coleman rem- inisces, "Messengers were now bringing *carloads* of telegrams to Inglis House. Actual carloads. One long wire came from a public-relations firm, guaranteeing Jonas a million dollars by the end of the year if he'd sign an exclusive contract. And a West Coast hospital decided overnight to rename itself Jonas E. Salk Memorial Hospital. It was a gimmick. The hospital's fund-raising campaign was on at the time. Jonas told me, 'Memorials are for dead people. I'm only half dead at this time. We better turn it down.' Hundreds and hundreds of requests came in for major speeches. Hundreds and hundreds of special awards were offered. Endless, endless. Basil O'Connor had left Ann Arbor in disgust on the twelfth. He called a day or so later: Someone wanted to erect a statue of Salk. No soap. And there were dozens of calls from Hollywood. Marlon Brando had agreed to play the part. The idea of a movie was anathema to Jonas and Donna. They blanched. Jonas finally said he'd allow a documentary, if the proceeds beyond a minimum profit went to support medical research. Nobody was interested in that. They wanted to make a Pasteur out of him. One Hollywood studio flew a bunch of manipulators east to try to talk us into something. They hounded me for weeks. Wherever I went, there they were. When I'd check into a hotel in New York or Boston they'd be lurking in the lobby. I'd go for a cab and find a couple of them sitting in it, waiting for me. They offered me the moon if I could get Jonas' signature. But this came later. Awful as the week at Ann Arbor was, it was only the beginning. Jonas got through it the way he gets through everything else—he goes his own way. 'To hell with them,' he says. I swear, the only people he really cares about and trusts are the mommas and poppas and kids of the world who don't ask anything of him but science."

The Salk children wanted to go home to Pittsburgh. "The baseball season had begun," says Donna. "They were unhappy in their exile."

"I wanted to get back to my lab," says Salk. "I thought, be- lieve it or not, that when I returned to Pittsburgh I could go back to my lab." Years passed before he was able to enter the laboratory with a mind free of distractions.

"There's still work to be done," he told a reporter when he and the family finally left Ann Arbor on Saturday, April 16, "and I hope to be allowed to do it."

An official welcoming committee met them at Pittsburgh Airport. Somebody thrust two dozen roses into Donna's hand. She smiled thanks. City officials were there, and Billy McEllroy and Tom Parran and other representatives of the University, and Val Bazeley, Jim Lewis, Don Wegemer, and Robert Rotundo from the lab. Salk was grateful that these people had come. "I saw you in Ann Arbor at a distance," he told Bazeley and Lewis, "but that's as close as I could get."

"Boy, I sure have had enough excitement," said Peter Salk, sipping a ginger ale while his father answered reporters' questions. Peter was eleven and not long after would make a profound observation. Hearing "Salk" on the car radio, the child said, "Dad, I'd rather be an ordinary person like me than famous and bothered like you."

A reporter asked Salk at the airport if he thought he and the family could resume normal life now that he had become famous. "I'm quite sure we can," he said edgily. "At least, we should have the opportunity to try."

The Salks had moved from suburban Wexford to a house in Squirrel Hill, near the University. The welcoming committee now directed them to Mayor Lawrence's car, which would take them home with a motorcycle escort. "Home we went," says Donna, "the sirens screaming and the cavalcade going in the wrong direction down a one-way street. When we got home we found a police guard posted at the house. The place was full of mail. Letters from everywhere on earth, from polio patients and the parents of polio patients, some of them enclosing dollars or shillings or francs. There were letters addressed to me in unformed hands, with money 'for you, yourself. Give none to research.' The letters were affecting, their messages so genuine, so free of complication or maneuver or device, so much more gratifying to us than the public ceremonies and the offers that kept coming from promoters. We had to get a new telephone with an unlisted

number and put the old telephone on answering service. Otherwise the house would have been unlivable."

Among the first messages from the answering service was a
request that five-year-old Jonathan Salk phone a friend of his.
He did so. The friend had seen him on television and now
reported that event. "Oh yes," said Jonathan. "I'm famous. And
so is my father."

After the Ann Arbor meeting, Lorraine Friedman spent a few
days in Chicago. "Like everyone else, I expected to come back
to Pittsburgh and go to work. Instead I found my desk piled with
mail. The University received about ten thousand letters and
telegrams during the first week. It took days and days to sort
through it all."

Salk had to submit to a press conference on Monday, his first
day back at the University. "I have a laboratory furnished by
public funds," he told the reporters. "Do I use it or do I become a movie star? No more scoops."

"He was getting testy. It got so he would willingly talk to no
reporters other than Ed Murrow and John Troan," says Tom
Coleman. "He was fighting for privacy as if his life were at
stake. When under pressure to appear at something sort of important but outside the scope of his work, he'd send one of the
polio kids who'd been in the experiments at the Watson Home.
We called them 'Salk Soldiers' and they invariably made a hit
and, of course, they loved the trips. Some of the toughest pressure during April came from the people in New York who were
putting on a Loyalty Day Parade. They wanted Salk and Salk's
parents. Jonas wasn't about to take time off for a parade, but
decided to send Jo Ann Long, one of the Watson soldiers, and
Jimmy Sarkett, from whom he'd got the Type III virus for his
vaccine. And he begged off for his mother and father, on grounds
that the old man's health wasn't too good. I got the kids to New
York and on the night before the parade there was a phone
call from some woman official. 'Regardless of what has been
said, Mr. Coleman, we are going to have the parents at the
parade,' she announced. 'No,' I said, 'that's out. You know it's
out.' So she said, 'You know what tomorrow is, don't you?' and

I told her it was a Loyalty Day Parade and she said, 'Now let me ask you something, something which I may need to look into further before the end of the night. Dr. Salk is *loyal,* isn't he? His parents are *loyal,* aren't they? Aren't they? Would the press be interested in their attitude toward Loyalty Day?' I got Dad Salk's physician to attest to his ill health, but the Loyalers picked him and Jonas' mother up the next morning anyway and took them to the parade and the old man had a fine time, waving to the crowd and meeting the Mayor and the Governor."

A 208-foot telegram, supposedly the largest in history, came to Salk from Winnipeg, signed with more than seven thousand names. Letters arrived from Africa, inscribed with marks instead of signatures. There was a new car, given by the town of Amarillo, Texas, and sold immediately so that the money could be sent back to Amarillo to buy vaccine for children. A silver plow was given to a museum. Truckloads of mail came every day, the cherished letters from common folk set aside for answers that never were written because there never was time: A form letter finally went out months later. The money contained in the letters went into a fund and was used eventually to defray research expenses.

"One day Danny Kaye's manager phoned," says Donna. " 'Do you want Danny Kaye to come over?' Jonas asked me. It seemed like a nice idea, and was. Jonathan lay on the floor, chin in hand, while Kaye made faces at him and chatted with us about juvenile delinquency. After he left the kids asked, 'Now can we have George Gobel over?' Ed Murrow wanted us to appear on one of his *Person to Person* programs, the ones in which celebrities were interviewed in their own homes. Jonas disliked saying no, because he was so fond of Ed. He almost consented but finally agreed with me that this was the sort of thing we could not do."

A board of distinguished physicians voted Salk the $10,000 Mutual of Omaha Criss Award. The University of Pittsburgh, the City College of New York, and New York University notified him that honorary degrees were in the offing. Mount Sinai Hospital tendered him a medallion. Governor George M. Leader of

Pennsylvania ordered a medal struck, and Congress agreed with
President Eisenhower that it should award a medal of its own.
General Rafael Trujillo announced that a street in Ciudad Trujillo would be named for Salk. Oslo, Norway, collected money
from schoolchildren for a painting of Salk. In Salk's honor the
Pennsylvania State Legislature created a $25,000 a year profes-
sorship in preventive medicine at the University of Pittsburgh
and he became its first holder. The office of Mayor Robert
F. Wagner of New York announced with regret that Salk had
declined the ticker-tape parade. The office spokesman reported
that Salk had answered, "I do not want any reception in my
honor in New York or anywhere else. I want to get back to my
laboratory. . . ." The city thereupon created eight Jonas E. Salk
scholarships of $3,500 each, to help college students go to medi-
cal school.

It did not end. When he went to Washington to discuss vaccine potency with Bill Workman, people plucked at him to thank
him, reporters followed him to question him. On one trip during
this period, he was sitting in the parlor car of a train when two
beminked ladies identified him, flung themselves to their knees,
and rained kisses on his hands. Jane Krieger wrote perceptively
of his attitude toward this sort of thing in *The New York Times
Magazine* after watching him in action at City College, where
he got an honorary degree:

> When he walked into the President's office in a dark suit,
> white shirt, and dark tie, the President, assorted deans and
> faculty members, the members of the Board of Higher Edu-
> cation and their wives, his father and mother, and some
> friends were gathered to greet him.
>
> Salk, looking self-possessed but not entirely happy, shook
> hands all around, kissed his parents, and allowed the public-
> ity people to put him into a cap and gown. As the photog-
> raphers posed him he looked embarrassed and winked
> impishly at a friend. His father said, "We have to be content
> with only a glimpse of Jonas now." A college official said,
> "Well, Jonas, you're certainly handling this well. I bet ten
> years ago you wouldn't have believed you could handle fame

so well." Salk said, "Ten years ago I wouldn't have believed
this could happen." Another man said, "Jonas, how can you
stand all the demands on you?" Salk said, "I've learned to
say no. I never dared to say no before. . . ." A reporter
said, "I hear you're trying to find an anticold vaccine now."
Salk said, "All I'm trying to do is keep my balance." He
turned to [a friend] and said, "When a reporter approaches
I generally find myself wishing for a martini."

The photographers finished, and the party moved out to
the corridor on the way to a private dinner in Salk's honor.
As they waited for an elevator, a lady asked Salk if he didn't
feel like a writer with a successful first novel published—
afraid he would never do it again.

Salk said, "I don't want to go from one crest to another.
And science isn't like novel writing. To a scientist, fame is
neither an end nor even a means to an end. Do you recall
what Emerson said? 'The reward of a thing well done is to
have done it.' " The lady looked puzzled and said, "Don't
tell me your head hasn't been turned by all this." Salk said
she reminded him of the farmer who saw the giraffe for the
first time, "Aw, there ain't no such animal."

Salk's plea to be left alone so that he might resume his work
was uttered at every encounter with the press, sometimes ir-
ritably: "He's lived in the dark of the laboratory for twenty
years," Basil O'Connor used to say to his National Foundation
lieutenants, "and you can't expect to educate him overnight.
Leave him alone. Don't pressure him. Anybody who sullies his
reputation by making a commercial character of him is through
around here."

"I am not a commodity. I am not a product," said Salk to
Stephan H. Alex and David Preston of the Foundation's public-
relations department. "And I am not a fund-raiser. It is not
proper to expect me to smuggle something about the March of
Dimes into my scientific remarks, and it's not fair." Alex and
Preston had gone to the American Medical Association convention at Atlantic City, where Salk was to accept the Criss Award,
among others, and read a scientific paper. Their job was to

remind the press of the connection between Salk and the March
of Dimes, and their immediate objective was to ask Salk's help
without antagonizing him and O'Connor. "The only technique
that ever worked," says Alex, "was to find out somehow what
Jonas was going to say in his paper. Then we could issue a
National Foundation release about it, tying in the March of
Dimes. But he seldom cooperated more than that. He felt that
he had been cheapened and compromised and endangered by
ballyhoo and wanted no more of it."

At Atlantic City, when Dr. Harvey B. Haag, President of the
American Therapeutic Society, presented Salk with the Oscar B.
Hunter Award and praised him as "a great doctor, a great scientist, a great human benefactor," Salk ventured the hope—for
perhaps the thirtieth time in public—that he and his laboratory
staff "will be allowed in the not too distant future to resume our
activities."

President Eisenhower wanted to present him with a citation in
ceremonies at the White House on April 22, during the first
flush of excitement about the vaccine and its developer. Donna
and the children also were invited. Salk dragged his feet. "I was
saying no to anything that wasn't scientific or academic and I
would have preferred to say no to this one," remembers Salk,
"until Oveta Culp Hobby got me on the phone and reminded
me that this was on the order of a command performance. I
didn't want the family involved any more than they already were,
but I had no choice."

The Salks left for the airport somewhat late. After driving for
a few minutes in chaotic traffic and rain, they realized that they
would miss the plane. "It didn't occur to any of us that we
could call the airport and have the plane held for us," says Donna. "So we stopped at a police station and got ourselves a motorcycle escort like veteran dignitaries and roared off to the airport, pursued by several dozen cars whose drivers had fallen into
line behind us to see where the excitement was." Tom Coleman
also made the trip, to provide public-relations succor and perform
a special, additional service that drove him half out of his mind
but was a great boon to Salk. "Jonas had learned that if some-

one other than him registered in a hotel as 'Jonas Salk' and he simply did not register, then the poor soul who was registered as 'Salk' would get all the nutty telephone calls and would be up half the night while people banged on his door begging for an audience. I was that poor soul. There is scarcely a major city in the United States in which I have not been locked up in a hotel room as 'Jonas Salk.' "

At the White House it was explained to Salk that Mrs. Hobby would say a few words and then the President would present the citation with a few words of his own and Salk would reply, "Thank you, Mr. President." But Salk had written an acceptance speech and was keen on giving it. "I couldn't just say thank you, as if I were entitled to the entire accolade," he says. "If I was going to be mixed up at all in occasions of this kind I at least had to make it clear that I wasn't the only astronaut, as it were. I knew that every time I appeared in the daily press it meant a greater accumulation of difficulties with my colleagues. So I could not accept honors—even from the President of the United States—without responding in such a way as to clarify the situation."

Salk was quite stubborn about this in the White House. "Sherman Adams got all flustered," says Basil O'Connor, who was there. "For Salk to speak after the President did would be contrary to protocol. We had quite a little go-around."

Tom Coleman recalls, "The idea was that nobody was supposed to overshadow the President. When Jonas asked me what I thought, I suggested that the ceremony be held in private, so that the President would not be hurt by having Jonas respond with remarks of his own. But they wanted the ceremony in public and finally consented to let Jonas speak after all."

Andrew Tully wrote in the Scripps-Howard newspapers the next day:

> A grandfather named Eisenhower stood in the White House rose garden and his voice broke for parents everywhere as he tried to thank Dr. Jonas Salk for helping save our children from polio.

No bands played and no flags waved. But nothing could
have been more impressive than this grandfather standing
there and telling Dr. Salk in a voice trembling with emotion,
"I have no words to thank you. I am very, very happy."

Behind the two men stood three little boys, Peter, eleven,
Darrell, eight, and Jonathan, five, sons of the discoverer of
the successful polio vaccine, and Dr. Salk's wife, tall and
slender and proud.

Salk now read his own speech:

At various times in our lives we stop, look, and listen—
to see where we are—and sometimes think not is it safe to
go ahead, but rather, how did we get where we are at the
moment?

When I received a call from the White House to come
here, it was as though I were receiving a call for someone
other than myself. It seems, in retrospect, that my dreams
have been devoid of hopes or expectations of ever meeting
the President, no less of receiving from him that which
you have just conveyed. My reward came to me, you might
say, in the quiet of the laboratory some two and a half
years ago, when a light glimmered through the darkness
with hopeful brilliance.

That this was something that others might someday see and
feel came about because of the untiring devotion of my staff
and of so many others who offered their assistance and
assumed responsibilities for large and important segments
of the work that needed to be done. I am sure you know
how I feel when you single me out for the warm and generous sentiments you have just expressed, and to receive this
citation. You have been in similar situations and I know
that your thoughts were of the foot soldiers who crossed the
Elbe and not of yourself.

If I were to say that I am honored on this occasion, I
would not be telling the whole truth. I say, rather, that on
behalf of all the people in laboratories, in the field, and
those behind the lines, I gladly accept this recognition of

what each of us has contributed, and I hope that we may
have the opportunity to see again in our lifetime the beginning of the end of other fears that plague mankind.

Eisenhower then gave a citation to O'Connor for the National
Foundation. The ceremony was over. The President turned to the
Salk children. "Let's go back in, boys," he said. He took them
into his office and gave each a ball-point pen and a pocket knife.
"Mr. Eisenhower," asked Darrell Salk, "what else do you do
besides play golf?"

"I paint and fish," said the President.

"So Darry launched an interminable description of a painting
he had done in school," says Donna Salk. "The President was
very patient about it." After they left the White House, she confiscated the pocket knives.

Salk was never at his best on occasions of this kind. His
speeches of acceptance invariably suffered from the awkwardness he felt when singled out by nonscientists for honors that scientists would have withheld. Yet, he could not refuse to accept
a Presidential citation and, when the nation's first Congressional
Medal for Distinguished Civilian Service was tendered him, he
could not refuse that, either. In fairness to his scientific peers,
he was unable to accept credit not due him; yet in fairness to
himself and Basil O'Connor and the millions who had made
his achievement possible, he could not pretend that only slight
credit was due him. In his acceptance speeches he tried to cope
with these nuances by philosophizing about the nature of scientific discovery and the meaning of acclaim, hoping to make
clear that his vaccine work was not quite what the laity thought
it was but was somewhat more impressive than his fellow scientists were willing to concede. The difficulties were multiplied
by his propensity for fancy rhetoric. He wrote his speeches as
if simple declaration were a penal offense. Their lumbering ele-
gances verged on pomposity, supplying to the occasion and to
him an exalted air that belied the humility he wanted so much
to convey.

When he accepted the Congressional Medal, he read a home-made parable that depicted the vaccine development in Biblical terms. Extracts deserve inclusion here to demonstrate what the man was going through at this time and what he was trying to do about it:

Imagine a tall campanile, or bell tower, that had been in the process of being built for a long time—one that was needed and wanted by the people, to be used to call them to defend their city and themselves against attack. For years they contributed so that they might someday have what they wanted. And, they gave still more: They gave of their time and effort, and they made personal sacrifice to build this bell tower, and to build it in a way that would be useful and would last. It had to be built soon and soundly because the attackers from without were getting stronger at each assault.

The tower was ready and was tested. When the bell rope was pulled the bell rang clear, and the people rejoiced. But, this moment was long in coming; there had been differences of opinion on how it could be built, how it could be made to work, how it could be finished. It could have been a Tower of Babel, but it was not. This was not chance alone—there were the leaders who recognized the need, the solution, and the means for its implementation. And so in togetherness the tower was built.

There was rejoicing and the giving of accolades. The pleasure and satisfaction of near completion could not be distinguished from the relief that came from the joyful dismissal of feelings of fear of an ever present and impending danger.

It was not, however, the rejoicing and the giving of accolades that provided the incentive that moved each to contribute—it was not for glory, but for use, that each gave what he could. When one useful contribution was placed carefully upon another, it was soon discovered that the whole was greater than the sum of the parts. When the whole was together, the feelings of gratitude of each man for his neighbor, for what each contributed for all and for each, was showered upon but one—and he was from among

the last of the many whose contributions were made near to
the end. But they knew that the end could not have come
without the beginning, and without all that transpired between the beginning and the end. . . .

And so—on an occasion such as this, when one reflects
upon the passing of time and of events and of distinctions
made among men—we realize the role of chance in time
and in place and in the opportunities that we encounter.
But, where there is freedom of opportunity, there then is
choice of what to do, what to take, and what to give in return. For myself, and I will speak, too, for those whose contributions came before, but whose lot it was not to become
a symbol for honor, I feel that the greatest reward for doing
is the opportunity to do more. . . .

When he got a Lasker Award in 1956, he scolded those who
insist on giving awards:

To be singled out as a symbol awards you with something
that was never intended by those who wish to do you honor.
You become the possessor of a feeling of dissatisfaction,
as well as the possessor of feelings of satisfaction.

You do not question the judgment of those who have made
so weighty a decision. And while you are pleased to have
had the opportunity to have played a part in something
that someone believes to have been time and effort well
spent, you can't help but think of those, unawarded, singly,
or as a group, who should be standing in your stead.

But, then, this is but a fleeting moment—and it is over—
and the wounds heal quickly. Because it is not the awards
made by men that give us the greatest reason for doing.
The real reason is known to each and every one of us.
Those who have experienced the feeling that comes with
finding out what they set out to learn or of discovering
something they didn't expect, have enjoyed the satisfaction
of a moment that could never again be exceeded but could
be equaled if they could do more. . . .

Life would be sad, indeed, if those who knew this feeling

were only those who have been the recipients of awards,
or those who will be singled out in the years to come.

A Nobel prize in medicine would have defined the social significance and scientific validity of Salk's work. He has been considered somewhat favorably at least once in the deliberations at
the *Karolinska Institutet* in Stockholm. However, Max Theiler
won the prize in 1951 for his live-virus vaccine against yellow
fever, and John Enders, Thomas Weller, and Frederick Robbins
won it in 1954 for their tissue-culture achievement, thus narrowing the terrain on which the developer of a polio vaccine might
gain foothold. More to the point, virologists on whom the
judges at the *Karolinska* depended for advice and guidance were
unconvinced that Salk should get a prize of any kind, much
less a Nobel prize. One member of the *Karolinska,* the influential
Sven Gard, was among the world's most energetic antagonists of
Salk's viral-inactivation theories.

Perhaps the most striking and unpalatable evidence of Salk's
alienation from his former peers in polio research is the refusal
of the National Academy of Sciences to admit him to membership. "Original work!" Tom Rivers barked when asked several
years ago how a worker of Salk's distinction could possibly be
excluded from the Academy. "You don't get into the Academy
without you've done original work!" he said, reddening. "Just as
you don't get the Nobel prize except for original work. Now I'm
not saying Jonas wasn't a damned good man, but there had been
killed vaccines before. Lots of them. And Formalin-killed ones
at that." Rivers was capable of great candor on some occasions,
but this was not one of them. As a veteran member of the
Academy—along with such other polio experts as John Paul,
Albert Sabin, Joseph Smadel, John Enders, and David Bodian—
Rivers knew perfectly well that the membership included numerous microbiologists whose work hardly matched Salk's in
originality or significance. Another member supplies a more
comprehensive explanation: "Jonas has been nominated repeatedly and has never come close to election. The factor of original

work has something to do with it, but not much. Over the years, election to the Academy has become a popularity contest. The election procedures are so complicated that if any faction in the candidate's field opposes him, he has no chance."

15

THE BETTER MOUSETRAP IS HARMLESS TO MICE UNTIL SOMEONE
puts it where the mice are. The Salk vaccine could prevent no
paralytic polio while gathering dust on warehouse shelves. If the
world's immunization programs were haphazard or desultory or
otherwise unintelligent, avoidable cases of paralysis would occur
and new headstones would commemorate human folly.

Having planned and underwritten the research, development,
testing, and evaluation of the vaccine, the National Foundation
arrived on April 12, 1955, at the outer limits of its active re
sponsibility. It had neither the funds nor the power to mount
the enormous immunization campaigns that could have brought
paralytic polio to a fittingly swift end. Only government could
do that. The Foundation had shown how, of course. The national field trial had demonstrated how easily mass vaccinations
could be administered in the schools. And then, while Francis
was at work on his data, Basil O'Connor had announced a
model plan for the distribution of the 27 million doses of vaccine that the manufacturers were producing for him while awaiting Francis' verdict. The Foundation was to get this vaccine before any could be sold to the general public through commercial
channels. The 9 million persons to be immunized with the allotment were those who deserved priority. First would be the almost
2 million Polio Pioneers who, serving as placebo controls, had
been injected with an inert solution during the field trial or, as
observed controls, had not been injected at all. Also, the more
than 400,000 youngsters actually vaccinated during the field trial

would each get a booster shot. And the remainder of the Foundation's vaccine consignment would go to the country's approximately 7 million schoolchildren of the first and second grades.

There would be no charge for the vaccine, which had been paid for in the first place with funds contributed by the public. Neither would any fees be charged by those who gave the injections. At this point objections were heard from the Chicago and Illinois Medical Societies, among others. The organizations suggested that physicians be allowed private fees when they injected the Foundation's free vaccine in their own offices. O'Connor declined this gambit. A mass immunization program was no occasion for business-as-usual, he said. The idea was to immunize as many people as possible as quickly as possible; he was confident that numerous physicians would willingly donate the brief time and small effort, just as they had in the field trial.

O'Connor's plans established a pattern for national action: centralized purchase of large amounts of vaccine at a reasonable price, rapid distribution of the vaccine for free inoculation on a mass scale, and first service to those most susceptible to paralysis. He had gone as far as he could. The next move was the government's.

In September 1954, after the National Foundation had made its deal with the manufacturers, Hart Van Riper visited Dr. Martha M. Eliot, Chief of the Children's Bureau of the Social Security Administration; he told her what was afoot and suggested that the time had come for the government to prepare for the stampede that undoubtedly would follow a favorable Francis report. Dr. Eliot agreed. On November 4, Van Riper wrote to the Secretary of Health, Education, and Welfare, Oveta Culp Hobby, requesting that "detailed plans for the distribution and administration of the vaccine, contingent of course on the licensure of the product, be worked out in cooperation with federal and state health authorities, the medical profession, and other groups which will be taking an active part in the program." Nothing happened. And when Martha Eliot approached Mrs. Hobby in this vein, she was told that it would be best to see how the Francis report looked before trying to plan anything.

April 12, 1955, came and went. No plans yet existed for the

immunization of the millions of Americans ineligible for the National Foundation's small allotment of vaccine. An official of the Department of Health, Education, and Welfare confided a few years later, "It would have been simple for the government to buy up all the vaccine and distribute it, but we were acutely aware that we then would have been in the business of providing medical care. Once that precedent was established, the next vaccine discovery would go the same way. We could not permit that. Our Administration had a different philosophy than that."

The simple necessity of eradicating paralytic polio was entirely too complicated for the government of the United States. The social mobilization, the moderate federal disbursements, and the slightly regimented, possibly unpaid medical services essential to rapid conquest of the crippling disease were, as the official explained, alien to the philosophy that the Eisenhower Administration shared with its loyal consultants at the American Medical Association. If the laissez-faire tradition of American medical economics were suspended for polio immunization, a menacing precedent would be set. Suppose a cancer vaccine were to be developed someday. Would the do-gooders then demand mass, government-sponsored immunization against cancer? The prospect was too dreadful to contemplate. The mandate was clear. The Administration elected to lie low. It botched what could have been a suitable magnificent conclusion to the nation's polio-research program.

On April 14, when questions were beginning to arise about the possibility of botch, the President directed Mrs. Hobby to report to him on "the best means of assuring equitable distribution of the vaccine." By this time, although the National Foundation was still without enough vaccine for its own program among the schoolchildren, hundreds of thousands of vials of the stuff were turning up in peculiar places. More than half a million doses went into commercial or other inappropriate channels before the Foundation got what it had contracted for. Shortly after April 12, for example, stockholders of Cutter Laboratories received from the firm's President, Robert K. Cutter, M.D., a cheerful letter that said, "You are probably well aware that Cutter is one of six companies producing polio vaccine. This has been one of our major projects for well over a year. . . . The National Institutes of Health have now licensed polio vaccine for commercial production. While we and the other polio vaccine producers have been going at top capacity to have as much vaccine on hand as possible, it looks like there may not be enough to go around.

"Here at the laboratories," continued Cutter, "we are already started on a program to vaccinate the children of our employees. Because the vaccine may be in short supply, I want to be sure that you as a Cutter shareholder also have the opportunity to have your children or grandchildren under eighteen years of age immunized against polio should you so desire.

"A coupon is enclosed which entitles you to vaccine for two complete immunizations; to be sent to your children's or grandchildren's physician. . . ."

Two thousand doses of Parke, Davis vaccine were dispensed in Cuba on April 13. Hundreds of thousands of doses arrived at commercial outlets throughout the United States. All over the country, physicians got token supplies for their own use—supplies that should have gone to young children through the National Foundation. The word spread rapidly: Some physicians had vaccine and were giving it to favored adults. Black marketing was rumored. Beleaguered public-health officers from one end of the country to the other wanted to know when their departments could buy vaccine. They seldom got a straight answer, because nobody really knew. On April 21, Oveta Culp Hobby conferred with manufacturers about these embarrassments, after which vaccine stopped reaching commercial hands. The next day she held a meeting among the manufacturers and representatives of medical organizations, where it was agreed that a National Advisory Committee on Poliomyelitis Vaccine should be established. The committee would have no enforcement powers, of course. On April 27, she met with fifty national organizations described as "broadly representative of the public interest," but excluding several of the consumer and service groups that had been most active in the field trial and were most anxious for a program of mass immunization. At this gathering the representatives of

the government extolled the virtues of a program in which nobody would be required to do anything, and representatives of
the general public pleaded for the exercise of government authority.

It was beginning to dawn on everyone that the polio season
would arrive before sufficient vaccine would be available to immunize more than a small fraction of the population. In New
York City the hue and cry was so impressive that a county medical society felt constrained to suspend a physician who had vaccinated his nineteen-year-old son and thirteen-year-old daughter.
Another medical society in that city reprimanded three physicians
who had vaccinated adults. The City Health Commissioner reported that she had located five physicians who had vaccinated a
total of seventeen adults. The Board of Health was so indignant
that it amended the sanitary code. Every medical prescription
for vaccine now was required to show the age of the patient.
"This," said a health official, "is to shame the doctors into following the voluntary priority."

Members of Congress, including Eisenhower's Republican Mi-
nority Leader in the House of Representatives, Joseph W. Martin,
declared in favor of federally controlled distribution. The President told a press conference that "there will never be a child
in the United States denied this protection for want of ability to
pay." And his press secretary elucidated, "If a situation ever
develops in this country where children are deprived of the vaccine because of inability to pay, the President would immediately
ask Congress for authority to permit the Secretary of Health,
Education, and Welfare to buy the entire output of the vaccine, other than that already allotted to the National Foundation
for Infantile Paralysis."

The manufacturers had announced that the retail price of the
vaccine would be $6 for the three shots that constituted a full
course of vaccination. Physicians, however, would be able to get
the vaccine for about $3.50. Declarations by county medical so-
cieties made plain that the patient would nevertheless pay $2 for
each shot, plus the regular fee for an office visit. In most places
the fee for one visit was described as "averaging" $5. The total
price of immunization would therefore "average" $21 per child.

On the other hand, the manufacturers were offering the vaccine to health departments at a wholesale price—from eighty to eighty-five cents per shot. Only a strong partisan of private medicine could believe that a $21 immunization was preferable to a $3 one. And aside from the compelling question of cost, one had to be a lunatic to suppose that the job could be done more expeditiously in the offices of private physicians than at schools and clinics.

Reasoning in this fashion, members of Congress gave Secretary Hobby some uncomfortable moments, demanding to know why she awaited a Presidential directive before turning her attention to the problems of vaccine distribution, and why her plans were toothless. She did not think her plans were at all bad. "We sincerely believe," she told a Senate committee, "that the program we have outlined will operate the fastest. I believe there can be no real argument on that. If this should break down, if some maldistribution should take place, if something that we cannot foresee should happen, of course, the federal government should always be in control of the situation." She was impenetrable. As to her failure to anticipate the need for adequate supplies of vaccine earlier than she did, she replied heatedly, "I think no one could have foreseen the public demand."

She finally sent up a bill under which Congress would have appropriated $28 million for grants to the states. According to her figures, this would be "sufficient to purchase the vaccine required to vaccinate 22 percent of all children through age nineteen who are not vaccinated under the program of the National Foundation for Infantile Paralysis." Basil O'Connor appeared at one of the Senate hearings on the legislation but declined to express an opinion about it. Besides being colorful, his opinion would have been illegal: The terms of the National Foundation's existence as a tax-exempt organization barred it, by law, from legislative activity. However, the following colloquy took place between O'Connor and Senator Paul H. Douglas:

> Q. When you had these shots distributed to schoolchildren in the first and second grades, did you provide free vaccine for all children or for only 22 percent of the children?
> A. All the children.

Q. In other words, no means test was imposed as to wheth-
er the children's parents could pay for the shots?
A. None.
Q. Did you hear any cries of outrage from children or from
their parents that they were being seduced by being furnished free vaccine?
A. No.
Q. No parents insisted that they should pay for the shots?
A. None that I know of. But they were not prohibited from
taking that position if they wanted to.
Q. Did you feel that you were undermining the medical
profession by furnishing those free shots?
A. No.
Q. Now suppose, Mr. O'Connor, that we were to decide
that in view of your splendid record we would like to place
at your disposal sufficient funds to immunize the third, fourth,
fifth, sixth, and seventh grade children. . . . Suppose the
government purchased the vaccine from the commercial producers, and then directed the commercial producers to turn
over the vaccine to you; would you be willing to accept the
vaccine?
A. Yes.
Q. If that were carried on, do you think the vaccine should
be furnished for 22 percent of the children, or for 100 percent of the children?
A. One hundred percent.

It would have cost Washington less than $100 million to pro-
vide the National Foundation with enough vaccine for all elementary schoolchildren not already covered by the Foundation program. Had the government preferred an even more substantial
head start against the disease, about $140 million would have
bought the vaccine needed for all Americans below the age of
twenty-one. These sums were positively inconsequential when
compared with the tax losses and other cumulative public and
private costs of treating and maintaining the permanently paralyzed survivors of the epidemics that would occur unless the new
vaccine were used as quickly and widely as possible. However,

the bill finally signed by President Eisenhower established a
fund of only $30 million, on which the separate states could
draw if they cared to give vaccine away to the needy. Traditionally, most states took their advice in such matters from organized medicine, just as Washington had. Local medical societies could be relied on to obstruct any immunization plan that
sought to combat polio with free or cut-rate mass immunization,
as if the disease were a public-health problem or something. The
federal program was therefore inadequate medically and scientifically, as well as financially. It guaranteed, in most places, that
the medical profession would be permitted to handle polio immunizations exactly as it treated upset stomachs. New Jersey,
for example, allocated only 25 percent of its vaccine to free
public programs. And the selective nature of these programs was
defined by the State Medical Society, which forbade its members
to participate in any undertaking that gave away vaccine, except
to paupers.

Although Jonas Salk regretted the myopic meanness of the
government's approach to polio immunization and might have
used his new prestige in a most salutary way had he chosen to
speak out, he resisted the temptation. In fact, he does not remember being tempted at all. "Vaccine distribution and public-health
planning were not my fields and not my responsibility," he says.
"Now, more than ever, I could not hope to attend to my own
responsibilities if I became embroiled in everyone else's. It was
the manufacturers' responsibility to produce safe, potent vaccine, and the Public Health Service's responsibility to police
this, and the responsibility of the Congress and the Executive
branch and the states and the medical profession and the National Foundation and other interested groups to make the best
arrangements they could for delivery of the vaccine to the public.
Obviously, it would have been better if paralytic poliomyelitis
were attacked nationally, concertedly, and immediately, but the
living realities of the situation were otherwise. Beyond all other
obstacles, there was not enough vaccine on hand to permit such
a program in the spring of 1955. No amount of exhortation or

criticism could have altered that. In any case, exhortation and criticism were not part of my role as a scientist."

On April 27, fifteen days after the vaccine was licensed for general sale, a crisis arose in which Salk's role as a scientist was subjected to harsh scrutiny and acrimonious debate. The national perplexity about what kind of vaccination programs to organize gave way to grave doubt whether there should be any vaccination programs whatever. The issue now was death. On April 25, Dr. William G. Workman, Director of the Laboratory of Biologics Control at the National Institutes of Health, learned that a Chicago infant had became paralyzed after inoculation with a physician's sample of Cutter vaccine. Workman remained calm. The child might have been carrying the infection before he was vaccinated. But word reached Bethesda the next day that five California children were paralyzed. They, too, had been given Cutter vaccine. Could all six cases be coincidence? Had something gone wrong with the Cutter vaccine? Was there live virus in it? Several hundred thousand schoolchildren covered by the National Foundation program were to be vaccinated with Cutter's product the next day. Should the government let this happen? On the evening of the 26th, Dr. James A. Shannon, Deputy Director of the National Institutes of Health, met in his office with Assistant Surgeon General David E. Price (a member of Basil O'Connor's Vaccine Advisory Committee); Dr. Victor Haas, Director of the National Institute for Allergy and Infectious Diseases, of which Workman's department was a part; Dr. Alexander D. Langmuir, Chief of the Epidemiology Branch of the Public Health Service's Communicable Disease Center; Workman; and two other officials of the Laboratory of Biologics Control, Drs. Roderick Murray and Karl Habel.

"We checked the manufacturing protocols which Cutter had submitted on its batches of vaccine," recalls one of these men, "and we saw nothing wrong. We did not find out until some days later that Cutter had been sending us its records only on vaccine that passed the safety tests. When we learned how many of its batches had failed to pass the tests, we got a much different picture, of course. The plant had not been producing safe vaccine consistently—which gave us a compelling reason to suspect that some of the samples had passed the safety tests only by chance and were, in fact, from lots which contained residual living virus. But we did not know this on the 26th. All we knew was that we had to try to interpret the six paralytic cases and make up our minds whether vaccinations should continue. We had to play safe, but we didn't want to undermine the immunization program. It was a terribly tense situation."

"We burned up the wires to learn all we could about the cases," says Alex Langmuir. "The California Health Department had just moved into a new building and it took a while to locate anyone. When we began to fill in the gaps I became as convinced as anyone could be at this stage that the cases were attributable to a common source, the Cutter vaccine. Each of the children had fallen ill a few days after inoculation. In each case, the first paralysis had occurred at the site of inoculation. No comparable outbreaks of paralytic polio seemed to be taking place among unvaccinated children in the same communities. I believed that our one small hope of avoiding catastrophe was to get the Cutter vaccine off the market at once. Bill Workman agreed. But the others voted to wait, figuring that it all might turn out to be a false alarm and that drastic action would be a mistake until we were more certain what was going on.

"At two-thirty in the morning Dave Price phoned the Surgeon General (Dr. Leonard A. Scheele) and told him what we had been doing and how we had voted. Scheele now did a very smart thing. He said, 'When the vaccinations start at eight-thirty out in California it will already be eleven-thirty here. That gives us most of the morning to consult other people. Round up all the key polio experts you can on a conference call and see what they think.' "

Sooner or later his gossamer tightrope breaks, and the office holder lands among the crocodiles. If they eat him, he is a failure. Leonard Scheele was a success. The tall, genial, unexcitable physician paddled impassively among the crocodiles, assuring them that all was well. And in time all was more or less well.

The contrasts between popular illusion and political reality have seldom been more noticeable than in the Cutter incident. If the sole concern of the Public Health Service had been public health, the tragedy could not have occurred. But other factors were involved. Scheele's budget, his procedures, and the size and disposition of his staff were regulated by law and tradition to ensure minimum interference with private medicine and the drug industry, the compulsions of which do not necessarily coincide with those of public health. This arrangement antedated Scheele. It antedated Eisenhower. It antedated Oveta Culp Hobby. And, of course, it antedated modern reality. But it was public policy, accepted by the electorate and reaffirmed in every session of Congress. Nevertheless, if the Cutter vaccine was actually causing paralytic polio, this same electorate and some of its Congressmen would demand to know why the Public Health Service had not prevented the disaster. From the White House down, nobody would be content with the truth, which was this: The personnel at the Laboratory of Biologics Control of the National Institutes of Health of the Public Health Service of President Eisenhower's Department of Health, Education, and Welfare could not possibly have superintended Cutter's vaccine production (or that of any other manufacturer) without transgressing budget, violating custom, and, in fact, stepping entirely out of character. The same mystique that impelled the government to prostrate itself in planning vaccine supply and distribution was operative in the Cutter incident and, to a considerable degree, explained it.

No sane spokesman for the Administration could invite attention to the relationship between these facts and the deaths of children. Scheele's position compelled him to avoid full, frank communication with the people, lest they lose confidence in the Administration, its methods, and its values. Furthermore, the concealment of certain facts was required by law. A statute enacted in 1905 prohibited federal officers to disclose information concerning business processes. Exceptions were permitted in cases of crime, but no crime had occurred in the Cutter case and none was alleged. Even if Scheele had wanted to rock the boat by explaining the paralytic illnesses and deaths in terms of his own department's failure to correct Cutter's laboratory practices, the law would have forbidden him to tell exactly how it happened. Hence, when officials of the National Institutes of Health testified in civil suits brought against Cutter by the parents of paralyzed children, they declined, on grounds of this law, to reveal everything they knew about the methods that the firm had employed in manufacturing the unsafe vaccine.

One does not become Surgeon General without learning how to survive bad bargains. Scheele was good at it. He endured the Cutter affair without once suggesting that the disaster was a disaster or that any party to it was other than a splendid fellow. The public never found out what really had happened. When time came to assign blame, he diffused it expertly. Those who deserved much got less than they deserved. Those who deserved little got more than they deserved. By such means Scheele contrived to save the Public Health Service and the Eisenhower Administration from the calamity of truth. In the process, he saved the Salk vaccine from the calamity of total misrepresentation.

This was a miracle. "The live-vaccine crowd wanted to kill the inactivated vaccine on the spot," says Jonas Salk. "If Scheele had been weak, they might have succeeded. Lord knows they tried hard enough. But Scheele behaved in a most constructive way, refusing to panic, assessing the evidence objectively and serving the interests of science, medicine, and the public as best he could in the circumstances."

"I think I saved the vaccine situation, yes," says Scheele, who is now a pharmaceutical executive. "I had good counsel, though. Jim Shannon—and this is no secret—had strong reservations about the Salk formula and the safety tests that were being used, but he did not want to scuttle the program. And Alex Langmuir, a staunch supporter of Salk's work, helped make me brave about it by being so brave himself."

On the morning of Wednesday, April 27, Victor Haas held the telephonic conference ordered by Scheele. Among the consultants were William McD. Hammon, Salk's colleague at Pittsburgh (and no fan), Tommy Francis, Joe Smadel, Jim Shannon, and Howard J. Shaughnessy, Chief of Laboratories of the Illinois Department of Public Health. Other polio experts were reached as the morning progressed. But not Salk. Nobody was terribly anxious to consult Salk. He learned about the paralytic cases only after the National Foundation did, later that day. The consensus

of the polio experts was that Scheele should "do something," short
of calling off the entire vaccination program.

At eleven-thirty that morning, with the inoculations about to
begin in California, Scheele talked by telephone with Dr. Malcolm
Merrill, California Commissioner of Public Health, who threatened
to call off the program unilaterally, rather than risk more cases.
When Scheele heard this, and heard the results of Haas's tele-
phone conferences, he told Merrill that he would ask Cutter to
recall its vaccine from the market pending a study of the cases.
Merrill then canceled the California inoculations, a fortunate move.
Some of the batches of vaccine scheduled for injection into Los
Angeles children on that day contained living poliovirus.

The Surgeon General of the United States Public Health Service had no power to order Cutter Laboratories, a licensed manufacturer, to withdraw its vaccine from the market. Scheele could
only request Cutter's cooperation. He got it immediately. He then
sent Drs. Karl Habel and William Tripp to Berkeley to inspect
Cutter's plant and records and question its employees in the hope of
turning up clues to what might have happened. The evidence
indicated that bad vaccine had been passing at Berkeley as if it
were good vaccine. Why? A good question. But, if employees had
been falsifying the company's records, pretending to follow production procedures that they actually neglected, two inspectors
from Bethesda could hardly expect to discover this during a
visit months after the fact. All the inspectors could do was take
the company records at face value, along with the assurances of
company employees that all procedures were peachy-keen. It
so happened, however, that Cutter's own records provided a partial explanation of what had gone wrong.

Of the twenty-seven lots of vaccine produced at the Cutter
plant, the firm's own safety tests had demonstrated that nine contained living virus. Because these batches were failures and un-
suitable for sale, Cutter did not even report them to Bethesda.
It was under no legal or administrative compulsion to do so, although National Institutes of Health officials declare that failures
of this magnitude usually were reported by manufacturers, if for
no other reason than to get technical assistance. Had Cutter submitted the protocols on the rejected batches, it is probable that

Bill Workman would have become suspicious about batches that had *passed* the safety tests. He would have invoked the dearly won principle of production consistency, which had been applied so stringently before vaccine was accepted for use in the 1954 field trial. He would have had the supposedly good batches of Cutter vaccine retested and might have found the live virus in some of them. But again, no law was broken. "Consistency" was undefined in the government's 1955 regulations affecting the manufacture of commercial vaccine. Cutter was within its rights to interpret the word any way it pleased. And it pleased to go about its business in the good old-fashioned way: If a batch of vaccine passed the safety tests, it was safe, statistical probabilities to the contrary notwithstanding.

Something else that Habel and Tripp found at Berkeley was already known in Bethesda but had caused no alarm there. The protocols on which Cutter logged the production of each batch of vaccine showed that the firm had adopted a most cavalier attitude toward Salk's inactivation methods. Where samplings of the virus mixture were recommended at five separate stages of the inactivation process, to see whether the all-important *rate* of inactivation was proper, Cutter usually had been taking only two samplings. Once again, no law was broken. Cutter had been manufacturing biological products successfully for many years, employing established procedures, which did not include plotting inactivation rates on graph paper. Habel and Tripp noted all this, including the fact that they had found nothing amiss in Cutter's procedures. Later they and Workman and other government experts were able to testify in the damage suits brought against Cutter that, as far as they were able to tell, Cutter's performance had been competent.

"My job," says Jonas Salk, "was to provide the understanding, but I could not force-feed it to my colleagues or to the Laboratory of Biologics Control or to Cutter Laboratories. I could offer it, and offer to help clarify it. It is sometimes true, and was certainly true in this case, that the *doing* part defies the understanding or ignores the understanding or overlooks the understanding. Therefore, when the doers enter and don't understand, we are in trouble. It took me very little time to know what went wrong in the

Cutter incident. The doers had not understood and had resisted understanding. And when some of them shook their fists at me and said, 'Nya, nya, you see, your inactivation process didn't work,' they were raising nonunderstanding to the level of a principle."

At four o'clock on the afternoon of April 27, after he had learned at last from New York and Bethesda that children were being paralyzed and that Scheele had asked Cutter to withdraw its vaccine, a shaken but self-possessed Jonas Salk issued a statement to the press: "I have just learned of the decision by the Public Health Service. It is difficult to say whether or not the association between vaccination and the reported cases is one of cause and effect or one of coincidence. When you realize how much investigation was done to verify each case in the field trials, then it is not difficult to appreciate that only after the same kind of thorough investigation can any valid conclusions be drawn concerning the reported cases. It would seem that what is being done is reasonable, namely that a thorough investigation of the reported cases is being made. . . ."

At a press conference in Washington, Scheele urged public calm. He said nothing about the circumstantial evidence that seemed to incriminate the Cutter product. It was being withdrawn only as a "safety precaution," he said, emphasizing, "I want first and foremost to assure the parents of children who have received an injection of poliomyelitis vaccine this spring that in the very best judgment of the Public Health Service, they have no cause for alarm." He continued to play variations on this theme for weeks.

Before the end of the day, word of two more cases, one fatal, came from Pocatello, Idaho. For a few minutes, Scheele and the Bethesda officials were relieved: Idaho was not Cutter territory. Only Parke, Davis vaccine was supposed to go to Idaho. But then someone pointed out that Cutter had sent many vaccine samples into Idaho. Sure enough, both of the Pocatello victims had been given Cutter vaccine. The theory that these illnesses were mere coincidence was even harder to sustain than in the California cases, since the polio season would not begin in Idaho for several weeks. Before the Cutter epidemic ran its course, there

were to be eighty-six polio cases in Idaho, seventy of them paralytic, five fatal. Twenty-five would occur in vaccinated children,
and the others among parents, siblings, and friends infected by
contact with the children. The contaminated vaccine finally caused
at least 260 cases, including eleven deaths, in twenty-five states
and the Territory of Hawaii.

On April 28, Scheele announced that he had established a
special Poliomyelitis Surveillance Unit at the Communicable Disease Center in Atlanta, "for rapid investigation of all cases reported as poliomyelitis." Alex Langmuir would be in charge.
Scheele urged the public to be calm. He said that the withdrawal
of Cutter vaccine did not imply that there was any correlation
between that product and the occurrence of poliomyelitis. "There
have been only three new cases of poliomyelitis reported among
vaccinated children in the past twenty-four hours," he said. "It
cannot be accepted that vaccine would provide protection so soon
after a first injection. According to the study of Dr. Francis,
moreover, the Salk vaccine is 60 to 90 percent effective after full
immunization. Thus in any large group of children who have
received the full course of immunization, it can be expected that
there will be some who will contract the disease. There is nothing
unusual about the polio picture across the nation. . . ."

Behind the scenes, Scheele addressed himself to one of several
things that were quite unusual about the polio picture. He ordered
the Laboratory of Biologics Control to test samples of all batches
of Cutter vaccine. This, of course, should have been done before
the government permitted the stuff to be injected into children.
No doubt it would have been done in time if Oveta Culp Hobby
or Scheele had obtained for the National Institutes of Health the
money and manpower needed to test the cataracts of vaccine that
inundated the place on and after April 12.

The head of the Laboratory of Biologics Control, Bill Workman, had demonstrated his cautious conservatism in negotiations
with Jonas Salk and the National Foundation before the field trial.
Although he had more confidence in industry (which he understood), than in Salk (whom he did not), he undoubtedly would
have liked to double check all commercial vaccine on a routine
basis for a few months, until assured that the six firms were

producing safe vaccine consistently. But he was hamstrung. So he had ordered a few spot tests of vaccine samples and relied mainly on the information contained in the manufacturers' protocols. If his staff was indulgent toward Cutter, accepting that company's decision to cut corners on Salk's new-fangled nuisance, the inactivation graphs, the attitude derived from a fundamental confidence that the vaccine manufacturers usually knew what they were doing. Which, indeed, almost all of them did.

Jonas Salk spent much of April 28 on the telephone. "We had a string of them set up in his office," Tom Coleman recalls, "so that he could talk to the panicked doctors who were calling from all over the country. They'd taken free samples from Cutter and had given shots to their wives and children and cousins and what was going to happen now? All Jonas could say was that their best bet was gamma globulin, just in case. At that early stage in the Cutter incident, it was still not clear to us that the cases we'd heard about were anything more than freak coincidence. But the threat was there, and rumors were starting that all vaccinations might be called off, not just those using Cutter vaccine. If that happened, Jonas' career would be up for grabs and I'm sure he knew it. I've never seen a man in a situation so difficult who was in such total control of himself. He knew, he just *knew* that if anything was wrong with Cutter vaccine the trouble would have to be found at Cutter and not in his theories. He'd been through it, you see. He'd been through it all. He'd tested it all. He'd explored every angle of it. And he knew. This is what held him together."

On Friday, April 29, Salk was in Bethesda for the first of numerous meetings at which he and other scientists attempted to understand and explain the Cutter incident and devise measures that might prevent a recurrence. With David Bodian, John Enders, Tom Francis, Bill Hammon, Foard McGinnes, John Paul, Albert Sabin, Joe Smadel, Howard Shaughnessy, and Dr. Edward H. Lennette, Director of the Viral and Rickettsial Disease Laboratory of the California State Department of Public Health, Salk had been appointed to a Special Committee to Consider Problems

Related to Poliomyelitis Vaccine. These leading scientists now became—by force of law—the accomplices of government and industry in withholding the truth from the American people. The obscure statutes and regulations that protected commerce by making certain of its relations with government as confidential as those of doctor and patient or lawyer and client now muzzled Salk and his colleagues. They could communicate with the people only through the Surgeon General. The transcripts of the meetings were impounded and have never been made public. To this day none of the scientists speaks freely of what took place in the conferences that began on April 29, 1955, but some say enough to make clear that much of the awful truth of the Cutter incident was obvious long before the government saw fit to reveal the smallest hint of it. It also is clear that, as the meetings continued, they became a death struggle between Salk and his scientific opponents.

Jim Shannon was chairman of the April 29 session. Other Public Health Service experts also were present, including Alex Langmuir, who made no bones of his belief that paralytic cases were attributable to the Cutter vaccine and nothing else. Bodian agreed. "The job," he said, "is to find out how it happened."

"Correction!" said Salk. "The job is to find out *what* happened." He was not yet ready to agree that the Cutter product contained living virus. Neither, at that first meeting, was Albert Sabin, who urged attention to the possibility that the cases were simply coincidental. Sabin also suggested that the injections of vaccine might have provoked paralysis in persons already infected, as injections of any kind could sometimes do.

Foard McGinnes asked an obvious question. What had the Laboratory of Biologics Control discovered about the Cutter product in the routine safety tests that preceded release of the vaccine to the public? There was no answer. He repeated the question at least once. There still was no answer. The government representatives were acutely uncomfortable. It began to dawn on the committee that no tests had been made.

"Much of the discussion," recalls a participant, "was at least implicitly concerned with the hot water in which the Cutter cases had dumped the government. If word ever got out that the Public Health Service had actually done something damaging to the health of the American people, the consequences would be terrible. Regardless of our diverse opinions of Salk and his vaccine, most of us were very much in sympathy with the government people. We felt that no lasting good could come to science or the public if the Public Health Service were discredited. Paradoxically, this recognition of the government's dilemma was a powerful influence in helping to save the polio immunization program. John Paul, John Enders, Bill Hammon, and Howard Shaughnessy were dead set against continuing the program. They wanted the entire thing canceled outright. Cutter cases were continuing to pile up, and these men genuinely feared that the vaccine manufactured by other firms would cause illness, too. Scientifically, they just couldn't see the Salk vaccine. Neither could some of the government people. They wished they'd never heard of Salk. But they could not buy the Paul-Enders recommendation and cancel all vaccinations without giving the public the idea that the vaccine never should have been licensed in the first place. People like Bodian and Langmuir sided with Salk, pointing out that no other manufacturer's product had yet caused paralysis and that there was no reason to expect such disaster."

By April 30, twenty-six cases of paralytic polio had been reported in children inoculated with Cutter vaccine. Having seen some of Cutter's protocols, Salk now realized that some tests of the inactivation rate had been omitted at the plant. The firm's failure to inform the government about its bad lots of vaccine also became apparent. Leonard Scheele recalls that Salk behaved with considerable aplomb. So does Salk, who felt that the evidence was becoming so plain and Cutter's mistakes so obvious that little more deliberation was necessary. If Cutter were now instructed in some of the procedures which it had not fully appreciated in the past, and if "consistency" were defined in the government regulations, and if the Laboratory of Biologics Control became more alert, no further trouble would arise. Wrong again. Trouble had barely started.

The committee appointed Bodian, Enders, Francis, Salk, Shaughnessy, and Smadel to study the government's regulations and suggest possible improvements. All manufacturers were asked to begin informing Bethesda of vaccine batches that failed to pass safety tests and were not being submitted for clearance. Scheele did not burden the public with information of this sort. He reported that the committee thought the vaccination programs should continue without Cutter vaccine. He reiterated his faith in the vaccine. He said nothing about the Cutter protocols and what they revealed about the firm's approach to Salk's inactivation method. He said nothing about the failure of the Laboratory of Biologics Control to test all batches of vaccine that it cleared for distribution. But he did indicate that everything was fundamentally fine and that nobody had anything to worry about.

Over the weekend, the Cutter toll continued to rise. Sabin now agreed with Enders and Paul that the safe thing to do was call off all vaccination programs. The Cutter cases were probably being caused by the virulent Mahoney (Type I) virus to which he had objected so strenuously in the past. The carefully controlled production and triple testing of the vaccine used in the field trial had eliminated unsafe batches. But no such care had been taken with the vaccine now being offered the public. This week, Cutter cases. In whose product would the Mahoney virus wreak havoc next week? At a meeting of the Association of American Physicians in Atlantic City on May 2, Sabin, Enders, and Paul met in a hotel room with Dr. William H. Sebrell, Jr., Director of the National Institutes of Health, and urged that all licenses to manufacture Salk vaccine be suspended immediately and all vaccine be withdrawn. They recommended a public admission that the product had been licensed prematurely. The vaccine simply was not ready for mass, commercial production. Honesty was the best policy. Human lives were involved. Sebrell was impressed by the scientists' argument. Even if he was not ready to swallow it whole, he could not brush it aside. These were the leading authorities in their field. Their stern warnings against further procrastination were already being echoed in Bethesda, where sentiment was turning toward suspension of all vaccinations pending the development of more stringent safety regulations and the retesting of batches previously cleared for public use. Jim Shannon now was in the polio situation full time and full strength. He regarded the present safety tests as inadequate. He believed that Salk's inactivation principles could not be

applied under conditions of large-scale manufacture unless the
safety tests were greatly improved. He believed that the Public
Health Service had only one sane choice: Withdraw all vaccine
temporarily to protect the public, or prepare to take down the
shingle and flee.

The list of Cutter cases grew longer by the day. Here, more
than in the machinations of his opponents, was Salk's pain. Each
new case report was a challenge to the air of scientific detach-
ment that he had cultivated for so many years. He was Jonas.
He had never been able to pretend successfully that the suffering
of others was none of his concern. And now the suffering of others
was attributable to a vaccine that bore his name. "I know it's
purely emotional," he said to a friend, apologizing for the sensi-
bilities that distinguished him as a human being, "but I cannot
escape a terrible feeling of identification with these people who
are getting polio." His grief and indignation were magnified by
awareness that the Cutter cases could not have happened if the
government and the drug firm had understood his scientific and
technical principles, the laws of nature. But now another law of
nature was at work—the law of self-preservation. Neither government nor Cutter could reasonably be expected to achieve in the
threatening atmosphere of the present an understanding that had
eluded them in the past. To preserve themselves they would be
compelled to mock him and his graphs and the claims he had
made about a margin of safety. In discrediting his science, they
would absolve themselves of error. And what would he do in
response? Did not the law of self-preservation also govern him?
He would fight. In his own way, of course. And not in public,
of course. His technical subcommittee was to meet in Bethesda
on Thursday and Friday, May 5 and 6. He would take that opportunity to review concrete facts in an appeal to reason. Surely
the experience of the field trial and the continuing recent success
of the Lilly and Parke, Davis vaccines—millions of doses of
which had now been given safely—proved that mystery had long
since departed from mass production. Any firm able to abide by
simple principles could produce highly effective, completely safe
vaccine in unlimited quantity. This was no conjecture. It was a
matter of record. It had been done. It was still being done.

"When he was in Pittsburgh, which was unusual during that period," says Donna Salk, "we sometimes had friends over in the evenings to discuss what was happening. Should he speak out in public? What should he say? Or should he continue to conform to the standards of public behavior expected of him and awaken one day to discover that his work had been discredited? And that he had been demolished in the process?"

Invariably his decision was to try to play the game according to its established rules. Throughout the Cutter episode he endeavored to project to the people a sense of confidence that matters were well in hand. His public deportment was almost as bland as Scheele's. Sometimes he overdid it, no doubt because he was unsuited to the role. At the height of national concern about the unexplained cases of paralysis, he told a reporter, "I am in the eye of the hurricane and where I am all is peaceful and calm," conveying an indifference that he did not feel.

In the meetings at Bethesda, where he truly believed that he was dealing with people ready to see him dead, he tried to behave as if the only problems in view were scientific ones. He later told Jane Krieger of *The New York Times* that "he didn't lose his temper, he used his temper." She wrote, "Sometimes when he was really angry at his critics, he would go back to his hotel room and write out, in longhand, a speech for delivery the next day. Then, having delivered himself of his anger, he would throw the speech in the trash basket and go to bed."

Convinced of his own rightness, he saw wrongness and evil in those who opposed him, yet he was not one to meet such opposition head-on, call it by name, and smash it to earth. He preferred, as he sometimes says, to "rise above" conflict and let the hatred and errors expend themselves below. A scientist who attended the Bethesda meetings in May says that Salk was less successful in these attempted levitations than he may have thought. "He gnawed out the National Institutes of Health, for failing to enforce their own safety requirements at the Cutter plant," says the scientist. "He was absolutely right, but this was not the best time to put the NIH people on the defensive. Another thing that bothered everyone was the way Jonas hung on night after night, arguing about the phrasing of the press releases, trying to save the image of his vaccine when the circumstances also required that something be done to save the image of the Public Health Service. Before long there was a distinct feeling that some of the government boys were dedicated to an attitude of 'it's either him or us,' and were so sore at him that they had less than even the usual compunction about trying to throw him to the wolves. Dave Bodian, who was very much on his side, said to him once, 'For Christ's sake, Jonas, will you please stop saying that the vaccine is absolutely safe? There is no such thing as absolute safety.' There we were in a desperate situation, trying to salvage as much of it as we could, and Jonas, no matter what he may now think, was making it tough on his friends. And it would have helped if he hadn't always been the first one to get to the news reporters during committee recesses. Obviously, he was frightened about himself and his work and where it was all going to end, but he frightened others into becoming much more antagonistic to him."

It was at one of the May meetings, Salk recalls, that John Enders faced him across the table and said, "It is quack medicine to pretend that this is a killed vaccine when you know it has live virus in it. Every batch has live virus in it." Salk's face falls when he tells the story. "This was the first and only time in my life that I felt suicidal," he says. "There was no hope, no hope at all."

Scheele was still forcing the public to guess under which walnut shell the pea was concealed. On May 6, he announced that no new batches of vaccine would be cleared for distribution until the subcommittee reevaluated production and testing procedures. He denied that the vaccine, as such, was "under suspicion" and urged the public to continue taking shots of vaccine already cleared. Thus, the vaccine already cleared was good and safe, although the yardsticks that had been used to determine its goodness and safety might have to be corrected. But nobody should worry about anything. As to the Cutter vaccine and whether it was the actual cause of the thirty-eight polio cases now associated with it, "We have to have a lot more evidence before we can decide."

The evidence was accumulating. Investigation of the Cutter

record showed that almost half of all the polio vaccine made at the plant had contained live virus. The principle of consistency might as well never have existed. During the meetings of May 5 and 6, Salk saw proof of this. But his committee colleagues and the government officials were equally impressed by other information. Much was made of reports by the manufacturers that every one of them had encountered difficulty with the inactivation process at one time or another. Much more was made of Jim Shannon's unshakable insistence that the safety tests had to be augmented before anyone could dare hope that the Salk vaccine was a reliable product. At four o'clock on the morning of May 7, the meeting broke up and Len Scheele told the press that all polio vaccinations should be suspended, perhaps for as long as a month.

"Salk was heartbroken," says O'Connor, who had arrived in Washington on May 6. "The poor kid. It was his vaccine and he knew there wasn't a damned thing wrong with it when it was made properly, but he was up against a juggernaut. I kept telling him to relax, that the truth would come out someday. He knew this was so. But what was happening was very hard for him to take. It would have been hard for anybody to take, wouldn't it? Nothing was wrong with his vaccine, and the government keeps repeating that nothing is wrong, but they pull the vaccine off the market anyhow, and wreck the public's confidence."

On Sunday, May 8, Scheele went on television. "As Surgeon General of the Public Health Service," he said, "I recommended the day before yesterday that vaccination programs against poliomyelitis be temporarily postponed.

"That decision was based on preliminary reviews of the recommendations of a group of scientists and medical experts who have been consulting with us on the problem that arose when a number of children developed polio after injections with the vaccine of one manufacturer.

"That review has been completed.

"We must all remember that, like many other vaccines and medicines, this one is not 100 percent effective. But the percentage of children who have contracted poliomyelitis after vaccination this year is very, very small. As of now, there are only fifty-two cases among more than 5 million who have been vaccinated.

"Because the Public Health Service believes that every single step in the interest of safety must be taken, we are undertaking, with the help of the manufacturers, a reappraisal of all their tests and processes. This can be thought of, if you like, as a double check. The manufacturers are cooperating magnificently with us —as they have been doing all along in this effort.

"We plan to make this reappraisal on a manufacturer-by-manufacturer basis and, just as rapidly as possible, release the vaccine. We hope that this process will result in a return of the vaccine to availability beginning in the latter part of the current week.

"Until that recheck is completed, we are repeating our recommendation that the vaccine program be temporarily postponed. This will cause some delay in the program. But we believe —and I am sure the American people join us in believing—that in dealing with the lives of our children, it is impossible to be too cautious.

"We have every faith that this vaccine—the brilliant achievement of an able scientist, Dr. Jonas Salk, whose work has been so generously supported by the National Foundation for Infantile Paralysis—is both safe and effective. I believe that this reappraisal will demonstrate that fact and that within a few days, all of us will be able to move forward in the fight against polio with renewed confidence.

"On behalf of everyone in the Department of Health, Education, and Welfare and in the Public Health Service, I want to extend thanks for the help that has been so fully and generously extended by so many of our scientists, physicians, and public-health authorities. I am sure that, in so doing, I am also expressing the sentiments of Americans everywhere."

In another declaration on that day, Scheele asserted, "The reason for the association between administration of the Cutter vaccine and the few cases of poliomyelitis that have developed after its administration has not been determined. The association is so definite, however, that until the precise cause is found the vaccine produced by this laboratory will remain suspended." All other laboratories would be permitted to resume sales as soon as their processes had been rechecked. And, "The Public Health Service has every faith that, within the ever-narrowing limits of human fallibility, the Salk vaccine is safe and effective." A virtuoso performance.

"Basil O'Connor tried every which way to talk me out of suspending the program," Scheele recalls. "He called me at all hours of the night. He threatened to have me fired. And Jonas was not at all happy, either. But the doubts that had been raised about possible flaws in the safety-testing procedures were too strong to ignore. The uncertain state of knowledge and the general air of controversy which existed at that time simply decreed that we take the safe way with this thing."

O'Connor remembers phoning Scheele. "I couldn't understand what he had in mind," says O'Connor. "Every day he kept saying that the vaccine from the other companies was good, which was true, and now he wanted to put a stop to its use. I told him that the press would knock his head off if some reporter was smart enough to ask how come he was having the manufacturers withdraw a safe vaccine. Naturally, no reporter ever asked the question. Or if any did, I don't remember reading Scheele's answer anywhere."

After Scheele announced that all vaccinations should be suspended, O'Connor had his publicity staff telephone this comment to the newspapers: "Apparently Dr. Scheele wishes a week's time in which to recheck batches of the Salk vaccine heretofore licensed by the National Institutes of Health. Since the licensing of the vaccine is the sole obligation of the United States Government through the National Institutes of Health, one has to yield to Dr. Scheele's judgment as to the desirability of a recheck, regardless of the delay caused thereby, and despite the fact that Dr. Scheele still asserts that the vaccine as originally checked is safe and sound."

And Jonas Salk said, after swallowing hard, "The United States Public Health Service decision expresses its desire to do all in its power to assure the continuous flow of safe and effective vaccine. The United States Public Health Service has the ultimate responsibility in matters of this kind that have gone beyond the research stage.

"As a scientist, my responsibility is to make certain that concepts are sound and founded upon experimentally derived evidence. Of this I am certain, not only because of work done in our laboratory but because of its confirmation as shown by the evaluation of the field trials. In making suggestions regarding application of these concepts to large-scale production, I have extended my responsibility as far as I can. The carrying out of this application cannot rest on the shoulders of any one individual but of necessity becomes the responsibility of those agencies directly involved."

On Wednesday, May 11, Bill Workman arrived at the Parke, Davis plant for the heralded "recheck." On May 13, Parke, Davis vaccine returned to the market, and two days later the "rechecked" Eli Lilly vaccine was back in circulation.

"The result of all the confusion," commented *The New York Times,* "has been twofold. First, the nation is now badly scared. Never before have reports of the number of polio cases been so widely publicized and so carefully studied. Millions of parents fear that if their children don't get the vaccine they may get polio, but if they do get the vaccine, it might give them polio. This fear was evident in New York State last week. The National Foundation for Infantile Paralysis, which is distributing the vaccine free to certain age groups, received enough of the cleared Parke, Davis vaccine for New Yorkers. But as many as 30 percent of the children who had applied for injections last month failed to turn up last week."

Senator Estes Kefauver said, "There was no excuse whatever for starting and stopping, scaring everybody to death. . . . It is one of the worst bungled programs I have ever seen." And Senator Wayne Morse spoke words of unarguable truth about the Cutter cases: "The federal government inspects meat in the slaughterhouses more carefully than it has inspected the polio vaccine offered by the drug companies to the parents of the nation for inoculating their boys and girls against this dread disease. . . ."

The Subcommittee on Minimum Requirements, which had met on May 5 and 6, was to reconvene on Monday, May 23. Salk looked forward to the session with dread. If he attended, the process started at the previous meetings would undoubtedly be ex-

tended. By his very participation he might be committed to the
rape of his own work, an act from which he could not later differentiate himself without provoking dreadful public controversy.
Salk spent the weekend in New York with Basil O'Connor. They
agreed that one of the worst shortcomings of the various scientific
subcommittees at Bethesda was their ad hoc character. With no
authority to make decisions, the groups were, for all practical purposes, cats-paws for the Public Health Service. What was needed
to rescue the polio immunization program was a small committee
of men like Bodian, Francis, and Smadel. They didn't want to kill
the Public Health Service and they didn't want to kill Salk and
they were in favor of prosecuting the polio war in which they
had been engaged for so many years.

On Saturday night, Salk sent Scheele a telegram from the
Waldorf:

AFTER FURTHER CONSIDERATION OF CONVERSATIONS WITH YOU
AND DR. SEBRELL LAST NIGHT, AM CONVINCED PROBLEMS IN-
VOLVED CAN BE SATISFACTORILY SOLVED IF PUT IN HANDS OF
SMALL COMMITTEE WITH POWER AND AUTHORITY FOR DECISIONS
THAT MUST BE FOLLOWED. MEMBERS OF COMMITTEE SHOULD BE
FULLY ACQUAINTED NOT ONLY WITH PROBLEMS INVOLVED IN BI-
OLOGICS CONTROL BUT WITH DEVELOPMENTS THAT ACTUALLY
TOOK PLACE PRIOR TO FIELD TRIALS AND UP TO DATE. THEREFORE
URGE APPOINTING TO THE LABORATORY OF BIOLOGICS CONTROL A
PERMANENT COMMITTEE CONSISTING OF BODIAN, FRANCIS, AND
SMADEL. . . . STRONGLY URGE THAT NO DECISIONS BE MADE WITH-
OUT APPROVAL OF THIS COMMITTEE. FEEL CONFIDENT THAT IF
THIS IS DONE PROBLEMS CAN BE SOLVED IN THE BEST INTERESTS
OF THE AMERICAN PEOPLE. IT IS IN COOPERATING WITH SUCH A
COMMITTEE THAT I BELIEVE I CAN BE OF GREATEST VALUE AND
IF THIS COMMITTEE IS APPOINTED I SHALL BE GLAD TO GIVE IT
EVERY ASSISTANCE. I AM EQUALLY CERTAIN PROBLEMS CANNOT
BE SOLVED BY AD HOC COMMITTEES THAT HAVE NO AUTHORITY.

Salk did not attend the May 23 meeting at Bethesda. He went
from New York to Pittsburgh and spent the day in his office, a
visiting celebrity. His absence from Bethesda was a huge embarrassment to the Public Health Service, especially since it co-

incided with a barrage from O'Connor. At a journalism awards luncheon of the Albert and Mary Lasker Foundation, attended by some of the country's leading science writers and their publishers, O'Connor took off the gloves and got tough. Discarding his prepared speech, he said, "So long as the Salk vaccine and its research were in the hands of the National Foundation, you had some intelligence, intellectual integrity, and total courage—and you had no politics whatsoever." He also said that there was no point in changing the government's vaccine-testing requirements until the truth about the present testing requirements and the truth about the Cutter vaccine were known. He demanded that Scheele release the information to the public without further delay.

Scheele was now in a more difficult spot than before. His public-relations spokesmen explained Salk's absence on grounds of a "prior commitment," an excuse that Salk promptly repudiated. And word came from Dr. Louis P. Gebhardt of the University of Utah, Salk's former colleague in the virus-typing program, that a shot of Cutter vaccine had killed a monkey, from which living Mahoney virus was subsequently isolated. To Scheele's discomfiture, but not O'Connor's or Salk's, the news of Gebhardt's discovery reached the newspapers almost as soon as it got to Scheele. And Hart Van Riper supplemented the news with a revelation that the vaccine being produced by companies other than Cutter was passing safety tests with greater consistency than had been achieved in the successful year of 1954. And, as if this were not fully sufficient to invite public attention to the contrast between reality and the confusing protestations of the Public Health Service, the vaccine manufacturers themselves were now beginning to growl. The firms had been willing enough to put on a show of silent solidarity with Cutter Laboratories and the Public Health Service. To help divert blame from Cutter and the government, they had allowed suspicion to be cast on their own perfectly good batches of vaccine—batches prepared according to the Salk formula. But now the performance was losing its savor. The Public Health Service had told the manufacturers to expect a new set of minimum production standards which would cost the manufacturers more time and money than the old regula-

tions had. In talking to reporters, manufacturing officials used reasonable words like "unnecessary" and unrealistic words like "impossible."

Scheele had danced his fandango as long as he could. The
law of diminishing returns had set in. The time for action was
now. At his invitation, Salk's committee reconvened on Tuesday,
May 24, this time with Salk, O'Connor, and Tom Rivers' Vaccine
Advisory Committee. Scheele took Salk's telegraphed advice. He
appointed Bodian, Smadel, Shannon, Workman, and Dr. Richard
E. Shope of the Rockefeller Institute to sit with Salk on a committee empowered to draw up new manufacturing requirements.
Salk, who was convinced, of course, that the old requirements
were adequate for any manufacturer who understood and observed his principles, accepted the assignment with a feeling of
vast political sophistication: The new minimum requirements
would be window dressing to make the government look good. The
show of activity would restore public confidence in the safety of
vaccination. Jim Shannon was no less eager to set to work, but
for different reasons. His statisticians had worked out new vac-
cine-sampling procedures, which would assure the validity of
safety tests even if Salk's precious inactivation graphs gave misleading results. The committee was able to complete its work
with little difficulty. Salk submitted to Shannon's obdurate belief
that larger samples of vaccine had to be tested than in the past
and that the tests had to be more elaborate. Shannon blinked
away his disagreement with Salk's graph, reasoning that whether
it provided automatic safety or not would now be of little consequence. Both men agreed with enthusiasm that the concept of
production consistency had to be defined and enforced, that an
extra filtration should be included in the manufacturing formula,
and that all batches of vaccine, good or bad, had to be reported
to the government. Bodian and the others, eager to see the polio
immunization program resumed, were relieved by the comparative
harmony of the meeting.

On May 27 the manufacturers were persuaded that the new
procedures differed in no essential from those of the past. Scheele
announced that vaccinations would be resumed. Salk declared

himself pleased. "The margin of safety," he said, "is now so clearly understood that only the grossest human error can upset it." His principles remained inviolate. If the manufacturer applied the right amount of Formalin at the right temperature and acidity and for the right length of time (as demonstrated by the slope of the graph), the vaccine would be just as safe under the new government regulations as under the old. Now as then, safety tests merely confirmed the graph. Now as then, the manufacturer's only problem was to make sure, by reference to the graph, that his procedures were in order. If they were, his vaccine would be fine.

When a reporter asked Salk whether live virus had actually been found in the Cutter vaccine, he shrugged. A good soldier.

The Cutter incident was authentic tragedy but spurious mystery. Whatever mistakes resulted in the manufacture and distribution of lethal vaccine by the California firm in 1955 were simple variants of mistakes made elsewhere in 1953 and 1954, when the victims were laboratory monkeys instead of men, women, and children.

The quasi-official guess about the firm's production difficulties is that its laboratory staff attempted to make vaccine of virus mixtures in which sediment had formed during weeks and months of storage. Because nothing in the government's minimum requirements suggested that such fluids be filtered immediately before the inactivation process, filtration was omitted at that stage. Virus particles imprisoned in the sediment were protected from the Formalin, remained alive, eluded the safety-test samplings, and ended by causing paralytic polio in human beings. This explanation is usually offered by government spokesmen in rueful but unself-critical tones, as when a man attributes the lateness of his train to the fact that it did not arrive on time. He explains nothing. He only describes. If crowded, he may smile wanly and observe that, the art of transportation being as rudimentary as it is, late arrivals are part and parcel of railroading. When pressed to explain the Cutter incident, past and present spokesmen for the Public Health Service declare that it was unavoidable in the circumstances. It was a consequence of the prevailing state of the art. Not enough was known about the mass production of polio vaccine, they claim, for anyone to anticipate and prevent the problems that arose at Cutter. Virus fluids had never before been stored for such lengths of time before conversion into vaccine. Therefore, how could anyone know enough about the sediment problem to require filtration immediately before inactivation?

Jonas Salk, who neither shared this view in 1955 nor dared to dispute it publicly at the time, now contents himself with philosophical declarations that there would have been no Cutter incident if the "doers" had understood his principles. But even this explains little. The truth is that the problem of sediment had been faced, recognized, and solved in 1954. Salk's own address to the Third International Poliomyelitis Conference in Rome that summer referred to the problem, making clear to anyone who bothered to listen that sediment could wreck the inactivation process.

If one cares to adopt Salk's position of helplessness against "doers," one concedes the likelihood that "doers" might not look into the bottles of virus fluid to see if there were any sediment, or, seeing it, might grant no significance to it. One also concedes that such people might omit three of the five tests of the inactivation rate recommended by Salk and the Public Health Service, thereby omitting three opportunities to notice that something was wrong. Furthermore, they might be so indifferent to the laws of probability, as embodied in the well-known principle of production consistency, as to remain unshaken by the failure of a third of their vaccine batches to pass their own safety tests. They therefore would do exactly what Cutter did: submit the other two-thirds for government clearance, get it, and distribute bad vaccine.

But where does this leave the licensing agency of the government? Is the government supposed to employ nothing but "doers?" The question answers itself. So that nobody would ask it, the government was impelled to make sure that nobody would know enough to ask it. The root facts of the Cutter incident had to remain as mysterious as possible for as long as possible.

In May, after the government's new minimum vaccine requirements were promulgated and accepted, Len Scheele set to work preparing an official report, a "white paper" in which he sought to tell as much about the Cutter incident as was allowed by law and the political exigencies of the situation. Early in June he and Jim Shannon gave a preview of this document to the convention of the American Medical Association. They presented to a symposium on polio immunization a paper that disputed Salk's inactivation principles without calling unnecessary attention to the millions of doses of safe vaccine that manufacturers other than Cutter had been able to produce. In reporting the paper and the symposium, *The New York Times* sounded a festive note: "The new Salk vaccine against polio is difficult to manufacture and no batch can ever be proved to be 100 percent safe before it is given to children."

One of the stars of the symposium was Albert Sabin, who complained that the results of the 1954 field trial no longer were valid now that manufacturing requirements had been amended and the formula supposedly changed. He dispensed a cautious hope, however. It seemed that his own strains of attenuated, safely infectious poliovirus might be just right for a new, safe, potent vaccine.

On Wednesday, June 8, Salk, Smadel, Bodian, and other members of Scheele's technical committee were shown a draft of the official "white paper." As expected, it was generous in its treatment of the Laboratory of Biologics Control and the rest of the Public Health Service. It shrouded the performance of Cutter in impenetrable mystery, also as expected. And, as indicated at the AMA symposium, it was vigorously forthright in its implications that much of the trouble had been due to incompatibility between Salk's original formula and the needs of mass production. After a certain amount of table-pounding about which none of the surviving participants are willing to speak, Scheele and Shannon agreed to have some of the language softened. The report was released on June 9 and made the following points:

1. *Salk was wrong.* "The original concept of vaccine preparation was that the process itself assured a wide margin of safety. . . . The total experience of the manufacturers now reveals that the process of inactivation did not always follow the predicted course." On this debatable assertion by the government rested, of course, the justification for the new safety tests. With the passage of time the assertion stopped being debatable. It became demonstrably erroneous. David Bodian eventually wrote in defense of Salk's work, "[The] inactivation data of manufacturers throughout the world show beyond a doubt that the inactivation rate of poliovirus, as established by Salk, is sufficiently approximate to a straight line . . . so that for practical purposes the time of inactivation . . . should be predictable from the slope of the line."

2. *Basil O'Connor and Salk had pushed everyone into a jam by demanding haste where care and caution were preferable.* "The Salk vaccine applies new practices in the production of viral vaccines," wrote Scheele. "The vaccine has progressed from the experimental level to large-scale production with unprecedented rapidity. This speed, reflecting the increased tempo of all medical research, created problems in biologics control amenable to solution only with the accumulation of knowledge and experience."

3. *Lacking knowledge and experience, the government had failed to make demands which it now would make.* ". . . The records which manufacturers were required to submit did not include certain data which are essential for an adequate assessment of consistency in performance. The protocols submitted related only to lots of vaccine proposed for clearance, and gave no information concerning lots discarded in the course of manufacture."

To apply all the new knowledge and experience, Scheele named Dr. Carl Larson as head of a new Division of Biologics Standards, replacing the Laboratory of Biologics Control. The new bureau would have 150 employees, as contrasted with the thirty-five who had been on Bill Workman's staff.

When Basil O'Connor heard about the Scheele report, he observed to the press, "News accounts do not indicate that the report throws any light on the Cutter situation, which was the cause of any difficulties that have arisen with the Salk vaccine. The report obviously gives only the Public Health Service version of the vaccine situation to date. . . ." A government official who was active in the Cutter case thinks O'Connor's statement was dirty pool. "O'Connor was always needling Scheele about Cutter. Why did he keep needling? It was unfair." But keeping the public confused and uninformed was not unfair.

Salk was more indulgent than O'Connor. He counted himself lucky that Scheele had withstood the arguments of Sabin, Enders, Paul, Hammon, and Shaughnessy and had saved the immunization program in a situation that might have destroyed it. Also, his Olympian view of men and events enabled Salk to understand the imperatives of Scheele's position in life. "The Public Health Service," he told reporters, "has taken concrete steps to solve vaccination production and testing problems. Dr. Scheele should be commended for this action. We must now allow time for the reorganization of the Public Health Service to take place and for its influence to be felt." A day later, after he had read Scheele's report and had noticed how slightly the original draft had been modified in his favor, he told the press that there were points "wherein I concur and wherein I do not." He disassociated himself from Scheele's contention that his original formula had not worked out in practice, saying ever so mildly, "Where problems have arisen, this has been because practice has not taken full cognizance of all the theoretical considerations that apply. This could occur because the phrasing of the minimum requirements allowed for differing interpretations."

A few days later he told Jane Krieger, "You find yourself projected into a set of circumstances for which neither your training nor your talents have prepared you. It's very difficult in some respects, but it's a transitory thing and you wait till it blows over. Eventually people will start thinking, 'That poor guy,' and leave me alone. Then I'll be able to get back to my laboratory."

On June 22 and 23, a learned panel of medical and scientific experts congregated before a subcommittee of the House Committee on Interstate and Foreign Commerce to help it decide whether the United States should, in the words of Committee Chairman J. Percy Priest, a Tennessee Democrat, "defray the cost of vaccine for those individuals between the ages of one and nineteen who might not be in financial position to pay for it themselves." The panel, assembled by the National Academy of Sciences, included Salk, Sabin, Paul, Enders, Francis, Rivers, Shannon, Smadel, and seven others. No time was wasted in socioeconomic discussion. The scientists were there to tell what they knew about the Salk vaccine. With Paul as panel chairman the talk quickly gravitated to the question uppermost in the public mind. Was the vaccine now safe for use? Sabin thought it foolhardy to seek the answer in mass inoculation. He urged that the vaccination program be called off until such time as a strain less virulent than the Mahoney could be found. His own attenuated strains might be just the thing. They were being tested right now. Better safe than sorry. Call off the program. He had with him a letter from Bill Hammon, who agreed with him and wanted to be on record to that effect. John Enders also agreed. They lost. Eight members of the panel voted to continue the program. Two abstained on grounds that they were only Ph.D's and not qualified to make a medical judgment. Paul had no vote, being chairman. Salk abstained because he was Salk. "I have in the past contributed in no wise to make administrative decisions," he said, "and I prefer at this point merely to remain in my role of investigator who provides the facts and the evidence upon which others who have administrative responsibility can then decide." In a separate vote everyone agreed with Sabin that if a strain more suitable than the Mahoney could be found, it should be substituted.

Basil O'Connor was in St. Louis. When he heard what Sabin had done, he wheeled out the artillery. "Coming from Sabin," he told the press, "this is old stuff. He's been using it for years. He used it in an attempt to stop the field trials of the Salk vaccine. Since then he's been using it on every possible occasion to stop the use of the Salk vaccine.

"For years Sabin has been trying to get what is called a 'live-virus' polio vaccine. Salk's vaccine is one using a 'killed' virus. There are no present prospects of Sabin getting a safe 'live-virus' vaccine for years. The National Foundation has supported Sabin's work to the tune of eight hundred and fifty-three thousand, three hundred and fourteen dollars, and seventy-one cents," said O'Connor, "and will continue to support him financially.

"The Salk vaccine is safe and effective. . . . In the United States, Canada, and Denmark, 7,675,000 children have actually received the Salk vaccine with no untoward results. There could be no better proof of its safety than this. No vaccine in the history of the world has ever had such a test for safety. Anyone who would seek to prevent its use for other than unanswerable scientific reasons would be acting neither as a scientist nor as a humanitarian.

"Since the scientific method was established every important advance in science has met with the twin obstacles, ignorance and envy. The Salk vaccine is no exception. The American people, who made the Salk vaccine possible through their contributions to the March of Dimes and their unprecedented cooperation in the field trials of 1954, are interested only in preventing paralytic polio in children and young adults not only in our own country but all over the world. Those who would prevent its use must be prepared to be haunted for life by the crippled bodies of little children who could have been saved from paralysis had they been permitted to receive the Salk vaccine. Let's get on with the job the American people want done. Let the U.S. Public Health Service tell us what happened in the Cutter situation, which is now two months old. . . . Let's prevent the Salk vaccine from being talked to death!"

"I am not against the vaccine program," explained Sabin to the Cincinnati Times-Sun. "I am against continuation of it with the present Salk vaccine. The milder viruses I have developed would be substituted for the dangerous ones. They would be 'killed' viruses, too, but if some live viruses slipped through they would be harmless."

Manufacturers tested this attractive theory in their laboratories.

They found Sabin's strains less antigenic than Salk's. As recently as the spring of 1965, the original Salk formula remained unchanged, having proved the most potent and, of course, completely safe.

The effects of the Cutter incident are unending for its paralyzed survivors and their families, and for hundreds of other paralyzed Americans who might have been protected against polio if the confusion and controversy of the time had not sabotaged the nation's vaccination effort. For example, in the summer of 1955, an epidemic broke out in Massachusetts, which had called off its vaccination program on the advice of a panel of experts. A study of the four thousand Massachusetts cases showed that paralysis occurred among the unvaccinated at a rate more than twice as high as among children who had been given one injection of vaccine.

On September 27, Hart Van Riper wrote to Jonas Salk:

> I am sure that you were as gratified as the rest of us to read in the New York papers the remarks made by our Governor on Sunday in which he indicated that, of the New York children who received one dose of vaccine the attack rate . . . was 4 per 100,000 as against 16 for children who had not received any vaccine and were in the same age group. This further confirms my confidence and makes me glad that at a press conference in Seattle two weeks ago I very pointedly made the remark that those who, by direct criticism or inference had persuaded any parent not to permit their eligible children to receive vaccine would have to settle with their own conscience the resulting paralysis of a child who might have been protected.
>
> We are slowly coming out of the woods and some of the rest of us are going to have some fun in the coming months after the beating we have taken for the last year and a half.

To which Salk replied:

As to "coming out of the woods," maybe you are out and don't know it. I hope that you will have all of the fun you deserve but I think that the fun will come just by sitting quietly and watching those who have gotten themselves out on a limb struggling to get back, without anyone trying to do anything to make their lives more difficult.

16

IN 1633 THE INQUISITION DEFINED THE PLACE OF SCIENCE IN THE social order. It sentenced Galileo to seclusion and commanded him to recite the seven penitential psalms once each week for three years. This did not settle the issue of whether the sun revolved around the earth, as the theologians said, or vice versa, as Galileo said, but it clarified more immediate questions, such as who was in charge of Italy at the time. Although enlightenment increases, practitioners of science as yet have no vote at the policy tables of the world. Science and the values for which it stands remain vulnerable. When scientific truth collides with the wishes of those in charge, scientific truth comes off second best.

The history of polio immunization in the United States is an example. The scientific controversy between Jonas Salk and Albert Sabin was adjudicated not by science but by commerce and organized medicine. The controversy was bigger than science. There was political hay and important money to be made of it. In due course, and for reasons remote from science, medicine virtually abandoned the Salk vaccine in favor of the Sabin. The social and medical consequences of this maneuver have been concealed. Scientific truth has been interred. Certain aspects of the story make the Cutter incident look like a pink tea.

"Things are never all black or all white," says the patient scientist to the irate layman. "They are various shades of gray." A fetching platitude. The difference between two shades of gray may be the difference between life and death. Nevertheless, let it be agreed that the Sabin vaccine is neither all white nor all black, but a shade of gray. It appears to have been an advantageous public-health tool in the Soviet Union, Czechoslovakia, Hungary, and other countries of Europe, Asia, and Latin America, which have fed it successfully to hundreds of millions of people. But the indiscriminate promotion of the vaccine in the United States has been a scandalous abuse of medical and commercial privilege, for which lucky members of the American public pay only with money and unlucky ones with paralysis.

"Let's pretend," says Basil O'Connor, who has become by default the nation's leading critic of the Sabin vaccine promotion, "that a vaccine has reduced the incidence of cancer by 98 percent. The disease is under control. It is vanishing. A great scientific victory. But now the American Medical Association and the United States Public Health Service and some drug companies come along and tell you to forget it. They tell you that cancer is still a menace, no matter what the record shows. They tell you that everybody has to take a *new* vaccine, whether they've already been immunized or not. What would you say if that happened? Would you say somebody was crazy? Ha!

"So now let's pretend," continues O'Connor, warming to his fantasy, "that the new vaccine has a special characteristic. It *causes* cancer. Not much but some. The old vaccine caused no cancer. It only prevented cancer. But the new vaccine is dangerous. Would you expect medicine and the government to change their minds and stop trying to sell the new vaccine to the American people? What kind of a dream world do you live in? Let's stop pretending. The Sabin vaccine *is* causing cases of paralysis. And the government does nothing about it but pussyfoot. I wonder whether anybody cares about *anything* anymore."

The prevailing state of American polio prevention is every bit as lunatic as O'Connor suggests. There is a *Through the Looking Glass* quality about it, as if bored gods had decreed that up was now down, old was now new, and right was now wrong. By 1962 it was obvious that the Salk vaccine had been more effective than even Salk himself had foreseen; the annual incidence of polio was diminishing to the point of extinction. The disease had become a medical curiosity as rare as typhoid. At this unlikely juncture, organized medicine and the Public Health Service joined manufacturers in a great crusade against polio, actively promoting the use of Sabin vaccine in mass immunization programs. Communities that had seen no polio for five or six years stampeded to vaccination stations for doses of Sabin vaccine. No distinction was made between persons who had already received a full course of Salk injections and those who had not. By the middle of 1964, over 300 million doses of Sabin vaccine had been dispensed—enough to inoculate more than 100 million persons. At most of the clinics the people were asked to contribute twenty-five cents per dose. Payment was never compulsory, but receipts were excellent. Most people paid, and some paid more than was asked. A highly conservative estimate of the American public's out-of-pocket expenditure at these vaccination stations and in the private offices of physicians between January 1962 and June 1964 would be $75 million. A generous sum to spend on a synthetic crusade. An overgenerous sum, when the list of casualties is considered.

As of June 1964 the Public Health Service had been notified of 123 cases of paralytic polio "associated" with the Sabin vaccine. That is, within thirty days of ingesting the stuff, 123 Americans had come down with paralysis. The Public Health Service eliminated thirty-six of the cases, because they had occurred in so-called "epidemic" areas, where natural infection might have accounted for the illnesses. The study concentrated on communities with little or no paralytic polio except in persons who had fallen ill after taking Sabin vaccine. Of the total of eighty-seven such cases, the Public Health Service decided that fifty-seven were "compatible" with the belief that the vaccine had caused disease. Forty-one of these cases had been the only instances of paralytic polio reported in certain counties for two and a half years.

Because a high proportion of the victims were adults, the Public Health Service declared on several occasions, but not loudly, that adults might as well take the Sabin vaccine only in exceptional circumstances, such as the threat of epidemic. Nobody paid much attention. Medical societies and vaccine manufacturers continued to urge persons of all ages to beat back the alleged menace of polio by swallowing Sabin vaccine. Between January and June 1964 only thirty-five cases of paralytic polio were reported in the United States—a tiny menace when compared with the annual average of 16,316 cases during 1951–1954. Of these thirty-five cases, the government disclosed (without emphasis) that twelve were "compatible," which means that they almost certainly were caused by the vaccine. For those who don't care to do their own arithmetic, these figures indicate that slightly more than one of every three new cases of paralytic polio in the United States during that six-month period probably was caused by the Sabin vaccine.* Nevertheless, the immunization crusade continued.

Reviewed in these bald terms, American use of the occasionally dangerous Sabin vaccine in a situation well-controlled by the invariably safe Salk vaccine seems an exercise in madness. Or, as the appalled but assiduously philosophical Jonas Salk says, "unreasonableness." In his view, of course, man's propensity for destruction and self-defeat are the main problems of the race. "Why doesn't man do what he should?" asks Salk. "Why does he do what he should *not* do? Until this fundamental problem of unreasonableness can be solved, laboratory discoveries will be of relatively little avail."

Salk has been a helpless and largely undemonstrative spectator to the introduction and promotion of the Sabin vaccine, events in which his own achievements have been trampled by misrepresentation. As always, he draws some comfort from his ability to regard himself as a depersonalized, ego-free droplet in the stream of history. At this stage in history, he tells himself philosophically, considerations other than those of public health influence the design of public-health programs. There is nothing much to be done about it, he says. One can point out the scientific errors on which such misbegotten programs rest, he says,

---

* Early in 1965, the government announced that only ninety-four cases of paralytic polio had been reported in the United States during 1964. The downward trend was no longer as precipitous as during the years prior to introduction of the Sabin vaccine, but it continued at a significant rate. Information as to how many of the ninety-four cases may have been caused by the Sabin vaccine was not available at this writing.

but one can hardly expect the begetters to agree that they have erred. In fact, one can expect them to respond by pressing their shoes against one's Adam's apple.

There can no longer be the slightest doubt that workers in the Salk Institute for Biological Studies or some similar establishment eventually will master the specific molecular processes of the human brain which embody and perpetuate unreasonableness. It is neither facetious nor fanciful to suppose that the scientists subsequently will develop a reasonableness pill to prevent or cure physicochemical calamities of that kind. Man then will be liberated to enter upon the next stage of human history. In the meantime, unfortunately, we primitives are compelled to attempt survival in the present stage of human history, a hard job. Pending delivery of the pill, the only peaceable defense against unreasonableness is truth—as much of it as we can obtain and absorb. Why, then, were the American people persuaded to spend tens of millions of dollars on a vaccine which is less safe than the Salk vaccine but which has never been proved more effective? The answer is accessible to anyone who can stand the sight.

The conclusion of the Cutter incident in the summer of 1955 permitted Basil O'Connor to get on with his plans for protecting the American people against paralytic polio. Visions of mass immunization campaigns under joint governmental, medical, and National Foundation sponsorship had dimmed, of course, before the Cutter incident started. The American Medical Association and the Eisenhower Administration were opposed. And then the frights and confusions of the Cutter inquiry dampened the public's eagerness for treatment with the vaccine. O'Connor's work was cut out for him.

In June 1955 a convention of the AMA confronted the issue of polio prevention. There had been 38,476 cases during the previous year. A safe, effective vaccine was now available. For persons whose first concern was the health of the American people, the main question was how to get the vaccine to the public as expeditiously as possible. But the AMA had other things on its mind.

"RESOLVED," said the AMA, "that the American Medical Association go on record as disapproving the purchase and distribution of the Salk polio vaccine by any agency of the federal government except for those unable to procure it for themselves . . . and . . . that the American Medical Association urge the Congress of the United States to allow the Salk polio vaccine to be produced, distributed, and administered in accordance with past procedures on any new drug or vaccine. . . ."

In November, the AMA convened again and resolved to condemn "the practice of voluntary health organizations and the government supplying vaccine free of charge to the public of this nation and insist upon immediate termination of such practices except the practice of providing this benefit to individuals . . . financially unable to pay for such services." The AMA also resolved that "the Board of Trustees be empowered and instructed to voice opposition in behalf of the physicians of the United States to these and any subsequent programs violating the principles of free enterprise and sound medical practices, calling attention to the willingness of the physicians of this country to cooperate in seeing that every deserving person in this nation will receive the benefits of preventive medicine if the honest need is made known."

Salk vaccine was gathering dust on the shelves of drug warehouses. Children were being paralyzed. The physicians' organization was too busy agitating about polio economics to take heed of purely medical matters. Naturally, the National Foundation persisted in its own efforts. Helped by thousands of physicians preoccupied more with health than with fees, the Foundation managed, by the end of 1955, to get vaccine into 10 million children. The Public Health Service reported that there were 28,985 cases of polio in the United States during that year—fully 25 percent below the average annual incidence of the previous five years.

During 1956, organized medicine again sat on its hands. The Foundation issued hundreds of thousands of pieces of literature, propagandizing in schools, factories, social clubs, churches, unions, on radio and television, in newspapers and magazines. By now about 30 million people had accepted at least one injection of vaccine. This was not nearly enough people and not nearly enough injections per person. On June 22, a disappointed Jonas Salk wrote to Surgeon General Leonard Scheele:

> I have observed, from newspapers reports, that unused vaccine is being returned from the public allocation programs of many states. This is unfortunate because at this late date it will undoubtedly be extremely difficult to have the relatively large amounts of vaccine available administered other than on a large-scale "emergency" basis. I am sure you are considering the implications of the altered relationship from one in which you were criticized for not having enough vaccine to one in which much of the vaccine now available, and soon to become available, may well go unused until too late. . . . The clarification of responsibility in this regard may well help activate those who, in fact, are responsible for administering those practices that become available for maintaining the public health. It would be unfortunate, indeed, for this situation to continue much longer, when the seasonal rise is so close at hand. Although you have made your advice known, I have the feeling that the responsibility for implementing this advice is not strongly enough felt, nor in the hands of those whose first interest is that of maintaining the public health.

Salk was talking, of course, about the medical profession in general and the AMA in particular. The AMA had just passed another resolution:

> WHEREAS, Distribution of free Salk vaccine has been extended to include many more than the indigent group, thus constituting unnecessary government spending; and
>
> WHEREAS, Distribution by government agencies has resulted in a bizarre, unscientific, and inequitable administration of vaccine, thereby casting disrepute on the private doctors of medicine and consternation, concern, and confusion on the general public; and
>
> WHEREAS, A much wider and more adequate protection of

the public would be attained through regular channels of distribution; now therefore be it *Resolved,* That the American Medical Association requests the United States Government to return the general wholesale and retail purchase of Salk antipoliomyelitis vaccine to normal, commercial channels and to cease governmental purchase of the vaccine in other than those amounts needed by the Public Health Service for essential public-health needs and for distribution to the indigent population of the nation.

During that summer, the consequences of the nation's failure to use the Salk vaccine were demonstrated in several epidemics. The worst was in Chicago, home of the American Medical Association, where 1,100 cases were reported. In December, the AMA Board of Trustees announced, "The AMA is in favor of encouraging the administration of poliomyelitis vaccine to the public, and is in sympathy with the efforts of those who are endeavoring to educate the public in its use. The AMA will lend its efforts through regular medical channels toward the encouragement of such use by the general public."

Still no word about mass immunization programs. Still no meaningful assistance in the fight against polio. Nevertheless, the Foundation was making headway. Only 15,140 cases of polio occurred in 1956. The Salk vaccine, even though applied spottily, had reduced American incidence by almost 61 percent in two years. In October, the Public Health Service declared that no child protected with a full series of three Salk inoculations had died of polio during the year. But only 9 million Americans had received three shots. Of the niggardly $30 million appropriated by Congress, barely $8 million had been spent by the states. The legislatures and public-health departments of most states were discouraged by organized medical pressure from supporting mass vaccinations.

Late in 1956, the American Academy of Pediatrics and the American Academy of General Practice stole a march on the AMA. Under quite considerable prodding from the National Foundation and from physicians horrified at the absence of medical leadership, the organizations decided to make "every doctor's office an immunization center." The National Foundation had been threatening to kick over the traces and, in defiance of organized medicine, demand that the public conduct "unauthorized" mass vaccinations in schools, factories, and churches. When the pediatricians and general practitioners showed signs of trying to fend off this collectivism with positive activity of their own, the AMA agreed to acknowledge the need for vaccination. It held a meeting in Chicago on January 26, 1957. One of the featured speakers was Jonas Salk, who discussed one of his favorite subjects, responsibility: "It would appear that responsibility for the problem of eliminating paralytic poliomyelitis rests with each individual for whom there is a need for vaccine, either for himself or for those for whom he is responsible. This responsibility is shared also by those who are in a position to bring this knowledge to him and help him avail himself of the necessary treatment."

Quelle delicatesse! Ours is a bland age. When Louis Pasteur set out to needle someone, he used a harpoon. No circumlocution for old Louis. "There is only one road which leads to truth, and one hundred that lead to error," he once said of an adversary whose thinking was comparable to that of the AMA. "M'sieu Colin always takes one of the latter."

Dr. David B. Allman, President-elect of the AMA, commended the path of truth at the January polio meeting. "All too often in the past," he confessed, "our energies have been expended in defending medicine's position rather than assuming the positive leadership which is expected of us. . . . It seems to me that we face a situation today where we have sacrificed thousands of lives, years of research, and millions of dollars in search of something that after we have found what we were looking for we refuse to use it. It doesn't make sense to me and I don't believe it is good medicine. . . . This is American medicine's opportunity to carry the ball—let's not fumble it now."

And President Dwight H. Murray, using a quotation from Pasteur ("Take interest, I implore you"), acknowledged that the time had come for the population to be inoculated, regardless of ability to pay. The AMA now issued an official statement opposing public apathy. It refused to favor mass vaccinations, of course. But its mere expression of interest and concern was enough to make of 1957 a banner year in the campaign against polio. In fact, by March, so many physicians had begun to dispense Salk vaccine to their patients that drug suppliers complained of a shortage. In Cleveland, Seattle, and a few other communities, the medical societies actually helped to organize mass vaccinations. Elsewhere, previously immobilized public-health departments obtained federal vaccine and gave it without charge to indigents, actual or professed. But most of the people could obtain vaccine only through the AMA's cherished "regular commercial channels"—on an individual basis, in exchange for fees paid to private physicians.

In Houston, Texas, a nurse, whose daughter was still in braces after an attack of polio, obtained enough vaccine at cost to give vaccinations at one dollar each to 750 persons in the basement of her church. The local health department loaned her the necessary equipment. A sympathetic physician supervised the injections. Six other nurses contributed assistance. The Harris County Medical Society stopped the program. "We do not consider this a proper way of going about vaccinations," it proclaimed. However, after an American Legion post retaliated with plans to give seventy-five-cent vaccinations and challenged the medical society to try to stop the project, the society relented. It announced that it would give shots at hospitals and clinics for a dollar apiece. Anybody who lacked the dollar would be given the vaccine for nothing and would not have to prove himself authentically indigent. A few weeks later the newly inaugurated President of the Texas Medical Association, Dr. Milford O. Rouse, complained that "there is no more reason for undeserved charity in medical care than for undeserved charity in the dispensing of newspapers, shoes, gasoline, or fire insurance."

Medical understanding of the urgency of polio immunization was only somewhat higher than this in Pittsburgh, home of the Salk vaccine. There, as elsewhere, the population was largely unvaccinated. Jonas Salk had called publicly for the vaccination of everyone up to the age of fifty before summer, a proposal that was ridiculed in print by the Pennsylvania State Medical Society. But the AMA's new eagerness to see physicians engage in polio prevention had improved the climate. With help from the National Foundation, Salk worked up a plan. The Junior Chamber of Commerce and other civic groups were ready to assist at immunization centers. Salk's plan went before the Board of Directors of the Allegheny County Medical Society and lost by a vote of seven to six. "Too much emphasis on mass inoculations and not enough on getting them to go to their own doctors' offices," explains someone who was there. "The decision would have been an awful embarrassment to the profession if it had ever leaked out, but it didn't. Thank God, Jonas was at the meeting and helped talk one of the directors into changing his vote. So now the plan was adopted, seven to six."

Salk and Basil O'Connor hoped that the Pittsburgh project would serve as a model for the rest of the nation. Movies would be made of the immunization centers and would be shown on television newscasts. Salk himself would be in the films, giving injections. A bandwagon psychology would develop. When state and local medical societies saw how much goodwill could be generated by such a program, they would move beyond the AMA position. Mass vaccination would become fashionable, and polio would finally be defeated.

But O'Connor and Salk had picked the wrong city, or the wrong year. The County Medical Society was immeasurably more interested in attracting individual, fee-paying patients to individual physicians for individual vaccinations than in detouring such patients to clinics. Accordingly, while the clinics were not altogether lost in the shuffle, much emphasis was placed on private treatment. The vaccination campaign fell far short of its objectives. Tens of thousands of Pittsburghers remained unimmunized.

"I dropped in on Jonas one day and found him seething," recalls John Troan. "The clinic idea was being shunted aside, but some doctors were making fortunes in their own offices. Jonas had just heard of one office which supposedly took in $3,000 in a single afternoon—giving shots at five dollars a copy to six hundred kids. 'What are you going to do with people like this? What are you going to do?' said Jonas. 'Six hundred kids

who have five dollars get vaccinated, and six hundred who do not
have five dollars do not get vaccinated."

Nevertheless, by the end of 1957 more than half of all Americans below the age of forty had received at least one injection
of Salk vaccine. Thirty percent had been given the full course of
three injections. Only 5,787 cases of polio occurred during that
year. The incidence was 86 percent below the 1950–1954 level
—an absolutely fantastic result. So fantastic, indeed, that some
scientists refused to agree that it was a result of vaccination at all.
"Just because the sun rises when the rooster crows is no reason
to assume that the rooster makes the sun rise," said a believer
in live-virus vaccines. "Polio ebbs and flows in unpredictable
cycles. Salk's vaccine undoubtedly affords short-term immunity
and, for as long as the immunity lasts, is somewhere between 60
and 90 percent effective against the paralytic forms of the disease. But it has no effect at all against nonparalytic polio. And
it certainly cannot be expected to protect people who have not
been vaccinated."

In science, as elsewhere, the Bourbons never forget anything
and never learn anything. Quite aside from any effect a hy-
pothetical cycle may have had on the incidence of polio between 1955 and 1957, the Salk vaccine was working phenomenal changes. Published reports by government epidemiologists
showed that outbreaks of the disease were now tending to concentrate in poor neighborhoods—especially Negro neighborhoods
—where few members of the population had been reached with
vaccine. During the Chicago epidemic of 1956, the paralytic attack rate among Negroes was almost eight times that in whites.
In 1957, the attack rate among Washington Negroes was four
times that of whites. *An unvaccinated Negro was more likely to
contract the disease than an unvaccinated white.* The phenomenon was similar to the "herd" effect noticed by Jonas Salk and
Tommy Francis in 1943 after their double-blind test of influenza
vaccine in dormitories at the University of Michigan. They had
found that unvaccinated students who lived in the same dormitories as vaccinated students caught less flu than unvaccinated
students whose dormitory mates were also unvaccinated. Obviously, the presence of a significant number of immunized per-

sons in a dormitory—or a neighborhood—affected the spread of infection by interrupting the chain of transmission.

Advocates of live-virus vaccines could not accept this idea and did not try. By virological definition, the only way to abolish polio was to infect a large majority of the population with a live-virus vaccine. After recovery from the minor infection, the individual intestinal tract would no longer be hospitable to polio virus, they thought. The tissue would be immune, they claimed. If a wild virus came along, it would be destroyed on the spot. That, and only that, was the way to break the chain of transmission. In any event, whatever disposition orthodox virologists may have had to study the phenomenal success of the Salk vaccine ended during 1958 and 1959, when the downward trend in polio incidence was reversed. In 1958, there were 5,787 cases—over three hundred cases more than in 1957. And in 1959, 8,425 cases were reported. Orthodox virology was not at all surprised.

In describing the polio epidemic that took twenty-two lives and left 312 persons paralyzed in Detroit during 1958, the Health Commissioner of that city, Dr. Joseph G. Molner, wrote, "The overwhelming majority of cases occurred near the downtown area of the city, an area that has a mixed population . . . an economically depressed population. . . . Before the epidemic the vaccination program was felt to be adequate and essentially similar to the programs in other metropolitan areas. Yet our program allowed a pocket of susceptible persons to be created of sufficient magnitude to support a major epidemic. Such pockets undoubtedly exist in other cities of our nation.

"A vigorous program for the protection of the public against poliomyelitis was conducted in Detroit through the private physicians as well as through schools, health centers, and our two city hospitals. It must necessarily be pointed out that the vaccine which was being used was that purchased by the state and was limited for a time for the use of persons between the ages of five and fourteen. The preschool age group and adults were not allowed the advantage of the vaccine other than that purchased by physicians through private sources. . . .

" 'Tis an ill wind that doesn't blow someone some good, and

this should be an object lesson to all of us in the curative arts, to energetically try to get the masses protected against this serious disease. Let us not, as physicians and public-health workers, be guilty of the same type of apathy that our constituents have demonstrated. . . ."

"In 1959," says Jonas Salk, "epidemics in Kansas City and Des Moines showed this same pattern of changed susceptibility. The Negro attack rate in Kansas City was thirty-two times higher than among whites of the upper socioeconomic group. But only five years earlier, in 1954, there had been an outbreak in which the rate among Kansas City whites was higher than that among Negroes! Nor was the new pattern attributable only to the lower incidence among whites. The susceptibility of Negroes had actually *increased* in the five years. This absolute increase could be explained in only one way: Before the vaccine, Negroes were more resistant than whites because the conditions under which they lived tended to expose them to harmless, natural, permanently immunizing infection during infancy. But after the white population began to be immunized by vaccine, the total reservoir of natural infection was reduced. Viruses that Negroes formerly brought into their community from white neighborhoods were no longer available. A certain proportion of Negro children no longer acquired natural infections and natural immunity in early infancy. So when an outbreak finally occurred, the unvaccinated Negro population fell prey to it at unprecedented rates. As Joe Molner wrote after the Detroit epidemic, the solution was to bring the vaccine to the people. This, of course, was not being done."

According to Salk, the incidence of polio rose during 1959 not only because of failure to immunize, and not only because this failure had created a new, aberrant socioeconomic pattern of disease, but because many batches of commercial vaccine had been below optimum standards of potency, a defect the manufacturers finally repaired. Another contributing factor, he feels, may have been an upward fluctuation in the natural cycle of the disease. "There was great hope," he says in astringent reference to his adversaries, "that the incidence would continue to rise after 1959. The statistics for that year gave tremendous impetus to the live-vaccine crowd. Sabin had been warning for years that the inactivated vaccine could never control polio and now, in black and white, here was the statistical evidence of the vaccine's failure."

In 1960, however, there were only 3,190 cases in the United States. And in 1961, there were 1,312—a reduction of 96.6 percent from the 1950–1954 level and, in fact, the lowest incidence ever recorded in the United States. As nearly as anyone could tell, polio was beaten. In 1962, there were 910 cases. Polio was indeed beaten. But Albert Sabin was not. In 1962, after his own promotional talents and the even more influential ones of Charles Pfizer & Company, Inc., and Lederle Laboratories had lined up the American Medical Association and the United States Public Health Service, the Sabin vaccine began to replace the Salk vaccine on the American market. And, for the first time in history, organized medicine crusaded for mass vaccination.

Hilary Koprowski, who developed a live vaccine against polio and fed it to human beings with excellent success before anyone else had a foot in the field, was as aggressive a campaigner as Albert Sabin and ever so much more colorful a figure. He fought tooth and nail for his vaccine, lost out to Sabin by inches, and says now that he is glad. "I consider myself the luckiest," he smiles. "I am able to retain my equilibrium. I have become neither a hero, as Salk did, nor a potentate like Albert. When Sabin was in Brazil the children sang beneath his hotel window. I would not like to be in such a position. Few scientists would."

Koprowski was bitterly disappointed when the United States Government licensed Sabin's vaccine instead of his. No evidence existed that either vaccine was safer or more effective than the other when fed to human beings. The government based its decision on the fact that two monkeys out of eighteen injected with Koprowski's Type I strain showed signs of paralysis. None of thirty monkeys injected with Sabin's Type I component showed such signs, although half of them later proved to have polio lesions of the central nervous system. Koprowski kicked up an enormous rumpus. In a letter to the AMA *Journal* he argued that a virus that caused lesions in monkeys was hardly preferable to one that caused paralytic signs. Not that monkey tests were crucial; he ridiculed the concept that a vaccine which, like his, had been given to 9 million human beings "without any ill effects" could be pronounced dangerous because of its damage to a few monkeys. He accused the government of adjusting its standards to suit Sabin's vaccine, rather than requiring that the vaccine suit the standards. His Type III strain, he said further, was superior to Sabin's and should have been accepted.

Most of the bitterness is gone now. "It's ancient history," Koprowski says. "And soon the dispute between the killed- and live-vaccine schools will also be ancient history. Now that it is becoming possible to isolate and purify and even synthesize the viral protein that confers immunity, the infectious part of the virus becomes unnecessary. Perhaps undesirable. Why introduce viral infection—even supposedly harmless infection—when you can supply the specific antigenic protein you need for immunization?"

He is the first important member of the live-virus movement to break ranks. By acknowledging the present trends and future prospects of immunology, he accepts the essential validity of Jonas Salk's scientific position. An exchange between Koprowski and Tommy Francis at a meeting of the New York Academy of Sciences in 1955 gives some of the flavor of the controversy that took up so much time in those days, when Koprowski and Sabin, spokesmen for orthodoxy, had become convinced that they were radical insurrectionists storming the walls of entrenched power. Koprowski said in a characteristic paper:

This is the fifth anniversary of the day when—after painstaking soul searching—a decision was reached to administer the TN strain of poliomyelitis in live form to a nonimmune individual. . . . Five years have not yet changed the Age of Doubt into the Age of Faith, but the administration of live poliomyelitis virus to human subjects is now considered only a minor sin, and anyone professing a milder view may even grant those committing such sins an escape from eternal damnation—though thinking like Josh Billings, "Give the devil his due, but be very careful that there ain't much due him."

. . . Now, a few words about future steps in live-virus immunization. Most of the work, so far, was accomplished in homes for the mentally defective. Other investigators are performing similar work among volunteers in prisons. If the research work continues at the present pace and remains limited to these population groups . . . by 1984 the inmates of asylums and of prisons in the United States will become the only two groups of society *permanently* immunized against poliomyelitis. . . . If certain scientists are still haunted by the specter of live-virus vaccines, they had better adopt toward this new era of immunization an attitude similar to that of Horatio announcing the appearance of Hamlet's father's ghost: "Look, my lord! it comes!"

Tommy Francis responded by recalling that Aristotle "belonged to the group that believed that women had fewer teeth than men, whereas all he needed to do was look in Mrs. Aristotle's mouth and make an observation. This serves only to emphasize that, however deeply we may be impressed by our opinion, the evidence gained by putting the thesis to test is, in the end, the deciding factor." To substantiate their beliefs, advocates of infectious vaccines were able only to cite the effectiveness of the smallpox and yellow-fever vaccines, remarked Francis; this, he said, was "a two-case generalization that deserves some scrutiny." Immunology suggested rather plainly that inactivated vaccines would also work against smallpox and yellow fever, to say nothing of measles and hepatitis.

"The two outlooks are, then, simply this," Francis continued. "Inactive virus vaccine is apparently a test of the straightforward hypothesis that antibody induced by the administration of antigen can provide protection without subjecting the recipient to harmful effects of even the inapparent infection. The other, through the use of modified active virus, seeks to induce antibody formation but wishes to add some undesignated advantage derived from assumedly harmless infection (I am not certain that any significant infection may not create undesirable tissue reactions). . . .

"Which of these approaches to poliomyelitis will be the more effective is, then, not a decision to be arrived at by authority and debate but by looking in Mrs. Aristotle's mouth and really making the observations. When the conditions are appropriate, tests should be made. This is the beginning, not the end. . . ."

Between 1953 and 1961, the National Foundation supported Albert Sabin's vaccine studies with grants of $1.19 million. The Cincinnati scientist's most powerful friend in court was Tom Rivers, who regarded him as an extraordinarily substantial worker. Rivers fully expected that the Sabin vaccine, when it arrived, would be the polio preventive of choice. Sabin was in entire accord with this view. Beginning in 1954, he pressed the National Foundation to support human trials of his steadily improving vaccines. Rivers was in no hurry. With the Salk vaccine approaching fruition, no reason existed to take chances with an infectious preparation. The Foundation was so conservative on this score that Sabin cast about for other support, consulting Herald Cox and Koprowski at Lederle Laboratories about the possibility of joining forces. Nothing came of this. In 1955, Sabin gave his vaccine to prisoners in the federal reformatory at Chillicothe, Ohio, after obtaining the necessary clearances from the government and from Rivers' Vaccine Advisory Committee. The results encouraged Sabin, but the Foundation persisted in its cautions, reinforced now by the success of the Salk vaccine. Until Sabin's was as undeniably safe as the Salk vaccine had been demonstrated to be before the 1954 field trial, the Foundation would be chary of large human experiments.

Unfortunately animal tests were not reliable measures of the safety of polio vaccines made with modified living viruses. The very process of modification might make the viruses lethal to monkeys but perfectly safe for human beings, or the process might have the contrary effect. This had always been one of Hilary Koprowski's most vehement contentions. To tell whether a live polio vaccine was safe and effective, the scientists had to depart from the prisons and mental institutions and feed the stuff to larger, more representative populations. After 1955, there was little hope that this could be attempted on a satisfactory basis in the United States. In the atmosphere of trepidation that followed the Cutter incident, neither the public, the medical profession, nor the government was ready to play guinea pig with living polioviruses. By the time reassuring demonstrations could be given in other countries, so many Americans would be protected with Salk vaccine, furthermore, that it would be enormously difficult to arrange a statistically significant, controlled American field trial comparable to that which Francis had conducted in 1954.

While puzzling over these difficulties, Sabin continued to improve his product. For his special benefit, Tom Rivers staged a conference at which Sabin was persuaded to adopt Renato Dulbecco's technique of growing viruses in microscopically thin layers of tissue. The colonies proliferating from the growth of a single virus particle could now be identified and isolated. This permitted Sabin to purify his nonvirulent strains to a most reassuring extent.

Early in 1957, Sabin's chief competitor, Koprowski, suffered a disaster. A Belfast scientist, George Dick, announced that two Koprowski strains caused paralytic polio in monkeys after passing through the intestinal tract of human beings. An American, Joseph L. Melnick, would later reveal that Sabin's strains displayed the same tendency to revert to virulence after human passage. Melnick asked an excellent question: "Under certain epidemiological settings, will the altered strains excreted by the vaccinees undergo progressive changes after several passages in the community and eventually reach a degree of virulence comparable with that of wild epidemic polioviruses?" However, it now was 1959, and Sabin was impervious to theoretical objections of that kind. He answered them with results, and overwhelmed them. His vaccine had been fed to millions of children in the Soviet Union, whose medical and scientific authorities declared the substance uniformly safe and effective.

In 1956, Sabin had sent samples of his attenuated strains to

Anatoli A. Smorodintsev, Director of the Department of Virology at the USSR Academy of Medical Sciences, Leningrad, and Mikhail P. Chumakov, Director of the Institute for Poliomyelitis Research, Moscow. Smorodintsev has confided to American acquaintances that Soviet preference for the Sabin vaccine was based less on scientific doctrine than on the practicalities of an emergent medical situation. An improvement in living standards had afflicted the Soviet Union with what the United States and other industrial countries had suffered several years earlier—a sharp rise in the incidence of paralytic polio. In 1957, polio struck ninety-four of every million Soviet citizens. Salk vaccine had been used with some success during that year, but Soviet industry found the inactivation process as difficult as American industry had, and Soviet science could draw on considerably less polio-research experience in attempting to correct the troubles. Also, the Soviet public-health departments discovered that the logistics of injecting three shots of polio vaccine into more than 200 million people were forbiddingly complicated. During 1957, when every child in Leningrad was inoculated with Salk vaccine, as few as 10 percent of the children in nearby rural areas got any. The prospect of being able to produce Sabin vaccine easily, and of handing it over in the form of candy balls for house-to-house distribution by nurses was most appealing. "Our inoculation program was a public-health measure, not a field trial," Smorodintsev said during a visit to the United States in 1964. "It was designed to suit our medical services. In attempting to inoculate a population the size of ours, could there be any serious confusion about whether to give away candy drops, when the alternative was injection requiring so much more apparatus and personnel? Our work with the Sabin vaccine must be viewed in terms of public health and not as a strictly controlled scientific experiment."

If Smorodintsev or any other Soviet scientist had bothered to speak in that vein during 1959 and 1960, a certain amount of confusion might have been avoided. Instead, the Russians moved in phalanx from one international polio conference to another, reporting one enormous, absolutely unqualified scientific success after another and standing shoulder to shoulder in support of Sabin's contention that all fundamental questions were now answered. Their reports were unsatisfactory to many American scientists, not so much for what they said as for what they left out. That the Sabin vaccine should reduce the incidence of polio by 60 to 90 percent after mass feedings was no surprise to anyone. But how many cases of polio did it cause in the process? In how many instances had other intestinal viruses interfered with the vaccine virus, destroying its effectiveness, as had happened frequently in Latin-American trials? And what did the Soviets mean when they diagnosed a case as paralytic polio? How uniform were their diagnostic standards? How reliable were their laboratory tests? The Soviets offered little information on subjects of this kind, having been engaged in a public-health enterprise rather than a full-dress, scientific inquiry into the safety and efficacy of the Sabin vaccine. On the other hand, it pleased them to report their serene conviction that the vaccine was fully safe and remarkably effective. They, and nobody else on earth, had been foresighted enough to recognize the virtues of the vaccine. They had lost no time in applying it widely, for the benefit of their people. As Sabin took pains to point out to his fellow Americans, the Russian accomplishment—vaccinating about 75 million people in not much more than a year—was a terrible reproach to our own science and medicine.

On October 15, 1959, after the earliest Russian feats had been throughly publicized throughout the world, Sabin urged that the United States Public Health Service stop shillyshallying, read the handwriting on the wall, and license his vaccine for general distribution. Tests on more than 12.6 million people in the Soviet Union and Czechoslovakia had proved the vaccine from 96 to 100 percent effective, he said. He also said that the material was "a hundred times cheaper to produce than the Salk vaccine," a statement which no longer echoes in the land now that medical societies charge twenty-five cents per dose.*

---

* During 1964 physicians who bought Sabin vaccine in small quantities paid about thirty-five cents a dose for it. They paid twenty-eight cents a dose for Salk vaccine.

Americans who were worried about the possible hazards of a living polio vaccine picked over the Russian reports with the avidity of scholars hunting for clues in the Dead Sea scrolls. In person, the Russians were no help. An American braced the high-flying Chumakov in Washington in 1960 and said, "Do you mean to tell me that you have given your candies to 50 million people without any adverse reaction?" And Chumakov bubbled, "No reaction. Absolutely none."

Smorodintsev reported that, before using the vaccine on a large scale, his group had fed it to 2,500 healthy children of preschool age and had found it entirely safe. Chumakov's wife, Marina K. Voroshilova, indicated to a World Health Organization conference, however, that it was impossible to "exclude the possibility" of the vaccine viruses becoming virulent after several passages through the intestinal tract of man. To avoid the dire results of infection with viruses which had reverted to type in that way, she and her husband had practiced what she called "the principle of mass and simultaneous immunization with live poliovirus vaccine covering the territory of a whole district, city, or region." This effort to immunize everyone at once, to avoid whatever paralysis might otherwise be caused by transmission to the unvaccinated of passaged vaccine virus, seemed reasonable. It was especially interesting by contrast with Smorodintsev's report that *he* vaccinated "no more than 60 to 80 percent of the population in the areas concerned." He used the unvaccinated as observed controls, whose polio attack rate could be compared with that of the vaccinated. Unfortunately, no intelligible comparison of the results achieved by Chumakov and Smorodintsev in their vastly different approaches to the work was ever offered. Had reversion to virulence been a problem in the communities serviced by Smorodintsev? Did vaccine-associated cases of paralytic polio occur with greater or lesser frequency in Chumakov's precincts? American experts throw up their hands. They say that comparisons of that kind are impossible, because of variations in diagnostic, epidemiological, and laboratory practices from place to place in the Soviet Union—problems little different from those Tommy Francis avoided in his 1954 field trial, when he imposed binding rules and regulations on every participating community.

According to Voroshilova, "In the Soviet Union there were no poliomyelitis cases on record which could be attributed to the immunization with live virus from Sabin's strains." But American scientists, including one who reads and speaks Russian, declare that in some regions Soviet health workers were instructed to report as vaccine-induced polio *no* cases of the disease that occurred during the first thirty days after vaccination. It would be precisely within this period, of course, that vaccine-associated cases would arise. Other Americans are not so sure that the Russians followed so curious a procedure, although, as I shall show, records exist of at least one Soviet vaccine trial where cases that occurred within ten days of feeding were ruled out. In any event, there have been numerous cases of Soviet polio that appear to have been connected by more than coincidence with the infective qualities of the Sabin vaccine.

The only Russian who seems to have studied the question for purposes of publication is Dr. O. V. Baroian, of the Ivanovsky Institute, Moscow. A proponent of inactivated vaccines, Baroian had been much heartened to discover that, despite all production difficulties, Russia's Salk vaccine was sometimes as effective as America's. He decided to attempt a strictly controlled trial of the Sabin. In thirteen towns of the Sverdlovsk and Orenburg regions in the Urals, he gave Sabin vaccine to 287,000 people, a placebo to 165,000, a Salk-type vaccine to 125,000, and nothing whatever to 20,000. He found the Sabin vaccine relatively ineffective against paralytic polio—an almost unbelievable conclusion when one remembers the good results attained virtually everywhere else. He also found that the vaccine caused paralytic polio at a rate approximating seven cases per million of population. He reported, however, that the paralysis was mild and temporary.

"There was an awful lot of ill feeling about the Baroian report," says an American who attended a Moscow polio conference in 1960. "The impression Chumakov and Smorodintsev conveyed of a Soviet immunology absolutely unanimous in its approval of the Sabin vaccine was now shattered. It was evident, even before Baroian's report, that several leading Russian workers were quite unconvinced about the vaccine. Not that we could find out exactly why. From our point of view, the Baroian study was interesting, but it was so complicated and was susceptible to criticism on so many grounds that we could do little but note its existence. If Sabin vaccine actually caused paralytic polio in as many as seven of every million people who took it, the finding would be less significant in the Soviet Union than in the United States. Any vaccine that could reduce Soviet polio incidence from ninety-four per million could, as a public-health measure, be allowed the deficiency of provoking mild paralysis in seven of every million vaccinees. In the United States the situation was much different, of course. By 1961, polio—both paralytic and nonparalytic—was hitting our entire population at a rate of only seven per million. We obviously wouldn't want to use a new vaccine which *caused* polio. If there had been any way of penetrating to the bottom of the Baroian study, it might have been helpful."

Dr. Dorothy M. Horstmann, the Yale polio worker, investigated the Soviet studies for the World Health Organization. She found that, in the city of Karaganda, in the Central Asian Republic of Kazakhstan, twenty-one cases of paralytic polio occurred during May and June 1959 among children recently fed Sabin vaccine. During the same period, only eighteen cases were reported among unvaccinated children in the same city. The health officials in charge of this part of the study ruled that cases occurring within ten days of feeding could be eliminated from consideration, because they might have been caused by natural infection (a view with which American scientists would not agree, unless other evidence to that effect were present). Even accepting this peculiar version of the incubation period of polio and eliminating cases that occurred within ten days, there were at least five cases of vaccine-associated disease. Since only 171,000 children had been vaccinated in Karaganda, the vaccine appears to have been implicated in paralytic polio at a rate of not less than thirty cases per million persons fed.

Picture a Cheshire cat riding a jet-propelled steamroller and you have the Albert Sabin of 1959 and 1960. International polio conferences were as frequent as the seasons during those years, and Sabin was at each, with his triumphant Russians. By late 1960 they and others had fed his vaccine to upwards of 100 million persons. The Russians still had no ill effects to report. All they had to report was success. For example, there had been 963 cases in Estonia during 1958, but only eight in 1959. Smorodintsev had passed Sabin's virus strains through eight successive groups of children without noticing any serious reversion to virulence. The Soviet scientist was openly contemptuous of the Salk vaccine, which "has not eliminated the danger of paralytic forms of the disease developing in triply-vaccinated children and has had no effect on the circulation of the virus among vaccinated subjects." Also, he found the Salk vaccine "wasteful . . . complex, expensive," and he pointed out that it involved "additional scarring of children because of the repeated injections required." Sabin himself could not have posed these aspects of the problem more cogently.

Jonas Salk attended some of the conferences. "It was like sitting in on the plans for one's own assassination," he says. "The atmosphere of intrigue and hostility was even more intense than in 1953 and 1954. In those years mine was the only vaccine in the picture and the battle lines almost drew themselves. But now you had Sabin and his vaccine, Koprowski and *his* vaccine, and Herald Cox and his Lederle vaccine, and each of them had their coterie. The vying for position was absolutely brutal. There were actual plots hatched to keep one or another vaccine report off one or another scientific program. And, long before a particular report was read, you heard a dozen whispered allegations about the lies contained in it and the number of deaths unmentioned by it. It was like Lisbon during the war—everybody hawking secrets to everybody else."

Sabin was very much in command, however. At every opportunity he called attention to the backwardness of nations that refrained from licensing his vaccine and abolishing polio. He enumerated the supposed shortcomings of the Salk vaccine. He raised his eyebrows in regret over the rising incidence of polio in the United States during 1959. And, whenever Koprowski or

Cox held up a hand, Sabin shot it off. He had tested Koprowski's strains personally and had found them sadly lacking—a charge that the sorely beset Koprowski disputed vociferously but unsuccessfully. Koprowski was now at the Wistar Institute in Philadelphia, having left Lederle Laboratories after a falling out with Herald Cox. Cox, promoting a vaccine made of virus strains only slightly different from Koprowski's, was benefiting from an aggressive publicity campaign by his employer. His particular selling point was a trivalent vaccine—all three types of virus in one palatable, permanently immunizing dose. When he got an opportunity to try it out in Dade County, Florida, where Miami is situated, the press was full of the big news. Sabin disposed of the matter easily—pointing out with his usual, gentle perspicacity that too many people in Miami had taken Salk vaccine for the test to mean anything, statistically.

After 412,000 doses of Cox vaccine were distributed in Dade County, only seven cases of polio were reported. A victory, said the Lederle people, until scientists took a closer look and discovered that five of the seven cases occurred in persons within two weeks after they had swallowed the Cox vaccine. No cases were reported in persons previously immunized with a full series of Salk vaccine. One man who got polio but had not taken the Cox vaccine turned out to be the husband and father of a family that had; he fell ill thirty days after his wife and daughter were vaccinated. The circumstantial evidence suggested that they may have infected him. Whatever now was left of the Lederle project perished later in 1960, when someone got the bright idea of sending some of the stuff to West Berlin. The Russians were giving Sabin vaccine to East Berlin. If unimmunized West Berliners got polio that summer, the free nations of the world would suffer a setback in their struggle for the hearts and minds of men. Unfortunately, the Lederle promotion had a similarly lamentable effect. Of thirty-four polio cases reported in West Berlin after the Lederle product was given to 280,000 children, twenty-three cases were among the vaccinated and only eleven in the unvaccinated.

What with the American polio outbreak of 1959, the glowing reports from Eastern Europe and the repeated assurances by Albert Sabin that his vaccine could eradicate paralytic polio in the United States, the Public Health Service was under great pressure to license the product. The Surgeon General, Dr. Leroy E. Burney, acknowledging that polio immunization had become a matter of cold war prestige, like bombs, had appointed an advisory committee to study the matter. Dr. Roderick Murray, Director of the Division of Biologics Standards of the National Institutes of Health, was chairman. Other members were David Bodian, William McD. Hammon, Alexander D. Langmuir, Joseph L. Melnick, and John R. Paul—a formidable group, representing a wide spectrum of immunological and epidemiological thought. While Burney discussed possible manufacturing standards with various drug firms, the committee assembled a report which suggested that, regardless of the testimonials from Europe, not enough was known about the safety of the Sabin vaccine. The subject of most acute concern was reversion to virulence: What would happen when vaccinated persons transmitted the vaccine virus to the community?

By 1960, the Public Health Service found it necessary to be heard again. The pressure had not subsided. The American people knew nothing about reversion to virulence. All they knew was that the Salk vaccine was being publicized as a disappointment. The Sabin vaccine was infallible and required no needle. You swallowed pieces of sugar, and after taking three of them you were immune for life. The National Foundation's immunization campaigns were losing ground steadily. Although vaccination campaign efforts were redoubled each spring, fewer and fewer Americans sought vaccination. The miracle cube of sugar was just around the corner. Why take the needle? On August 24, 1960, Surgeon General Burney announced that he had a new report from his committee. "On the basis of these recommendations," he said, "it is considered that live poliomyelitis vaccine is suitable for use in the United States. It is now possible to visualize the licensing . . . for manufacture and sale. . . ."

The committee's unhappiness was poorly concealed in the language of its report. It recommended that Sabin's virus strains be the ones approved for American use, noting, however, that his Type III strain "has less than optimum immunogenic capacity and shows a tendency to change its neurovirulence characteristics after passage in man." It urged that a "superior Type III strain" be sought. It pointed out that the promise of lifelong immunity after one dose of each of the three types of virus was without basis: "The committee concludes that the field data now available indicate that while good levels of immunity can be obtained under certain conditions, such levels can only be assured by repeated doses." It warned that the Sabin vaccine could not accomplish more than had been achieved with the Salk vaccine unless "a unified national program" were followed. It neglected to mention that polio incidence in 1960 was at a new low, thanks to the Salk vaccine. It put the country on notice (not that any significant number of people ever read these pronouncements), that improper use of the Sabin vaccine would be inadvisable; unless entire communities were vaccinated at one time, the unvaccinated might be infected by virulent viruses excreted by the vaccinated.

The only feature of the situation altogether pleasing to the Public Health Service was that there seemed no possibility of having to take responsibility for the Sabin vaccine until late in 1961 or early in 1962. It would take that long for manufacturers to satisfy all government safety requirements. But the pressure continued. Lederle had now jettisoned the Cox vaccine in favor of the Sabin. And Lederle's arch-competitor in the production and sale of antibiotics, Charles Pfizer & Company, Inc., was already making Sabin vaccine in England and was pushing hard to open the American market. Between the two companies and the tireless Sabin, the Public Health Service got little peace. "They did everything but picket Bethesda with signs warning us to 'Repent Before It's Too Late,' " remembers a close observer. "Congressmen were telephoning to find out why Burney was delaying the licenses. There were rumors of legislative investigation and one heard talk of the 'polio gap' between Russia and the United States—like the 'missile gap.' "

On November 22, 1960, Jonas Salk tried to remind the American Medical Association that the growing concern about American polio immunization could be allayed by vaccinating the unvaccinated with Salk vaccine. He had tried to make this point in conversations with Burney and with the AMA's Executive Vice-President, Dr. F. J. L. Blasingame. He now wrote to Blasingame:

> If I were to specify what I had in mind when I came to see you it would be the following: First, to consider with you means whereby the prevalence of paralytic polio could be further reduced by vaccination before the summer of 1961, at least to an extent comparable to that which has already been accomplished in some of the Scandinavian countries or Australia, where vaccine administration, especially in the younger age groups, has been much more complete than in this country. Secondly, to consider whether or not some initiative on the part of the American Medical Association, and its county medical societies, might not be of great value if the local societies were to declare that they will take the lead and will enlist the support of local service organizations and voluntary groups as fully and completely as necessary to accomplish the desired objective. It is hardly necessary to point out that if specific programs were organized under the auspices of the county medical societies, the community could be saturated with vaccine. I doubt that an effective country-wide vaccination program can be carried out without this kind of medical society initiative and support and I can see great value in bringing about the further reduction in incidence of polio by a voluntary community contribution of this kind.

Neither Blasingame nor Burney answered the letter. They had other fish to fry. In February 1961, partly to show activity and partly to prepare the nation for the mass immunizations that were considered a necessary safety precaution in use of the Sabin vaccine, the Public Health Service held a meeting at its Communicable Disease Center at Atlanta. Salk, O'Connor, Sabin, and Tom Rivers were there, along with numerous other scientists and the representatives of veterans' groups, service clubs, and organized medicine.

"Unbelievable," says Salk. "Because the inactivated vaccine had not been taken to the people and there were still some cases of polio, the assumption was made that an infectious vaccine would do the job better. It was impossible to stop this, but we wanted very much to delay it if we could. There was a scientific point at issue. In a sense, our field trial of the inactivated vaccine principle was still in progress. We knew that, if the other vaccine were kept out of the community until the end of 1961, the decreasing incidence statistics would be inescapable proof that the inactivated vaccine could eradicate polio. The implications for the control of other viral diseases would be strong."

Basil O'Connor and Tom Rivers almost came to a parting of the ways at Atlanta. Rivers not only was convinced that the Sabin vaccine was ready for licensing but was giving interviews in which he predicted that it would eliminate epidemics. This riled O'Connor, who was as anxious as Salk that the inactivated vaccine be allowed another year of activity against polio, without the statistically confusing assistance of a second product. Moreover, O'Connor was upset because at least one of every four Americans below the age of twenty-one had not been vaccinated with a full series of Salk shots, while more than 15 million doses of the preparation languished in manufacturers' warehouses.

"What are you people talking about?" snapped O'Connor at all comers in Atlanta. "There is no Sabin vaccine yet. Go on home and get your children protected with the Salk vaccine." He took the floor of the meeting to make much the same point, complaining that all this public discussion of a product not yet available for use was encouraging the American people to remain unvaccinated while awaiting the new marvel. Some of the Public Health Service officials present were quite put out by O'Connor's unconcealed belief that they were acting as advance men for a commercial promotion and that they were doing so at the expense of polio prevention. They protested that they were only being foresighted, preparing for the day when the new vaccine would be available.

A few days later, the *Journal* of the American Medical Association rendered great service to this cause. It published a letter signed only "M.D., Wisconsin," which referred to the low potency of certain batches of Salk vaccine released for public use. The letter asked, ". . . is it true that by next year the oral vaccine will have solved this problem?" To answer the inquiry and banish confusion from the minds of its 180,000 readers, the *Journal* selected one of the most vocal of all Jonas Salk's critics, Dr. Herbert Ratner, Director of Public Health of Oak Park, Illinois. In Ratner's oft-publicized view, the Salk vaccine was sometimes unsafe and sometimes ineffective. As early as 1955, the health officer had circulated among science writers at medical meetings, declaring, "I am the devil's advocate. The Salk vaccine is bad."

In his answer to "M.D., Wisconsin," Ratner agreed that the potency of the Salk vaccine had usually been below snuff. "It is now generally recognized," he declared, "that much of the Salk vaccine used in the United States has been worthless." He did not trouble to explain how American incidence of polio had diminished by 92 percent in five years of Salk vaccination. The vaccine, he said, was "an unstandardized product of an unstandardized process." He concluded that, when the live-virus vaccine became available, "a complete course of vaccination is indicated, irrespective of the number of injections of the Salk vaccine given."

John Troan, who was now stationed in Washington as a Scripps-Howard staff writer, noted the remarkable coincidence which found an anonymous letter to the *Journal* being answered by Dr. Herbert Ratner, of all people, at exactly the time when the big putsch was starting in behalf of the Sabin vaccine. The *Journal's* editor, Dr. John H. Talbott, professed surprise at the reporter's interest. Ratner, he said, was a qualified health officer whose opinion "must carry weight."

Troan obtained a pointed comment from Salk. "The fact that polio continues to occur," said Salk, "is not due primarily to failure of the vaccine but failure to use it."

The AMA complained about Troan's story to every newspaper that published it. The whole thing was "sensational" and unfair, said the AMA. But its *Journal* hastened into print with an editorial by Surgeon General Burney, who called the Salk vaccine "effective," urged its wide use, and echoed Basil O'Connor in saying, "The possibility of a new vaccine will further encourage procrastination, either by individuals or communities." Burney then said that the oral vaccine would probably be available "in the months ahead," and that its advent should be planned for, even while vigorous campaigns were conducted for immunization with Salk vaccine. The editorial went on for more than a page of close print and, for that reason as well as its author's occupational habit of carrying water on both shoulders, was less effective than Ratner's pithy distortions had been. In April, the *Journal* returned to the subject, this time with a statement from the AMA's Committee on Polio Vaccines, which said that the Sabin vaccine would not be available in 1961 and that Salk vaccine should be used. The AMA had now reaffirmed its position as unbiased guardian of the nation's health without, however, lifting a finger to complete the job of eradicating polio.

On June 28, 1961, the House of Delegates of the AMA, in convention assembled, committed an act unprecedented in the organization's colorful 114-year history. It voted approval of a commercial product that had not yet been licensed for public use—the Sabin vaccine. Moreover, the House voted that the vaccine be administered on "an intensive, integrated, and coordinated basis," because "only by such an approach can a high proportion of persons be immunized in a reasonable period of time. Repeated experience in numerous communities has shown that routine vaccination programs fail to reach many individuals, especially those who need immunization the most." This, said the AMA, on the advice of its Council on Drugs, was "an opportunity to eliminate poliomyelitis as a significant public-health problem. . . . This opportunity can only be realized if physicians in each community take the lead in initiating, supporting, and participating in such programs."

At last! Programs of mass vaccination! Not only that but programs of mass vaccination "involving public and private, official and voluntary organizations as completely and actively as possible." This kind of socialistic undertaking had been rejected

by the AMA throughout its history. It had been rejected with
more than ordinary emphasis as recently as 1955 and 1956, when
mass use of the Salk vaccine was imperative. And now, when
mass vaccination no longer was necessary, but a simple, concerted effort to deliver vaccine to the unvaccinated *was* necessary, the AMA was all out for collectivism—but with another
vaccine.

The AMA's reasons were political. For years it had been
engaged in an increasingly difficult rearguard fight against "Medicare" legislation, which threatened to provide hospital and nursing care for the aged by extending the Social Security laws. The
new Kennedy Administration was supporting the labor movement
and other humane interests in advocacy of the bill. The policy-
makers of the AMA felt that organized medicine's Scroogelike
public image was a handicap in the legislative struggle. Previous
efforts to refurbish the image had failed; they consisted mainly
of propaganda and only slightly of improved medical services.
Organized medicine needed to demonstrate as quickly and conveniently and tangibly as it could that the first concern of each
and every American physician was the health of the American
people. The Sabin vaccine, a brand-new product for which magnificent claims were being made, was ideally suited to the AMA's
purposes, permitting the exercise of medical civic-mindedness at
the local level, where everyone could see it and be impressed.
The Salk vaccine could not be used for that purpose, of course,
without provoking questions as to why it had not been employed
on a mass scale years earlier.

Seldom has the arm of coincidence seemed longer than in the
no doubt coincidental association of the drug firm, Charles Pfizer
& Company, Inc., with this historic change in AMA policy. Quite
by chance, a former medical director of Pfizer's Laboratories Division, Dr. William C. Spring, Jr., was secretary of the AMA
Council on Drugs when it presented to the House of Delegates
its extravagantly biased review of the virtues of the Sabin vaccine. And, shortly after the House approved the report, the con-
ventioning physicians and representatives of the press attended
the world premiere of a Pfizer film called "The Next Step,"
which was all about the Sabin vaccine. Before the house lights

dimmed, Dr. Leonard W. Larson, President of the AMA, made
a speech lauding the vaccine. And after the film had been shown,
Larson posed for photographs with officials of the drug company. A National Foundation staff member who witnessed these
proceedings noticed, with some pain, that the film neglected to
mention that the March of Dimes had financed the development
of the Sabin vaccine. He wrote in a memo, "We paid for the
wedding but everyone else is romancing the bride."

To help local medical societies organize effective programs of
mass vaccination and sell large quantities of Sabin vaccine,
Charles Pfizer & Company, Inc., provides the societies with volumi-
nously detailed kits. Included in the cartons are organizational
instructions, canned newspaper, radio, and television testimonials
by high officials of the AMA, sample posters, leaflets, and miscellaneous material which, for want of a better word, might be
described as inspirational. One such item is a reprint of several
pages that appeared originally in the January 19, 1963, issue of
the AMA *Journal*. It describes the mass vaccinations accomplished
by the Maricopa County and Pima County Medical Societies of
Arizona. The programs were a great success. No fewer than
754,000 persons paid an average of about twenty-five cents a
dose for each of three doses of Sabin vaccine. Some paid more,
some paid nothing; it worked out fine. In evaluating their results,
the authors of the article could only guess, of course, whether
the promotion had been of any use against polio. They assumed
that it had.* Their evaluation of the program referred to "good
protection against the wild spread of poliomyelitis viruses." They
then said, "Probably of even more importance are other less tan-
gible values of the campaign. One of the first obvious results of
this program was the improved relations between the organiza-

* In 1953, Maricopa County had 287 cases of polio. In 1960 there were
only five, and, in 1961, six. In 1962, the year of the medical society's
big vaccination program, there were three. There also were three in
1964. In Pima County, where a high of sixty-one cases was recorded in
1952, incidence had fallen to one case in 1960 and two in 1961. No
cases have been reported there since the medical-society program.

tions that worked together to provide this program for the counties. The other important result is the improved image of the Medical Society in the eyes of the public."

An editorial in the same issue of the AMA *Journal* commented:

> The trend of the past two decades has been toward the division of community responsibilities, with the field of communicable disease prevention being allocated more and more to governmental and voluntary health organizations with minor consideration of the private physician's role in this field of medicine. . . . Once in a while, however, an opportunity presents itself for the private physician and the medical society to assume their natural leadership in the community in disease prevention. Such an opportunity was provided with the licensing of the oral polio vaccine. It is to the eternal credit of the private physician and the organized medical society that they voluntarily assumed the responsibility for conducting mass immunization programs to prevent polio. . . . As the authors of the article point out, the immunization against polio was only one of the values of these campaigns. Other values, such as the change of public image of the medical society and the private physician, the organization of communities for health activities, the inspiration found by voluntary groups, and the medical knowledge imparted to the citizens, were of great value.

On June 26, 1961, when the AMA's imminent approval of the Sabin vaccine was revealed in the newspapers, Jonas Salk was in Atlantic City, delivering a speech to the National Education Association about some of the biological aspects of man's struggle to outgrow what Salk called "his subhuman heritage." He later told reporters, "I left the plane and stopped at the airport to get a sandwich and saw my name in a big headline and said, 'What did I do now?' I bought the newspaper, didn't buy the sandwich and that afternoon I gave some very deep thought as to what do I do now, when I have avoided for so long commenting on the very things that were now being said, but now by an official body. Do I say nothing and therefore leave the im-

pression that surely this must be true or else Salk certainly would
have said something about it?"

Basil O'Connor says, "This was the only time I have ever
seen Jonas get mad enough and *stay* mad enough to fight back.
When the AMA finally did him the courtesy of sending him a
copy of the report adopted by its House of Delegates, he sat
down and wrote a brilliant rejoinder."

"Of course I was mad," says Salk. "And of course I fought
back. I did so knowing very well that my motives would be misconstrued. People would think that Salk was defending himself
against Sabin, or defending his 'product' against Sabin's. But a
scientific principle was at stake. For years I had been trying to
advance that principle in the only appropriate way—in communications to the scientific world. I had avoided public controversy as best I could. But now public controversy had been
thrust on me. By misrepresenting the inactivated vaccine principle to the country's physicians and to the general public, the
AMA had done a disservice to the interests of medicine, science,
and the public health. I felt it was my responsibility to set the scientific record straight."

The physicians of this country [Salk wrote to the AMA]
and the public are interested in the control of polio. They
are less concerned with whether this is accomplished by a
killed-virus vaccine or a live-virus vaccine; and in this they
are joined by the writer of this communication. The people
are interested in a vaccine that is safe, effective, and available. Their own experience makes them aware of the fact
that polio has been sharply reduced by the killed-virus vaccination procedure that has been practiced in the United
States. Factual evidence substantiates the view that failure
to use the vaccine which has been available for six years in
the United States has prevented the earlier eradication of
polio in this country. They understand that this is related to,
if not wholly caused by, social and economic factors which,
in turn, are related to a deeper social problem.
Without evidence, the physicians of this country and the
public have been told repeatedly over the past several years,

and by many, that a live-virus vaccine *may* induce longer lasting immunity than a killed-virus vaccine, and that a live-virus vaccine will eradicate not only the disease but the virus as well, which *cannot be expected* to be done by a killed-virus vaccine. The dogma has been that a live-virus vaccine is essential for the effective control of a virus disease and that this cannot be accomplished by a killed-virus vaccine. The experimental and field experiences with a killed-virus vaccine for polio have been successful and the dogma is no longer scientifically tenable. . . .

Not only is scientific justification lacking for the proposed new vaccine program but the *evidence* is notably lacking to support the *need* for "change-over" from one form of vaccination procedure to another and for revaccination of the entire population. . . . This venture on the part of the AMA into the realm of public health—to solve a problem that is solving itself—is difficult to understand.

This is a most perplexing situation. The AMA claims that mass programs for live-virus vaccine application are necessary to complete the task of fully protecting the United States against polio. The opportunity has existed for some time, and still exists to accomplish this by the use of a killed-virus vaccine, and yet the introduction of the use of mass procedures, which could be of value to prevent polio *now*, in the summer of 1961, is being reserved for the time when a "change-over" will become possible to another vaccine. In fact, on 22 November 1960 by letter the AMA was urged to take the initiative to accomplish mass immunization with whatever vaccine was then available toward the end of eradicating polio completely. Neither the AMA nor the United States Public Health Service, which was informed of this request, responded to this suggestion. . . . What are the facts? What are the reasons? Does our arrival at the destination of complete control over polio need to await the advent of "new equipment" *reputed* to be *how much* "better"? Need we wait to get there faster, and with not as yet demonstrated certainty, when we can get there sooner? How many have not already arrived and why? Those who have used the available equipment seem to be arriving safely; whole segments of communities in the United States and other countries have done so successfully. Why is it implied that the available equipment is inadequate and will soon be obsolete? Many who, for lack of understanding, or lack of a sense of responsibility, have not used the available equipment, are now offered justification for indecision and inaction by believing that "the scientists themselves can't decide." Decisions in science should be made on the basis of evidence. What is the evidence?

The report of the AMA Council on Drugs had said that the live vaccine "may" give longer immunity than the inactivated. Salk pounced on this, pointing out that some of his earliest experimental subjects still were immune nine years after vaccination. "One cannot say how long immunity *may* last," Salk wrote, "one can report only *how long it has lasted.*" Obviously, it was impossible to be certain that the Sabin vaccine would provide immunity of greater duration, for the theory had never been tested.

Salk reviewed the "herd effect," showing how the inactivated vaccine had protected unvaccinated as well as vaccinated Americans. He reported that Type II poliovirus was no longer detectable in the American population and that Type I also seemed to be disappearing—phenomena that he said might have been predicted, because the Type II component of his vaccine was the most effective and the Type I next most effective.

Thus, it would seem clear [he went on] that the *need* is for vaccination of the *un*immunized. The crux of the problem lies here. The AMA recognizes the importance. . . . They have proposed, for the first time, a program of mass use. . . .

Has the council taken cognizance of the virtual absence of Type II virus in the United States since the killed-virus vaccine has been used? If virus in the community is sharply declining with the use of killed-virus vaccine, would not the introduction of live-virus vaccine reverse this process by reintroduction of virus into the population with opportunity for multiplication and mutation? Would not children then be unnecessarily exposed to the experience of infection with three polio viruses when, under present circumstances, the ideal is rapidly approaching—namely, avoidance of exposure to polioviruses? Would not reintroduction of virus be a large step backward? . . .

Studies have been done that show fear of the needle is not a significant factor in individuals not having come forward, or not having brought forward their infant and preschool children to be immunized. A priori it is difficult to believe that so large a segment of the young parent population is fearful of a needle, whether for themselves or for their children, when injections are required for so many purposes, including immunization against other diseases which can never be converted into preparations that could be administered orally. In spite of the lack of specific knowledge on these points and the evidence for effectiveness of the killed-virus vaccine . . . the AMA implies that the expected gain from a "change-over" will be due to the change in *vaccine preparation* rather than to the change in *administrative procedure*. This assumption cannot go unchallenged. Attention should be called to the virtual elimination of polio in Sweden and Denmark, as well as other countries, where killed-virus vaccine has been used, as well as to the reported successful control in Czechoslovakia and Hungary and other countries where live-virus vaccine has been used. Might this suggest that the methods of distribution of medical service may be a factor to consider when the two kinds of vaccines were used with equal success? . . .

No issue is taken with the House of Delegates or its councils or committees for their desire to approve the use of a live-virus vaccine for polio. Nor is issue taken with their desire to apply mass vaccination procedures for the use of live-virus vaccines. Issue is taken for failure to acknowledge scientific facts and for recommending action based upon a medical dogma that can no longer be maintained in the light of scientific evidence and of experience in practice. Issue is taken for failure to acknowledge the degree of individual and community protection that has resulted from killed-virus vaccination and for failure to acknowledge evidence for durability of immunity. All of this opens to question the justification for the conclusions reached with respect to the action of the House of Delegates in a matter that concerns the health of the nation. The House of Delegates is

establishing a precedent in endorsing medications or biologi-
cals still in the stage of development and in recommending to
physicians which medications they should and should not
use. . . . Responsibility for the awkwardness with which the
country has proceeded in the past several years toward the
control of polio cannot be ascribed to the vaccine that has
been available but must rest with all those who have the
authority and the power to influence and to administer preventive measures that are available but who place questions
of procedure above purpose and goals.

It is superfluous to say that the sincerity of the AMA's desire to bring about the end of polio as soon as possible is not
questioned, but their sincerity would be conveyed and expressed more convincingly if they were to declare war on
polio to the finish under AMA leadership, starting now, and
with whatever vaccine preparations are available to be applied by mass vaccination techniques. While this might imply
a tacit admission that this should have been done sooner, it
would be more acceptable than to make it appear that the
proper vaccine for effective immunization is not yet available.

Leroy Burney had been succeeded as Surgeon General by Dr.
Luther L. Terry. On August 3, 1961, Salk wrote to Terry, having
heard that the Public Health Service's Special Oral Poliomyelitis
Vaccine Advisory Committee (which now included Albert Sabin)
was to meet in a few days to discuss licensing the vaccine. Salk
implored the Surgeon General to keep the Sabin vaccine off the
market until 1962, so that nothing might becloud the meaning
of the 1961 incidence statistics. By the end of 1961, Salk said,
"the full potential of a killed-virus vaccine will have been decisively revealed."

A result such as this [he continued] relates not only to
poliomyelitis, and to the United States, but is of broader
meaning with respect to virus diseases generally and for people the world over. The value of this experiment is, in part,
related to the possibility of introducing, into combination

with the three strains presently contained in the killed-polio-
virus vaccine, viral antigens for additional diseases of man,
whether these be for the common childhood diseases, or the
poliolike diseases of the central nervous system, or even the
viral antigens that may later be found to cause, or to have
a causal relationship to, the leukemias or other neoplastic
conditions. The total number of viral or other antigens, as
for diphtheria and tetanus, that could be included in a single
vaccine is yet to be determined but indications are that it is
more than ten and might be one hundred or more. . . .

On August 17, 1961, the Public Health Service licensed Sabin's
Type I vaccine for distribution to the American public. It licensed
the Type II vaccine on October 10. It did not license the Type
III vaccine until March 27, 1962. Members of the Advisory Committee were still afraid of the Type III's skittish tendency to
turn virulent. "Technical difficulties" at the manufacturing plants
were given as the official reason for the delay in licensing.

The committee proceedings were secret, and still are, in com-
formity with the 1905 law and more recent regulations which
forbid government disclosure of manufacturing problems. The
unspecified "technical difficulties" are known, however, to have
been connected with the instability of the Type III strain. To
this day, in fact, manufacturers and government remain unsure
whether any particular dose of Type III vaccine is harmless.
Some experts believe that illnesses attributed to the reversion to
virulence of vaccine virus in the intestinal tract are actually
caused by virulent viruses that escape the manufacturers' safety
tests. A colony of the attenuated Type III virus used in the vaccine may not be entirely homogeneous. It may contain virulent
particles or particles which, having begun to revert to virulence,
complete the transition while multiplying in the intestinal tract.

A participant in the Bethesda discussions which preceded licensing of the vaccine confides, "Reversion to virulence has
never been understood by the public. We speak of the virus
being virulent *after* passage through the human intestinal canal,
but we really mean that the change has taken place *within* the
intestines. The person who takes oral polio vaccine is not im-

munized by the viruses he swallows, but by their progeny, which develop during infectious multiplication in the intestines. Some of us who were close to the licensing situation *knew*—that's the only word for it—that cases of paralysis might occur and—if they did—would be attributable to the Type III vaccine. It was impossible to overlook Joe Melnick's demonstration that Type III vaccine virus passaged through children was sometimes virulent enough to paralyze monkeys. His work was beyond dispute. Even with the most indulgent attitude toward the optimism of the Russian reports, you had to be worried about feeding that vaccine to people. You can take my word that members of the Advisory Committee lost sleep over the thing."

Nevertheless, it is difficult to imagine how the government could have defended a decision to delay the licensing any longer than it did. The manufacturers apparently had learned how to produce a Type III vaccine that conformed to the Public Health Service's safety-test requirements (which are claimed to be the most severe in the world). Industry, medicine, the press, Congressmen, and reputable scientists were clamoring for release of the vaccine, citing the wonders it had wrought in other lands. The nation had been conditioned to believe the vaccine essential to the obliteration of polio. The Public Health Service had allowed itself to play a leading role in the conditioning process. The government was committed. The vaccine was licensed. Insiders held their breath.

Within four months of the release of the Type III vaccine and the beginning of the AMA's mass campaigns, it was evident that more cases of paralytic polio were occurring in persons fed Sabin vaccine than could be excused as coincidence. Notwithstanding the achievements reported in Russia, and regardless of the implied promise that ingestion of three sugar cubes moistened with Sabin vaccine would confer lasting immunity, cases were piling up. By the end of August, the Public Health Service was confronted with official reports of sixty-two cases in which Sabin vaccine had been administered within thirty days of the onset of symptoms.

No known laboratory test could prove beyond all doubt that a given case of polio had been caused by the vaccine. If the polio victim's blood showed that his illness had been caused by a Type III virus, and if his feces contained such viruses and if he had swallowed Type III vaccine two weeks earlier, one could still not *prove* that the vaccine viruses had induced disease. If the viruses retrieved from the patient resembled vaccine viruses rather than "wild" viruses, one could suppose—as proponents of the Sabin vaccine readily supposed—that the vaccine viruses had simply taken over the intestines, driving away the wild viruses responsible for the paralyzing infection. If, on the other hand, the fecal samples yielded Type III viruses that seemed to resemble wild viruses (as vaccine viruses sometimes do after they have reverted to virulence), one could decide that the wild virus had somehow driven off the vaccine viruses and had caused disease. Either way, nobody could prove the vaccine guilty.

To minimize controversy by remaining as close as possible to provable fact, the Public Health Service's Advisory Committee accepted no polio cases as "compatible" with the possibility of vaccine-induced disease unless every circumstance pointed in that direction. Accordingly, the committee eliminated vaccine-associated cases that occurred in communities where natural infection was known to have broken out concurrently. For example, Type III cases among Texans fed the Type III vaccine were eliminated, because an epidemic of Type I disease was in progress at the time! Furthermore, even when vaccine-associated cases were the only ones reported in their respective communities, they were eliminated unless adequate laboratory evidence of polio was available to supplement clinical evidence of the disease. In addition, the committee ruled out patients whose cases may or may not have been associated with the vaccine, but whose vaccination records were missing from the local reports. Cases of that kind totaled 186 by the end of 1962.

On September 15 the Advisory Committee met (Sabin was out of the country at the time), performed its processes of elimination, and found eleven cases of Type III paralysis "compatible" with the theory of vaccine causation. It also found one case of Type I. Most of the victims were adults. Only three of them had ever taken Salk injections. On September 20, Surgeon General Terry suggested to the nation that the use of Sabin's

Type III vaccine "be limited to preschool and school age children and to adults at high risk, i.e., those traveling [abroad] and those living in areas where Type III epidemics were present or impending." Mass vaccinations with Type I and II should continue in all age groups, he said.

Later, five more "compatible" Type III cases were reported. Four had occurred in Nebraska, bringing to eight that state's total of such cases. No other polio was reported in Nebraska during 1962.

In December, the Advisory Committee met again, eliminated some cases it had previously accepted, and added some new cases. It now reported eleven "compatible" Type III cases for the year. Of these victims, eight were over thirty years of age. Of seven Type I cases for which the vaccine seemed responsible, four victims were over thirty. Two additional cases, which occurred in unvaccinated household contacts of vaccinees, were reported as "compatible" with the spread of virulent vaccine virus. "Because the need for immunization diminishes with advancing age," said the committee, "and because potential risks of vaccine are believed by some to exist in adults, especially above the age of thirty, vaccination should be used for adults only with the full recognition of its very small risk."

This phrase, "full recognition of . . . very small risk," with its conflicting subtleties, could have issued only from a government bureau. Basil O'Connor was convinced by now that the Public Health Service was whitewashing the problem—much as it had sought to whitewash the Cutter problem. He wrote to Anthony J. Celebrezze, Secretary of Health, Education, and Welfare (with a copy to President Kennedy):

> The Surgeon General is encouraging the use of the live-virus vaccine, which entails a "very small risk," when, in fact, there is no need of its use at all. . . .
>
> Possible future polio epidemics, in view of the results of the use of the killed-virus vaccine, call for some stretch of the imagination, but, in any event, if one's imagination leads him to think the public should still further be protected against epidemics, that can readily be accomplished by further use of

the killed-virus polio vaccine, with respect to which there is no "very small risk" or risk at all.

An analysis of the Public Health Service's own reports for the year 1962 suggests that whitewash was, in fact, being applied. For example, in contrast with the inability of the Surgeon General's committee to agree that more than eighteen post-feeding cases were probably vaccine-induced, the record shows twenty-nine cases (a) in which symptoms began within thirty days of feeding, and (b) which were the only cases in their counties during the year.

The difficulties faced by those members of the Surgeon General's committee who were not convinced in advance of the live-virus vaccine's safety were illuminated by the courageous David Bodian. In an article he published in the *Bulletin of the Johns Hopkins Hospital* and called "Poliomyelitis: Pathogenesis, Policy, and Politics," Bodian, himself a member of the committee, managed, without violating Public Health Service canons of secrecy, to show which way the wind was blowing with the Sabin vaccine promotion. The wind was blowing from the AMA and from the public-relations offices of the vaccine manufacturers. Bodian wrote:

> The introduction of a new and incompletely evaluated product by means of crusadelike community-wide programs involves publicity in which any hint of lack of confidence is thought to be intolerable. Thus assurances of complete safety were so much taken for granted that the Surgeon General's committee found it impossible to evaluate a certain number of cases of paralytic poliolike illness occurring within thirty days after feeding of Sabin's strains because attending physicians had not considered the possibility of vaccine-related cases and had failed to obtain specimens essential for a complete diagnostic work-up. Repeated instances of delayed reporting of cases and of reluctance to report cases illustrate further that there are human factors which prevent us from obtaining a complete picture of the possible incidence of oral vaccine-induced paralytic poliomyelitis. It appears that with vaccines, as well as with drugs, the attending physician

is often unwilling to anticipate, understand, or admit the occurrence of undesirable reactions. . . .

Although experience has shown that a newly licensed product requires further evaluation in large-scale use, the Public Health Service appears to have no built-in mechanism for a carefully planned, gradual introduction of a new vaccine, so that definitive evaluation can be developed before the licensed vaccine is distributed in an indiscriminate way. It seems to me that this . . . brings pressure upon the licensing agency to hold back licensing until an intuitive decision can be made concerning presumptive safety, and then to yield, almost apologetically, to premature pressure for mass use throughout the country.

In retrospect it seems that the need for an intermediate stage of oral vaccine introduction and evaluation should have been especially apparent because of the existence of a sharp division of opinion among the scientific community in the field of immunization. In a general way, many virologists have been heavily in favor of the live-virus approach to immunization, and are highly protective of the oral poliovaccine as an example of what can be accomplished by this new approach. Many immunologists, conversely, do not feel that live-virus vaccines are the answer to the needs for immunization against the many disease-producing viruses which now afflict the human race. Their candidate, as it were, is the multiple killed-virus antigen. There is nothing wrong with this difference of opinion, and its existence may have contributed to the fortunate circumstance that the killed-virus poliomyelitis vaccine was properly introduced by means of the most scientific field trials of an immunizing agent ever to be executed. One wonders why so little attention was given to the desirability of a similar intermediate stage of oral vaccine introduction. . . .

During the summer of 1962, Canada's health authorities withdrew the Sabin Type III vaccine from public use, four vaccine-associated cases having been reported among 4 million persons who had taken the preparation. Michigan also banned the Type III, after fifty thousand vaccinations produced two cases. Elsewhere in North America, the "full recognition of very small risk" recommended by the Public Health Service resulted, as one might expect, in no recognition of any risk. County medical societies continued to urge persons of all ages to take the vaccine. So did public-health departments. "Let's face it," says a public-health officer. "The risk was awfully small. If you think the Sabin vaccination programs were a golden opportunity for the medical societies to look good, what do you think they were for some health departments around the country? They were a chance to work closely with organized medicine and get public visibility for their own programs. To come out of the woodwork, you might say. The health departments were afraid that, if they told adults not to take the vaccine, the adults would keep the children home, too, and the vaccination campaigns would be failures. So they took the small risk."

A high official of the Public Health Service says, "We were appalled when we saw how the drug companies and medical societies ignored the warnings. In Washington, they took a full-page ad, showing an old lady and a little baby. 'Nobody's too old or too young,' said the ad. We could do nothing about it but keep our fingers crossed."

In response to one of Basil O'Connor's observations that the Public Health Service seemed to be encouraging national disregard of its warnings, and was not just standing helplessly by, Surgeon General Terry wrote in a letter, "We have pointed out the potential hazard, especially in those over thirty years of age, and urged local authorities to weigh this very small risk in developing their programs. When the decision has been made locally as to which age groups will be included in mass programs, we have been happy to lend our support to these undertakings."

By the end of 1963, Charles Pfizer & Company, Inc., leader in the field of Sabin vaccine promotion, reported that more than six hundred mass vaccination programs had used its brand of the product in the United States. More than 70 million Americans had taken a full course of Sabin vaccine, whether Pfizer's or somebody else's. According to the reports of the Public Health Service, eighteen "compatible" cases of paralysis occurred during 1963 among persons whose symptoms began within thirty days

of taking Sabin vaccine. As usual, numerous vaccine-associated
cases were excluded—especially those reported in so-called "epidemic" areas, where cases of the natural disease had also been
found. Of the eighteen cases, sixteen were attributable to the
Type III vaccine. Only forty-two Americans aged fifteen or older
contracted paralytic polio during that year—but fourteen of the
cases were attributable to the vaccine. Federal health officials
were unmistakably nervous but kept silent. Silence was also noticeable among medical societies in whose jurisdictions paralytic
cases occurred after vaccination. State and local medical journals,
which in other circumstances might have remarked on the association of the vaccine with illness, now managed to overlook this
phenomenon. And the vaccination crusades continued.

"TO END POLIO EVERYONE MUST HAVE ALL 3
DOSES OF SABIN ORAL VACCINE," trumpeted the leaflets
distributed by the Suffolk County, New York, Medical Society in
March, April, and June of 1964. Like hundreds of other medical
societies, the Suffolk group called its project "SOS"—for "Sabin
Oral Sundays."

"Who should take this vaccine?" asked the leaflet, rhetorically.
"All persons over the age of three months," it answered. "Everybody—even senior citizens!"

"I have had Salk shots," continued the leaflet. "Should I take
Sabin Oral Vaccine too?" The answer was unequivocal, but unsup-
portable by scientific evidence: "By all means. Everyone must
take Sabin vaccine to eliminate polio. Salk provides temporary
immunity and requires 'booster' injections at intervals. Sabin
vaccines give lasting protection against all three kinds of polio,
and only Sabin prevents you from being a carrier of the dread
disease and transmitting it to your loved ones and neighbors."

There had been no polio in Suffolk County during 1963. There
had been two cases of polio in Suffolk County during 1962.
There had been no cases in 1961. Basil O'Connor, who had
conferred on himself the unrewarding chore of attempting to
impress the medical societies with the anomalies of their position, wrote to the President of the Suffolk Society. He quoted
from the leaflet. He reviewed the county's polio statistics. He
then set to work with his flail:

How, may I ask, can you justify this kind of high-pressure campaign to sell over 2 million doses of live-virus vaccine when the Salk killed-virus vaccine has long ago eliminated polio as a public-health problem in Suffolk County? Surely the people of the county are worthy of the kind of medical and public-health leadership that mobilizes resources to deal, not with nonexistent problems, but with such real problems as infant mortality and the chronic diseases that confront the people of all parts of the country.

... What do you mean by "lasting" protection: one year, ten years, a lifetime? . . . How can you say that any new vaccine that has been in commercial use for less than three years gives lasting protection? The Salk vaccine has been in successful use for nine years, which should lead *you* to believe that it gives three times "lasting protection"! Is this not gross hucksterism at its worst?

He wrote a similar letter to Nassau County, New York, where there had been only one case of polio since 1961, but where an "SOS" program was under way. And to Potter County, Pennsylvania, where there had been no cases in almost four years. And to Greene County, Pennsylvania, where there also had been no cases in almost four years. And to Stanly County, North Carolina, where the last case had occurred in 1957. And to Northampton County, in the same state, where there had been no cases since 1956. And to Wayne County, Mississippi, where the last case had been seen in 1955. And to Hampden County, Massachusetts, where there had been only one case a year in 1962 and 1963. And Bergen County, New Jersey (no cases since 1961); Essex County, New Jersey (none since 1961); Union County, New Jersey (same); Hudson County, New Jersey (one case in 1963); St. Marys County, Maryland (no cases in nearly five years); and to Franklin County, Georgia (likewise). He wrote scores of such letters and got several dozen answers, most of them huffy. One of the more candid and less irate responses came from Robert F. Sullivan, M.D., of Carnesville, Georgia, who said, ". . . had the medical society not seen fit to endorse the Sabin oral vaccination drive, it would have appeared to represent utter irresponsibility, in the face of such a high-potency publicity campaign as was conducted in Atlanta earlier this year. Our citizens would certainly have felt deprived of an opportunity to cooperate in a program to stamp out a disease as they had been educated to do. . . ."

Many of the replies informed O'Connor that the campaigns had been carried out on the advice of the United States Public Health Service.

In June 1959 a group of women in the Bethel Park suburb of Pittsburgh organized a polio immunization clinic to get Salk vaccine into the neighborhood children. With publicity from *The Pittsburgh Press,* the movement spread quickly throughout Allegheny County. Families that had put off inoculation when the price at doctors' offices was five or six dollars per shot now turned out in force. More than half a million injections were given, some for one dollar, some for less. Public-health nurses and individual physicians donated their services. Fraternal societies, neighborhood business associations, and parent-teacher groups staffed the dispensaries. Werner Siems, who wrote most of the articles for the *Press,* remembers, "Salk himself was very interested in the campaign. He had been upset by the failure of the earlier vaccination drive to reach as much of the community as he thought it should have. He wanted this drive to be a big success. But he was fearful about seeming to be his own salesman. He asked to be left out of the stories as much as possible, and would help me plan and write them only in an indirect way. He'd say, 'Now, if I were going to approach a problem of this kind, I would emphasize that which appeared most likely to achieve . . .' and so on and on. And by the time his circumlocution was ended and you cleared the cobwebs from your head you discovered that he had practically dictated your story for you without admitting that he was a participant in it. I became quite fond of him. When the clinics—there finally were about 360—had trouble getting physicians, he helped recruit docs from the medical school faculty. The result was that Pittsburgh became the first major city in the country to rid itself of polio. Salk was overjoyed. There wasn't a single case in 1961 or 1962."

In 1963, three unvaccinated residents of Allegheny County had polio. In 1964, amid publicity to the effect that the "Salk Era" was at an end, the County Medical Society conducted Sabin Sundays. Salk's friends in Pittsburgh tried to shield him from some of the more mendacious publicity about the "threat" of polio "running wild" in Pittsburgh unless everybody took oral vaccine. They refrained from mailing such press clippings to him at La Jolla. But he found out what was going on, regardless. One day he sat in his office at the Institute for Biological Studies, shaking his head and grimacing. "Doses of oral vaccine are supposed to be given at least six weeks apart," he said. "If the doses are given at shorter intervals, one type of virus may interfere with the other. This is basic. The manufacturers say so in their instructions to physicians. The Public Health Service says so. Everybody says so. But in Pittsburgh they are giving the doses only a month apart. And, to catch people who don't show up on the regularly scheduled dates, they give make-up doses between times. They negate their own principles. This has happened in community after community. In the meantime, the pockets of unimmunized people throughout the country are still not being covered fully by these campaigns. Not as they should be. Who do you think shows up at the clinics? The vast majority are people who have already been vaccinated with the inactivated vaccine."

But the casualties, the people who came down with paralytic polio after taking Sabin vaccine, were in almost all cases persons unprotected by Salk vaccine. And in almost all cases they were adults, whose susceptibility to severe paralytic polio has always been greater than that of children. In the summer of 1964, the Public Health Service had no choice but to act. More than half the cases of paralytic polio reported in the country during the first six months of the year were associated with the oral vaccine. Fully a third of the cases were "compatible." The "very small risk" had become no larger, but was increasingly difficult to explain away. To say, as some had, that no effective medical cure or prophylaxis is ever completely free of risk was an explanation that would not wash—because the Salk vaccine was effective and free of risk. No cases of polio had been attributed to it since the Cutter incident. How could the government continue to help promote indiscriminate use of this risky new vaccine without leaving its flanks exposed to scandal and political recrimination?

And so the Public Health Service acted. It did the absolute minimum. It disturbed nobody. It made a recommendation, the significance of which could be grasped only by the best informed and most alert. Its act, however, tidied up the government's record. If the roof finally fell in on the Sabin vaccine promotion, the government would be able to show that it had tried to direct commerce and medicine toward the path of righteousness.

On September 23, 1964, the Public Health Service announced that persons over eighteen years of age should be reserved in their eagerness to take Sabin vaccine. Like the historic "full-recognition-of-very-small-risk" document of 1962, which had recommended conservatism among persons older than thirty, this new press release was couched in language of the greatest delicacy. It emphasized the positive. It muddied up the negative. It disengaged the Public Health Service from the hook by pretending that the latest reduction in the recommended age limit for vaccines had been "forecast" in earlier advices. It was so ambiguous, and its construction diverted eye and brain so effectively from the real issue that *The New York Times* buried the news at the bottom of a rearward page, and other important newspapers neglected to publish it at all, not realizing that one of the most toothsome scandals of modern medical history was there, beneath the surface. The press release deserves immortalization here, at least in part:

> A special advisory committee to the Surgeon General of the Public Health Service, Department of Health, Education, and Welfare, urged today renewed drives by local communities during the fall and winter to vaccinate the younger age groups against poliomyelitis.
>
> The report was prepared by a Special Advisory Committee on Oral Poliomyelitis Vaccine and was made public today by Surgeon General Luther L. Terry.
>
> The committee's report said that the age groups to be immunized and the vaccine chosen for use should be determined locally. The committee said, however, that in its view the oral vaccination of persons over 18 should "generally be

recommended only in those situations in which unusual exposure to poliomyelitis might be anticipated, such as epidemics, entry into military service, and travel to other countries. . . ."

Dr. Terry, in releasing the report, said that the Public
Health Service was accepting the committee's recommendations. He pointed out that the shift in emphasis away from
adults toward younger age groups was forecast in a committee
report of December 1962. The Advisory Committee at that
time emphasized the importance of concentrating on the immunization of younger age groups and noted a "very small
risk" incident to the use of the oral vaccines in persons 30
years of age and over.

On the second page of the release one discovers that the new
recommendation was "based on an exhaustive analysis of 87
reported cases of poliolike illness associated with the administration of oral vaccines which have occurred in nonepidemic areas
since December 1961," and that the committee "believes that at
least some of these cases were caused by the vaccine."

"To a scientist things are various shades of gray," says one of
the principal officials of the National Institutes of Health. "But
to an administrator they are either black or white, yes or no—
license the vaccine or withdraw the license. That's what eventually will have to happen if cases of Type III polio persist with
the continued use of oral vaccine."

Meanwhile, interesting developments seem to be afoot in the
Soviet Union, whose supposed lead in polio prevention was so
influential on the public-health policies of the United States.
Soviet scientists tell their American colleagues that the promise
of lasting immunity has not been fulfilled by the live-virus polio
vaccine. In some Soviet health districts, the public is urged to take
the vaccine annually. In others, the incidence of polio has de-
creased at what Soviet experts describe as a most disappointing
rate. One Russian says, "As an interim public-health measure, the
oral vaccine was useful. But for the future, we look toward in-
jectable vaccines containing antigens against many diseases. This
cannot be accomplished with live viruses, because they would

interfere with each other. For swift immunization requiring the fewest possible separate doses, purified killed viruses are the thing." Dr. V. M. Zhdanov, Director of the Institute of Virology of the Soviet Academy of Medical Sciences in Moscow, is now at work on a vaccine which will contain—in one shot—antigen against eight diseases, including polio, influenza, and measles.

Which is exactly the sort of thing Jonas Salk has been advocating all along.

17

WHEN THE WORLD MAKES A PERSONAGE OF A MAN BY PUBLISHING his name in headlines, hanging decorations around his neck, and anointing him with oratorical oil, it places him in a new and transforming frame of self-reference. His existence has been validated by recognition. He is a certified committer of feats. He is on display. An environment once ignorant of him now cherishes expectations of him. He may hate this or love it or be deluded in some way by it but he cannot possibly be indifferent to it. It affects his style. He can no longer move from task to task as he did in the years of his obscurity. He now must proceed from accomplishment to encore. What does the new public figure do for an encore?

Behind the ivy, where academic scientists are sequestered for their own good and the benefit of us all, it has long been customary to reward accomplishment by making an encore impossible. Fame, as understood in the world outside, is rare here, but professional recognition is not. The man who earns large amounts of recognition becomes a jewel in the university's diadem. The institution then makes an administrator of him. Even if he wanted to do any more work, he would now be unable to. The dinner jacket is not a laboratory smock; there are no microscopes, tissue-cultures, or linear accelerators on the podium where the distinguished guest lecturer stands; the meeting of departmental heads differs from the scientific seminar. So the administrator goes gray at the temples and full in the jowl and putters when he can in the small laboratory he reserved for himself when he crossed

[394]

over to the other side. If he had refused the promotion and stayed with the troops, would he have remained a prolific and/or a significant investigator? This is a moot question, which probably can be answered only in terms of specific individuals, and never with certainty. A prominent scientific thinker who has been chief of a large research establishment says, "Scientists are like poets or other self-opinionated types. Most of them are burned out after the age of forty. The only reason many of them don't booze themselves to death is that society pays them to waste time, absolving them of responsibility and blame. When I was running an institution my main administrative problem was how to get scientists aged forty or more out of the laboratories and into sinecures so that space could be made for more productive men." He jests—but in earnest.

During the field trial of his vaccine, Jonas Salk consented to go the traditional route. He agreed to become head of a new department of preventive medicine at the University of Pittsburgh School of Medicine. On April 12, 1955, when Alan Gregg advised him to do only that which made his heart leap, and when it became evident to Salk that his new prominence allowed him to make such choices freely, he recognized that an administrative position in a department of preventive medicine was not for him. He resolved to avoid it. "I was an immunologist," he says, "and my first interest was in experimental medicine—life, people, ideas. I wanted an unstructured situation where almost anything would be possible. The world was open. Knowledge was expanding. I wanted to be in the thick of things. I could not see myself voluntarily withdrawing to administration and lectureships at this stage of life."

One of Salk's friends at the medical school recalls, "During the honeymoon phase, when the vaccine was an accomplished fact and before there was any serious threat to the idea that here was the final conquest of a disease, Jonas began to feel that it would be nice to tool up for new, bigger, and better activities. To him this meant getting out of the cellar of the Municipal Hospital and setting up a decent establishment. At that point, of course, he was considered an invaluable asset by the trustees of the University. He wanted to do immunology and experimental

medicine in a free setting? Fine. He wanted to be Commonwealth
Professor of Experimental Medicine instead of Commonwealth
Professor of Preventive Medicine? Done. He would like a wide-
ranging biological institute of his own? Great. Local philan-
thropists bought the Municipal Hospital for $1,400,000 and
turned it over to the University for Salk's use. Everybody was
happy. In 1957, the hospital became Salk Hall, where Jonas
was to organize his new Institute for Experimental Medicine. It
never got off the ground."

The University was in rapid transition, of which the salient
feature was a new chancellor, Edward H. Litchfield, board chairman of Smith-Corona, the typewriter company. "Litchfield put
everything on a business basis," says Salk's friend. "He acquired
new buildings. He drew up tables of organization. He appointed
a profusion of vice-chancellors and deans. Vice-Chancellor in
Charge of Coca-Cola Machines. That sort of thing. He flew all
over the country in a private airplane. He was a big-time operator.
He fully recognized Jonas' value to the University, but he could
not permit him to function outside the established hierarchy, the
limits of which were clearly delineated on the new organizational
charts. Jonas could have a research institute in Salk Hall, but not
an autonomous one.

"Now, Jonas had proved to himself years earlier that he was
at his best in an amorphous setting. If his position required him
to be an organization man and sneeze in unison with everyone else
and live according to the dictates of a corporate wall chart, he
would be unable to function. His goal in life was to be left alone
to do his work. He felt he had earned this. So he got stubborn
about it. He and Litchfield negotiated and negotiated without
agreement and without making anything of the projected institute.
By 1958 Jonas kind of gave up on the idea as far as Pittsburgh
was concerned, and by the following year he knew pretty much
that he was going to leave altogether."

Distractions upset Salk. They rout him from his bench. A
friend of his once likened him to the author who cannot face the
typewriter in contentment until twelve sharpened pencils of identical length are at his elbow, the temperature of his office is exactly

seventy-three degrees, the dogs and children are exiled, and the telephone disconnected. To measure up to his admittedly perfectionist standards of work, Salk must feel free of every material, emotional, and spiritual deterrent. His position as a public figure has, of course, multiplied such deterrents and, not surprisingly, has worsened their effect on him. His unsettled position at the University preyed on his mind for years, obstructing him. His search for a new place to roost, his musings about what kind of a place it should be, his decision that it should be an independent institute in La Jolla, his negotiations with potential colleagues and employees and financial supporters and architects and builders and management experts and fund-raising counselors and lawyers consumed years of his time, during which he ran his laboratory as much by remote control as in person. Throughout these years of trying to situate for productive scientific work, the day never passed when he did not say to himself or to Basil O'Connor or some other handy sympathizer, "I've simply got to get back to the lab."

In May 1956 he wrote apologetically to Edward F. Stegen, a National Foundation publicist who had been begging him to send some updated biographical material:

> I hope you will not take personally my neglect of correspondence. . . . I have found that this past year has the kind of impact that is not unlike the effects of a war. I hardly know which part of the ruins should be cleared away first. I know how simple it would have been to have attended to this at the moment but this, and a thousand other things, seem to be put from place to place. I am now working through one of many piles and in the attached you will find suggestions for changes in the biographical information, to bring it up to date.

Here is what he sent Stegen as biographical information:

> The following represent addenda to the biographical background . . .

Parents—Father a manufacturer, now retired.

Brothers—Herman Salk, Palm Springs, California—veterinarian. Lee Salk, clinical psychologist, Allen Memorial Institute, McGill University, Montreal, Canada.

Children—All three a year older.

Awards—I suppose the Criss Award, and a long list of other awards, from a large number of organizations, all of which have not been catalogued as yet. Apart from these there is the Chevalier, French Legion of Honour; the Presidential Citation; the Medal of Congress; the Medal of Merit from the Governor of Pennsylvania; the honorary degrees—LL.D. from the College of the City of New York and University of Pittsburgh; Sc.D. from New York University, University of Michigan, and Roosevelt University.

I don't quite know what to add concerning recent events or the recent state of affairs other than that I am making every effort to return to a more normal activity and, especially, back to constructive work. This is made exceedingly difficult by all that needs to be done in those areas that had to be neglected this past year, particularly in relation to work, and because of the incessant requests to attend functions and to speak to both medical and lay groups. It has been necessary, so as not to offend the sensitivities of any and, particularly, to make it possible to create time to think and work, to decline the invitations of all, apart from going to receive the Presidential Citation and the Medal of Congress and the medal from the Governor of Pennsylvania and honorary degrees only from those universities and colleges with which I have some association.

I have attended none of the many functions at which honors of various kinds have been bestowed on me. I have attended only those medical and scientific meetings at which I have presented new information or such meetings as are related to the progress of the work we are doing. I have found a great many who have extended invitations most understanding and generous in their consideration.

The work we are doing at present is concerned with observations on the conditions necessary for producing immunity in every individual vaccinated, as well as in prolongation of immunizing effect. In addition to the work on polio, a num-

ber of other problems have been under investigation for
some time but at the present there is little that we wish to
comment upon.

An acquaintance asked him to join a group that proposed
to devise and foster new means of coping with the world's
population growth. The idea fascinated Salk. He would have
loved to join some of his intellectual equals in an effort to
prescribe remedies for a problem so vast, but he could not give
the time. He refused even to attend a conference, explaining in a
letter during 1957:

> I, too, can and do dream—I have found that in the realm
> of reality I must limit myself to those dreams that conceiv-
> ably I could fulfill, or else, in the attempt to do more, I
> would do less. At this very moment, when the tide has not
> yet receded, I cannot welcome a new wave that would keep
> me from resting after a long, hard swim; when what I want
> to do most is to place my feet on earth that does not move
> with the wind and the tide. The time that I have taken for
> thought about these matters has been borrowed—but the
> rate of interest is high. I cannot now afford to increase the
> burden further . . . and cannot yet indulge myself in the
> extra pleasure that a meeting would now afford. . . .

Whenever he could, and as best he could, he returned to the
laboratory and attempted to pick up the threads of his research.
Between 1955 and 1960, beleaguered and distracted though he
was, he managed to report new findings and new concepts which
elucidated the immunology of polio, explained the action of the
vaccine, and announced—perhaps decades before the fact—the
certain advent of the day when immunization with polyvalent
killed-virus preparations in infancy will protect man not only
against all known viral diseases but against whatever cancers,
degenerative afflictions, and other organic disturbances may be
the delayed results of cellular changes induced by supposedly
"minor" viral infection. While Salk was not "back to the lab" in

the true, Salkian, perfectionist sense, he was in the lab enough and did enough while there to hold his franchise.

In January 1957 he wrote to Henry Kumm, the National Foundation Director of Research:

> To focus your attention more sharply on our principal interest, I believe that the term "viral latency" best describes the biological phenomenon underlying the disease problems that interest us the most. . . . I am considering the possibility that certain acute processes . . . may also produce the preconditions for the emergence of disease symptoms later in life. For this reason, we shall continue our interest in those viruses that are capable of causing acute infections of the central nervous system as well as viruses that manifest the phenomenon of latency.*

A few days before writing this letter, Salk joined other scientists at the New York Academy of Sciences to help honor Basil O'Connor with a Conference on Cellular Biology, Nucleic Acids, and Viruses. He read a paper in which he explained his views of the importance of early immunization against all known viruses:

> It is known [he said] that severe hypertension and gastric or duodenal ulceration can occur as a result of certain types of damage to the CNS [central nervous system], and that poliovirus infections have produced such effects. It would be of interest to know whether or not poliovirus infections could cause . . . damage to brain-stem centers that might not result in clinically manifest symptoms until a later time, under circumstances of growth, aging, or other stresses. . . . One cannot escape reflection upon the possible consequences that might ensue as a result of the *prevention* of similar kinds of damage to other portions of the CNS infrequently

---

* The propensity of some microorganisms to remain in the system, in a state of parasitic equilibrium, for years at a time until something upsets the equilibrium and induces a flare-up. The best-known example is herpes simplex, the cold sore, but the phenomenon has been noticed in chicken pox, shingles, and certain respiratory infections. It also is known to occur in bacterial infections such as syphilis.

affected by the polioviruses. Many other viruses invade the
CNS. There are those that are known to be the cause of
common childhood diseases [such as measles and mumps],
and still other viruses are being recognized that can cause
CNS syndromes simulating nonparalytic poliomyelitis. What
persistent effects are caused by such viruses? Do such
viruses disappear from the CNS . . . or do some remain
latent . . . as seems to be the way for herpes simplex and of
varicella [chicken pox], each of which causes characteristic
lesions if reactivated under a variety of circumstances later
in life? Might there be a correlation between an earlier virus
infection and certain derangements of the nervous system
that might not be attributable either to hereditary factors,
or be totally explainable by environmental influences or by
life experiences alone? [A reference to mental and emotional
disturbances.] Might the latter, and the stresses involved
therein, bring out symptoms and signs of disease that might
not have been manifest if a primary poliovirus infection, or
some other of the many possible virus infections of the CNS
had not occurred? . . . Is it reasonable to consider the possibility that a mechanism might be operative in some virus
infections of the CNS that is analogous to the way in which
the spirochete of syphilis contributes to the causation of general paresis?

   . . . Should not parasitism of man by viruses be prevented
and would this not be particularly desirable for viruses that
can infect cells in the CNS, exerting effects far out of proportion to the number of cells involved?

   . . . Since it does seem that the presence of the antibody
barrier in the bloodstream could and does protect the
CNS from invasion, would it not be logical to contemplate,
therefore, the extension of studies in the direction of creating
an immunologic barrier against the invasion of the CNS by
all viruses? And, in time, as can be expected with the less
obvious consequences of poliovirus infection [referring to
the spinal curvatures and muscular weaknesses suffered by
persons who have had polio but may never have known it],
light might then be shed on the cause of disease that may be,
but is not now, attributed to the immediate or delayed effect
of the activity of some virus.

The speech was widely publicized by the press and caused more than slight ire among virologists of the live-vaccine school. In the first place, it was not so much a report as an exercise in conjecture. Worse, it implied the existence of good reasons to refrain from feeding live, infectious viral vaccines to people: If Salk's latency theory was at all valid, infectious vaccines might do more than immunize against one disease—they might set the stage for another disease.

Salk was fully aware of this implication and had every intention of running it to earth someday; even as he read the speech, however, his mind was roving in another direction—cancer. During 1956, Elsie Ward had discovered some peculiar cells of monkey-heart tissue growing in one of her laboratory flasks. What made the cells interesting was their ability to propagate themselves continuously. If polioviruses would grow on them and, having done so, were as antigenic as when grown in cultures of monkey-kidney tissue, enormous economies could be effected in vaccine production. Instead of having to sacrifice thousands of animals to obtain their kidneys, producers could cultivate these heart cells in vats and have an inexhaustible supply of tissue. Cells of this kind were not unknown but had not been used in vaccine production; they usually were of human origin and resembled human cancer cells too closely for comfortable use in the manufacture of vaccine. But here were monkey cells. Were they safe for humans? Were they safe for monkeys? Would they induce cancerous growths in the animals? Salk tested this. The cells seemed harmless to the creatures. Next step: humans. His first experimental subjects were cancer patients. The monkey cells tended to multiply in them. Sometimes tumors formed. But normal persons, whom Salk recruited at a nearby prison, rejected the cells. No tumors formed. The normal immunologic apparatus rejects any foreign protein, which is why it is not yet practical to transplant organs from one human being to another.

What defect in the immunologic equipment of cancer sufferers made their bodies receptive to implants of monkey-heart tissue? Did this same flaw account for the proliferation in them of cancer cells, which were aberrant products of their own tissue and should have been sloughed off as immunologically alien? Could molecular

studies reveal the nature of this phenomenon? If so, Jonas Salk
would learn something fundamental about cancer. He also would
learn something about organ transplantation.

   In scenarios, there is never any lasting problem about what
the new hero should do for an encore. The developer of the polio
vaccine bestows an anticancer preparation on the world. At fade-
out, he waves cheerily to the audience and hoists sail for the
next triumph. Because he knew that everyone was wondering about
his choice of encore and that the merest hint of his activities
would cause an unattractive hubbub, Jonas Salk became more
secretive than ever. Nobody at the University was able to pry
from him any but the most guarded generalizations about his
cancer experiments. In 1957, the daily procession of cancer
patients into his hospital aroused curiosity, which resulted in
newspaper reports of an impending "milestone." Salk announced
truthfully, "We are not now working on a cancer vaccine. We are
doing basic studies on the nature of cells. This has no practical
significance at this time."
   In his reports to the National Foundation, he was careful to
emphasize that the first purpose of his experiments with the cancer
patients was to determine whether monkey-heart tissue might be
safe for use in the growth of poliovirus. When pressed by reporters, the Foundation issued a formal declaration to that effect but
pointed out that there was nothing unusual about a man of Salk's
stature experimenting with cancer cells: ". . . there are many
similarities between cells that are sick because of virus invasion
and cells that are sick because of cancer."
   Occasionally, Salk confided to selected friends that he was
"onto something." In 1964, at least four years after he had
virtually abandoned the project to concentrate on the establishment of his Institute at La Jolla, he intimated to a friendly visitor
that other investigators of the immunology of cancer had still not
overtaken him. "I have lost time," he said, "but I have not lost
ground. I haven't spent nearly enough time in the lab, of course,
but I haven't been idle intellectually. Many thoughts have arisen.
Many concepts. When the Institute is finally operating smoothly

and I can return to the lab with a minimum of distraction, interesting things may happen. . . ."

Salk's failure to report new experimentation in recent years is,
of course, grist for his detractors, many of whom cite his silence
as evidence that the well is dry. "The laboratory can be a lonely
place when you have no ideas," says one celebrated medical
scientist. And another mentions the problem of the encore: "Jonas
outsmarted himself with that vaccine promotion. He painted himself into a corner. He became a god. From that point forward he
could not be wrong. He had to be right. Not only right, but
big. Now, how the hell can anybody do serious scientific investigation with a burden like that? There's no mystery about Jonas'
long silence, no mystery about his refusal to discuss his work
with people who used to be his friends. He's afraid."

Salk has heard all this. Some of it has even been said to his
face. He tries to be nonchalant. "I can only dance to the music
I hear," he says. "The incredible experience with the polio vaccine made it possible for me to think in terms of something beyond
preventive medicine, beyond a department of microbiology, beyond routine virus research. So a negative situation had led to
something positive. Which led in turn to something negative—the
promise of an institute of experimental medicine at Pittsburgh
collapsed. The possibility of bringing together leading workers in
diverse fields and freeing them to collaborate with each other
without departmental or other administrative barriers proved to
be a mirage. I thought for a while of simply returning to my
work, just as if nothing at all had happened, but the attraction of
the biological institute concept was too powerful. An institute of
the kind I had been discussing with Leo Szilard and Robert
Oppenheimer and other people with minds of scope seemed essential to the rapid progress of biology at this juncture in the
history of man. And Basil O'Connor agreed. He was ready to
support such an institute—ready, as usual, to provide the environment in which both of us could accomplish more than could
otherwise be accomplished. So you might say that this was the
music I heard and that it was more compelling than anything else
in life. And, yes, it took me away from my lab. But in getting
away from my lab, I have been able to help create not just a new

lab but a dynamic new setting—and not just for myself but for some of the most productive and imaginative biological scientists in the world. I find it interesting that the people who pooh-pooh the idea of the Institute and say that I should have stayed in my lab at Pittsburgh are often the same people who had no particular regard for the work I did at Pittsburgh."

In his prophetic speech to the 1957 Conference on Cellular Biology, Nucleic Acids, and Viruses in New York, he did not mention an institute, but explained why he thought conventional modes of biological investigation were wanting:

"The time is drawing to a close when one can hope to find full understanding of many more disease processes through one discipline alone. Full understanding . . . of the properties and interaction of viruses and of cells, and the role of the organism of which these are a part, is far from complete. There are many viewpoints and areas of interest and there are differences in techniques used by the physicist, the chemist, the biologist, the physician, and the epidemiologist. Where cause and effect relationships are not clearly apparent, new insights come either from probing more deeply or from looking at the familiar from the unfamiliar viewpoint of another discipline."

The dynamics of biological research has moved many of its more creative practitioners from the observation and classification of organisms to the study of cells and molecules. Genetics has departed from its former preoccupation with the gross characteristics of fruit flies. It now ponders the physicochemical events that determine why and how one assemblage of atoms is the cell of a fruit fly and another the cell of a man. In these explorations —at what scientists themselves admit is the threshold of life's deepest secrets—physicists and chemists lead the way. The traditional distinctions between physics and chemistry have vanished in the light of new knowledge and new techniques. So have the barriers between the physical sciences and biology. The skills of chemistry and physics are indispensable to and, by now, scarcely distinguishable from those of modern biology. Only through merging its forces by tearing down the walls that separate them can science hope to proceed rapidly toward mastery of the submicroscopic processes that determine and control the differences among forms of life—or between life and nonlife, or health and disease, or youth and age.

Jonas Salk resolved to encourage cross-fertilization of the sciences by creating an environment favorable to collaborative interchange among men able, as he says, to "distinguish the relevant from the less so." The Institute that he sought to establish at Pittsburgh and that he finally built at La Jolla is therefore unique. Its goals, its organizational concepts, and, above all, the members of its faculty were chosen with the present and the future of biology in mind. The significance of this is made plain by Warren Weaver, Chairman of the Board of Trustees of the Salk Institute, Vice-President of the Alfred P. Sloan Foundation, and former Vice-President for the Natural and Medical Sciences of the Rockefeller Foundation. Weaver, an engineer, mathematician, and theoretical physicist noted for contributions to electrodynamics and the theory of probability, has been for years (not at all contradictorily) a world leader in the promulgation and support of molecular biology and genetics. He says, "The timing of the creation of this Institute is exactly right. This doesn't often happen in history. We are just at that moment in the liberation of biology when an institution of this sort, of this quality, with this kind of vision ought to be created. I think our timing is perfect.

"The whole structure of educational and research organization in our country, if I am not completely wrong about it, requires a profound modernization. It's rather ridiculous that the full organizational structure of a modern university differs fantastically little from the organization of the University of Paris five hundred years ago. Well now, has nothing happened to knowledge in five hundred years? Have we not advanced in a way that requires a different organizational structure in our universities and colleges and in our research institutes?

"I think it's very difficult to make the necessary experimental changes within the traditional institutions. They inherit so much

from the past—from departmentalization, for example. I used
to be the chairman of a department and I know how they are
handled. The chairman of a department has a *budget* and this
belongs to him; he has a certain number of professorships assigned
to him. Is he going to give these away to other fields that are
intermediate fields? Well, you can bet that he's not going to do so!

"And as long as this system exists, I don't see any real chance
of welding together the whole of science into a unified force
that will really affect the future of man. I think you've got to
start in some other way.

"The Salk Institute carries with it none of these impediments
of the past. There are no departments in the old classical sense.
If you would look at the records of the men who are members of
the staff, you would be surprised and perhaps almost shocked to
read what they have been and what they now are. A very considerable number of them started out by being trained in the
physical sciences—and then they saw the light and moved over
into the biological sciences. And, of course, essential in the
structure of the Institute from the very beginning are scientists
who are interested not only in science but in the whole range of
the humanities, the creative arts, the whole artistic and esthetic
and philosophical side of man's life."

Here, in the substance of the Institute's work, more than in
the organizational structure that promised to expedite the work,
lay the deepest interest of Salk and the Institute's principal supporter, Basil O'Connor. O'Connor had such goals in mind even
before he and Salk became friends. At the Second International
Poliomyelitis Conference in Copenhagen, during September 1951,
O'Connor said: "Scientists never cease to be awed by the fundamental simplicity of the universe. Its orderly arrangement has permitted men of perception to determine and translate many of the
laws of nature and duplicate natural phenomena in the laboratory.

". . . The same orderliness is not evident in human nature. Man
does not always act in a reasonable manner. He has been given the
gift of free will. And he is subject to his emotions, which defy prediction. Man not only fails in his understanding of man, he usually
fails to understand himself. What is worse, before he reaches the

age at which he has an opportunity to exercise his reason, he has been subject to prejudices, insecurity, privation, illness, and unfortunate experiences over which he has no control, but all of which influence his attitude toward other men and his ultimate role in society."

To O'Connor and Salk alike, the promise of molecular biology transcends the prevention or cure of disease. As Pierre Charron wrote in 1601, "The true science and the true study of man is man." Salk concurs. He calls the Institute "an assault on the unreasonableness of life." In 1961, he told an audience at the Massachusetts Institute of Technology: "I find it difficult to dismiss the idea that the basic question of the present time, perhaps underlying all others, is a biological one and concerns our understanding of the nature of man.

"Biologists have developed a degree of understanding of their subject that makes possible the interpretation of, or speculation about, many aspects of human life. Many of the facts of biology have been assembled into structures of ideas . . . on the basis of which man might develop a more reasonable and realistic view of himself and of his fellowman."

In another speech he said:

"It was inevitable that life itself would someday become one of man's principal interests and outstanding concerns. While man has long been conscious of the different manifestations and effects of life, only in relatively recent times can it be said that he has begun to discover and discern the nature of the organization and processes of life. The remarkable recent advances in understanding the structure and function of the minutest elements of living material have not only fired man's imagination and increased his understanding of life but have put almost within his reach means of great power, which will also subject him to the greatest test yet of his sense of responsibility. He will soon have to make judgments of the greatest moment that could be for good or for bad. Soon again he will be at his own mercy; this time not with respect to atomic power but with respect to the control that he may ultimately be able to exert over the material substance of life, of which he himself is made and, therefore, over the life of future generations. Will he use this knowledge and this power wisely? . . .

"Why, you might ask, am I now interested in such a pursuit, and why am I not concentrating immediately and exclusively on studies oriented toward preventing or curing disease? I will attempt to answer this and other questions which I have had to ask myself. First, I will say that I was trained as a physician. In the course of my scientific career I have, from time to time, become absorbed in questions that have not had an orientation toward . . . diseases. When I have thought about the magnitude of man's many problems, I recall the feelings that have accompanied the tendency to concern myself with such basic questions in biology as could affect the human condition and for which new knowledge was necessary. . . . I confess my sensitivity to suffering and a desire to reduce it; I am sensitive to discontent, unhappiness, and destructiveness in life, and would like to see these reduced, too. It is my feeling that this can best be accomplished by a scientific approach essentially similar to that employed in the solution of other complex problems in biology. Through the development of basic understanding in biology, necessary preventives and cures will come wherever possible. The need man has is for the development of the means for prevention of those ills in the human condition that arise from active processes of disease, from active frustration of man's potential, or from its passive nonfulfillment. When we speak of man's potential, we consider man as a biological organism, and it is his potential in body and in mind of which we speak."

In other speeches he has said, "Will not fundamental knowledge about the human mind, which now seems accessible, permit the life sciences to present man with a new and comprehensible view of his own nature? Will this not lead to the acceptance of new, universal human values?"

Warren Weaver again: "I have never in my life had anything to do with a development that I think is as important as the development of the Salk Institute for Biological Studies. I think that in terms of science and in terms of the total life of man it is the most important development that I have ever known."

Basil O'Connor says, "Jonas had a little list of the people he wanted to work with at the Institute. He didn't stop flying back and forth to Europe and negotiating and sweating and worrying and writing letters and modifying organizational details until he had corraled eight of the ten men on the list. I used to say to him, 'For God's sake, Jonas, does it have to be these people and no other? Are these the only scientists on earth? Does the future of the human race depend on these few people?' But he insisted that these individuals, working under the same roof, would be uniquely compatible with each other, complementing each other, inspiring each other, getting more done in that way than they could separately, and getting more done than any other group could. He called them a 'critical mass' from which a chain reaction would come. He wore himself to a frazzle and he wore my patience to the bone, but as usual he ended with what he felt was necessary. He got his men. Because he got them, the rate of discovery in biological science is going to accelerate. I'm sure of it."

When the Salk Institute for Biological Studies began operations in temporary quarters in 1963, the following scientists were on its faculty:

Jacob Bronowski, distinguished British mathematician-philosopher, wrote the celebrated report "Effect of the Atomic Bombs at Hiroshima and Nagasaki," and later became Director-General of Process Development of the National Coal Board of Great Britain. At the Massachusetts Institute of Technology, he was both a professor of physics and a professor of literature. His books, *The Common Sense of Science* and *Science and Human Values,* are classic elucidations of the role of science.

Melvin Cohn, a New York immunochemist and biophysicist, worked at the Pasteur Institute for several years and in 1956 received the Eli Lilly Award in bacteriology from the Society of American Bacteriologists. His primary interests recently have been studies of antibody formation, enzymes, and the genetics of protein synthesis.

Francis H. C. Crick, British physicist and chemist, turned to molecular biology after contributing to the wartime development of radar and magnetic mines. In 1962 he shared a Nobel prize with J. D. Watson and M. H. F. Wilkins for their discovery of the molecular structure of the basic genetic material, desoxyribonucleic acid (DNA). Crick has recently been studying the brain.

Renato Dulbecco, a physician, bacteriologist, virologist, geneticist, and physicist, won a Lasker Award in 1964 for demonstrating that viruses can cause cancerous changes without actually multiplying in the cells that they corrupt. His plaque technique of virus cultivation paved the way for Albert Sabin's polio vaccine.

Edwin Lennox, a former theoretical physicist with the Manhattan Project, contributed significantly to quantum electrodynamics and neutron physics and then became a microbiologist. He worked with Cohn at the Pasteur Institute and, at this writing, is collaborating with him on studies of antibody formation.

Jacques Monod was Chief of the Cellular Biochemistry Service at the Pasteur Institute and Professor of Biochemistry at the Sorbonne. Monod is celebrated for his studies of protein synthesis and bacterial adaptation to environmental change.

Leo Szilard, the great genius of theoretical and nuclear physics, was a pioneer of computer theory, patented the idea of the cyclotron, collaborated with Enrico Fermi on the world's first self-sustaining nuclear chain reaction, was instrumental in alerting Franklin D. Roosevelt to the military possibilities of nuclear fission, and spent the last years of his life struggling against the sociopolitical consequences of the atomic bomb. He had been talking to Salk about an institute since 1956 ("His role in life was to pollinate, like a bee," says Salk), and became a resident Fellow at La Jolla in 1964, a few months before he died. At the end he was at work on characteristically advanced theories bearing on the nature of memory, aging, genetic mutation, and antibody formation.

Salk and Warren Weaver also are Fellows of the Institute. In September 1964 they were joined by Dr. Leslie E. Orgel, of Cambridge University, a brilliant worker in theoretical chemistry, who had become interested in the simple chemical reactions presumed to have produced the small molecules essential for the origin of life.

As O'Connor indicates, Salk had no easy time persuading these scientists that his plans were more than a pipe dream. Above all, each of them had to be convinced that, even if Salk were able to construct this ideal scientific environment, the Institute would remain ideal under his leadership. The odor of Ann Arbor had permeated every corner of science. Salk was suspect.

"I don't know why we are the way we are," he wrote to O'Connor at a time of anguish. "I have to keep trying to realize that, except for a feeling of partnership with you in this undertaking, I am responsible to no one and consequently should approach this new opportunity with the anticipation of pleasure at being able to do, with the greatest freedom, something that is given to few to do. This has been the story of your life—one major contribution after another. I would like for us to get over, as quickly as we can, the feeling of despair that we've never done anything and that we're deceiving ourselves in what we're now trying to do. . . . I know we will quickly be on top of a rapidly growing and rewarding creation. The idea of having a place where science and philosophy and human values and the significant in life are artistically combined in a new synthesis that will live and grow is worth the fight. . . ."

It took him months, and in some cases years, to convince the others that he did not regard the Institute as a monument to himself, and that the freedom he sought for himself there would be equally accessible to his colleagues. And so they finally joined him. Their work together began. And the Institute rose out of the ground, a soaring edifice, a monument to the aspirations of man.

There is gray in Jonas Salk's hair. His skin is tan from the Southern California sun. His waist has thickened. Persons who have not seen him in years and have abandoned hope of ever hearing from him again ask whether he has changed inwardly. His steadfast secretary, Lorraine Friedman, has a good answer: "How in the world would anyone expect him to go through what he did and be the same as when he started? Nobody else was the same. The American people weren't the same—they now had a vaccine. Basil O'Connor wasn't the same—he had proved a point. Why should Doctor Salk be the only one?"

Someone else who knows him well says, "He hasn't changed. He's just more so. He still hates to be told what to do. He still can't stand being wrong. He still hates to antagonize people. He still hates to face unpleasantness head on. He still believes that everything will turn out his way—the right way, the perfect way—in the end, and he still ducks, swerves, and does Immelmann turns while waiting for opposition to expend itself. His susceptibility to pain remains limitless, but so does his ability to endure and outlive it."

A present colleague says, "Some of these things aren't easy to take or easy to understand. But this is the way Jonas is. The Institute is the blood of his blood and the soul of his soul. It is his life. He wants it to be just right in every particular. His definition of 'right' may vary from yours or mine, of course, and so may his notion of how to achieve 'right.' But we cherish him. He is the only man in the world who could have put this Institute together. He is the catalyst. And the reasons why he has given years of his life to it are good reasons. The scientific and social issues which interest him are important. All-important."

And Jonas Salk says, "I couldn't possibly have become a member of this Institute, you know, if I hadn't organized it myself."

Not very long ago, Lorraine Friedman said in a letter, "Dr. Salk is back in the lab and happy as a lark to be there."

I asked him about this and he answered, "Interesting things are happening. Life goes on. . . ."

Author's Note

JONAS SALK IS TOO YOUNG AND ACTIVE TO BE AN APPROPRIATE subject for a formal biography. His new triumph, the Institute for Biological Studies, is in its earliest stages. His careers as laboratory worker and scientific organizer-philosopher are not yet at zenith. His greatest contributions lie ahead. Nevertheless, this is a somewhat biographical book. For Salk's sake, and my own, I should like to emphasize that he neither sought nor was granted an opportunity to censor the manuscript. He did not see it until it was in print. The book is my fault, not his.

He submitted to interviews only after years of merciless badgering. The interviews took three weeks and left both of us limp. I had imposed cruelly on his time, his attention, and his emotional resources. In defense, he had frustrated me by electing himself superintendent of relevance and taste, limiting our conversations to subjects that he thought suitable. He seldom talked about himself except in terms of his work. He preferred on most occasions to discuss concepts rather than people or events.

In one of our first talks, I tried to question him about his school years, hoping to unearth the origins of his scientific outlook.

"I was quite sure that you would probably want to do something like that," he said uncomfortably. "I thought about it just briefly this morning and I feel that the best that could be accomplished, the best approach to this problem, to this question, is to treat it as one treats a scientific problem. . . ."

"I'd like to start," I said. "You went to Townsend Harris. . . . You took physics. There were no other science courses."

[415]

"Yes," he said. "Everybody took that."

"You took physics, and that was all," I encouraged.

"I tell you," he said, "this line of questioning does not excite me at this point."

"I don't know whether this line of questioning is as apparent as you think it is," I replied. "You were talking earlier about the killed-virus principle. I just want to get to the roots of that. I have nothing else in mind."

"I understand that, but you are jumping to a point instead of reaching a point," he objected.

"I want to *find* a starting point," I said.

"Yes," he said, "and this we can do only in retrospect. I think you'll discern a starting point. But I can't find it for you."

"I see," I said, unaware that I had asked him to find a starting point for me. "Well, why did you go to medical school?"

"That's another matter," he answered. "You see, that's another question, and in asking that question you might find the answer to this other question."

"That's why I asked it," I confessed.

"I'm also saying that one has to deal with these things obliquely, and you'll find them by serendipity," he said. "You'll pick them up, but not by direct confrontation. . . ."

"Tell me what happened," I begged.

"Well, in relation to what?'" he asked. "I think we will find the generalizations, or the examples for the generalizations, by examining certain details. Now, what details should we be exploring and discussing at this time? I think it is too early at this stage of our discussion to deal with that period of time."

"Okay," I said.

"Because that ought to come as the preface—last," he said.

It never came at all. Even if one put the preface last and the epilogue first and allowed the interviewee to ask and answer his own questions, vast areas were taboo. As he had warned, serendipity was the only hope. When he caught me infiltrating terrain that he had staked out as too personal or as irrelevant to his vision of what my work should encompass, his alarm and displeasure were noticeable. His primary wish was that I grasp the rudiments of immunological theory, so that I might report his work and his views ungarbled. His secondary wish, with which the first intertwined, was that I go home as soon as possible and leave him alone. At first he approached these goals gingerly, suggesting that my burden was too heavy and my pace too arduous for my good. I should leave La Jolla for a few months, he said, to ruminate and digest the material I had obtained there. I should return at an unspecified date for a cram course in immunology. I declined to go. I was afraid he would find my absence so salubrious that he would never see me again. I said that I had a more efficient idea. I would prolong my stay, I said. I would withdraw to the library of the Institute and study immunology until I had learned enough to satisfy him. We could then resume our chats. He was livid. He gave me armloads of books and papers to read. Three days later I returned for a quiz, which I passed.

He was quite pleased. But when I resumed my questioning, he blew up. He no longer was oblique. He no longer spoke of my burdens but of his. "I can't stand any more of this," he said. Neither could I. We agreed to meet twice more, to discuss the live-virus vaccine controversy. And we did. I could see that he regretted his anger, an emotion he seldom reveals to anyone. And I regretted having tortured him.

During my weeks with him, I became convinced of the accuracy of an impression I had acquired at earlier meetings in the East. The man becomes absolutely conscience-stricken when he thinks he is misusing his energy. He decides what should be done for the good of whatever scientific project happens to be uppermost in his considerations, and he then sets forth to do it. When people or events interfere, which happens all the time, his remorse surpasses his annoyance. He feels that he is misappropriating himself, doing disservice to science and to the world. If he were an ordinary man, this attitude could be interpreted as a kind of vanity. But Salk's responsibilities are unique. They are discharged in an environment for which few other human beings qualify. Salk calls it "the growing tip of advancing knowledge." If he sometimes behaves as if what is good for Salk is good for the world, he has reason to do so.

I would not like to spend the rest of my life with him and do not expect to be invited. But I consider him a man of authentic greatness. I hope this book conveys a sense of that.

The information about Salk's background, youth, and early manhood was supplied by relatives, friends, classmates, and former neighbors. For much of what I know about the history of polio and virology I am indebted to Dr. Theodore E. Boyd, of the National Foundation. I picked his brains for days and cribbed shamelessly from a history he is writing. I thank Mr. Basil O'Connor for sitting through thirteen lively interviews and for helping to open many doors. I thank Dr. Saul Benison, of Brandeis University, who is preparing a formal history of the Foundation. His recorded interviews with Tom Rivers, which he plans to publish, supplied me with many insights which, if not for Dr. Benison's labors, might have died with Tom. I also thank Gabriel Stickle, of the Foundation, for nursing me through my ignorance of statistical principles.

Among the scores of scientists, physicians, government officials, health officers, journalists, nurses, laboratory technicians, and miscellaneous plain folk I consulted in my eighteen months of research, many are quoted by name. Others prefer to remain anonymous. I thank them all. Special thanks are due John Troan, of the Scripps-Howard Newspaper Alliance; Natalie Paine, of the Columbia Broadcasting System; and Michael O'Connor, of *The San Diego Union,* for documents and clippings of great value. Extra-special thanks go to Drs. David Bodian and Joel Elkes, of Johns Hopkins University; the Honorable David L. Bazelon, Chief Judge of the United States Court of Appeals; Dr. and Mrs. Leslie A. Falk, of Pittsburgh; and Dr. Warren Weaver, Vice-President of the Alfred P. Sloan Foundation, each of whom helped me understand more about Salk the man and Salk the scientist than I might have been able to figure out for myself.

I am grateful also to Albert Q. Maisel, for insisting years ago that there was a story in the National Foundation. Mr. and Mrs. Stephan H. Alex, of Washington; the Honorable Helen R. Cobb, of San Diego; Dr. and Mrs. Harry M. Weaver; Lucile Cochran,

R.N., of the Watson Home; and Dr. and Mrs. Melvin Cohn, Mr. and Mrs. William Glazier, and Mr. and Mrs. Bernard Conal, of La Jolla, all befriended the wayfarer and have his lasting thanks.

It is customary to thank one's family for standing by during the ordeal, but I think this particular ordeal calls for an apology to Gladys, Nancy, and Johnny Carter. No apologies to Herbert M. Alexander and Bucklin Moon, of Trident Press, but thanks. And many thanks to Chuck Cameron, for salvaging some interview tapes I had almost ruined, and to Carolyn Hoff, for her expert editorial and secretarial assistance.

Index

Adams, Sherman, 294
Albert Einstein College of Medicine, 263
Alex, Stephan H., 292–93
Allegheny County Medical Society, 350, 389, 390
Allen, George E., 16
Allman, Dr. David B., 348
Amarillo, Texas, 290
American Academy of General Practice, 347
American Academy of Pediatrics, 193, 201, 347
American Journal of Public Health, 257
American Legion, 228, 349
American Medical Association: Council on Drugs, 371, 372, 377; Cutter incident, 333; fees, 302; House of Delegates, 244–45, 371, 372, 374–76, 378; *Journal*, 151, 154–55, 156, 158, 163, 164, 165, 166, 167, 246, 257, 262, 354, 370–71, 374; Murdock and, 149, 171, 176, 236; Sabin and, 179, 180; Sabin vaccine, 341, 354, 370–72, 376–78, 381, 384; Salk vaccine, 244–45, 256, 259–60,

292, 344–47, 348–49, 350, 368, 370–71, 376–79
American Public Health Association, 23, 199, 256
American Society for the Study of High Blood Pressure, 52
American Red Cross, 27, 197, 224, 226
American Therapeutic Society, 293
Archimedes, 72
Aristotle, 356
Armed Forces Epidemiological Board, 46, 56
Armed Forces Influenza Commission, 48, 51, 69
Armstrong, Dr. Charles, 21, 62–63, 81
Army Medical Center 171
Army Medical Corps, 69
Army Specialized Training Program, 49
Arsenal Elementary School, Pittsburg, 317–18
Associated Press, 264
Association for Research in Nervous and Mental Disease, 251, 263
Australia, 368

Avery, Dr. Oswald T., 34, 35, 249
Aycock, Dr. W. Lloyd, 63

Bailey, Dr. Mary Lynch, 217, 218
Barber, Dr. Bernard, 88
Barnard College, 88
Barrows, Raymond, 149
Baroian, Dr. O. V., 362, 363
Bauer, Louis H., 149
Bazeley, Percival L., 141, 212, 288
Bell, Joseph, 176, 183, 184, 185, 186, 187, 193, 194, 202
Benison, Dr. Saul, 90, 144, 176
Bennett, Byron L., 69–70, 212, 214, 279, 280
Berg, Roland H., 16, 166
Bergen County, N. J., 388
Berlin, 365
Bethel Park, Pa., 389
Billings, Josh, 356
Biological sciences, future of, 405–8
Biologics Control Laboratory, see Laboratory of Biologics Control
Birthday Ball, 13–14, 18, 19, 20, 21, 23, 24
Blakeslee, Alton, 272
Blasingame, Dr. F. J. L., 368
Blumenthal, George, 37
Boisen, Morton, 218
Bodian, Dr. David, 124, 174, 246, 299: Cutter incident, 317, 318, 319, 323, 328, 330, 333, 334; Immunization Committee, 125, 175, 195; polio research, 59, 63, 64, 80, 100, 108, 109, 112, 132, 133–34; Sabin vaccine, 262, 366, 384–85; Salk vaccine, 221, 222, 225, 234–35, 250
Boston, 8
Boyd, Dr. Theodore E., 58, 132, 278
Brahe, Tycho, 88
Brandeis University, 90
Brando, Marlon, 281
Brockman strain, 110, 111

Brodie, Dr. Maurice, 20, 21–22, 23, 24, 58, 63, 69, 129, 197
Bronk, Detlev W., 257–58, 273
Bronowski, Jacob, 410
Bulletin of the Johns Hokpins Hospital, 384
Burnet, Sir Macfarlane, 60, 141
Burney, Dr. Leroy E., 366, 368, 370–71, 379
Byoir, Carl, 13

California, University of, 52, 102
California State Department of Public Health, 310, 317
Canada, 385
Cancer, 399, 402, 403
Cannan, Dr. R. Keith, 32, 35
Cant, Gilbert, 216
Cantor, Eddie, 16
Carlton Hotel, 236
Celebrezze, Anthony J., 383
Census, United States Bureau of, 243
Charles Pfizer & Company, Inc., 354, 367, 372, 373, 386
Charron, Pierre, 408
Chase, Merrill, 218
Chemistry, 405
Chemotherapy, polio, 58–59
Chicago, Ill., 347
Chicago Medical Society, 302
Chicken pox, 60, 400, 401
Children's Hospital, Cincinnati, 63
Chillicothe reformatory, 357
Chumakov, Mikhail P., 359, 361, 362
Cincinnati Times-Sun, 337
City College, see College of the City of New York
Clayton, William, 16
Cochran, Lucille, 137–38, 139, 279
Cohn, Melvin, 410
Cohn, Victor, 225
Cold sores, 400, 401

Coleman, Thomas J., 285–87, 289, 293–94, 317
Colfax School, 220
College of the City of New York, 30, 31, 290, 291, 398
Columbia Broadcasting System, 157
Columbia University, 149
Common Sense of Science, The, 410
Communicable Disease Center, Atlanta, 309, 316, 368
Conference on Cellular Biology, Nucleic Acids and Viruses, 400, 405
Congress, vaccine investigations by, 306, 311, 327, 336, 367
Congressional Medal for Distinguished Civilian Service, 2, 291, 296, 398
Connaught Laboratories, 125, 278
Consistency principle, 225–26, 314, 319, 324, 329, 330, 332, 334
Copenhagen, University of, 113
Copernicus, Nicholas, 88
Coughlan, Robert, 166, 216
Covert, Cathy, 271, 272
Cox, Dr. Herald, 63, 109, 143, 172, 357, 364, 365
Cox vaccine, 365, 367
Crick, Francis H. C., 410–11
Criss Award, 290, 292, 398
Culver, Bettyann, 118
Cutter, Dr. Robert K., 303–4
Cutter Laboratories, 208, 216, 217, 242, 303–4; defective vaccine, 309–38, 340, 344, 358, 383, 390
Czechoslovakia, 341, 378

Dade County, Fla., 365
Darwin, Charles, 3
de Kruif, Paul, 18, 19, 21–22, 23, 24, 231, 233
Denmark, 378
Depression (1929–39), 31–32
Des Moines epidemic, 353
Detroit, Mich., 352–53

Dick, George, 358
Diphtheria, 33–34, 214, 380
Distemper, 102
Division of Biologics Standards, 334, 366
Doherty, Henry L., 13, 14, 18
Douglas, Paul H., 306–7
Ducas, Dorothy, 180, 229–30, 235, 236, 269
Dulbecco, Renato, 248, 358, 411

Editor and Publisher, 271
Eggs, 98, 100, 103
Egypt, 8
Eisenhower, Dwight D., 268, 291, 293, 294–95, 296, 303, 308
Eisenhower Administration, 208, 303, 311, 312, 344
Eli Lilly, 198, 199, 208, 211, 217, 221–22, 242, 257, 321, 327
Eli Lilly Award, 410
Eliot, Dr. Martha M., 302
Emerson, Haven, 10, 11
Emerson, Ralph Waldo, 292
Encephalitis, 102, 151, 214
Encephalomyelitis, 75
Enders, Dr. John F., 86–87, 88–90, 92, 112, 117, 144, 248: distemper, 102; field trial evaluation, 260, 261; Immunization Committee, 125, 126; Nobel prize, 60, 299; Salk vaccine, 144, 145–46, 317, 319, 320, 323, 335, 336; Second Polio Congress, 113, 114–18; Third Polio Conference, 246; tissue culture, 60, 86–94, 96, 105–6, 114–15, 116, 128, 135, 161, 185, 188, 198, 264, 299
Epidemics: encephalitis, 102; influenza, 45, 50, 51; polio, 65, 104, 347, 352-53
Essex County, N. J., 388
Estonia, 364
Evans, Dr. Charles A., 60, 87, 116, 171

Fame, nature of scientific, 3, 50, 394–95
Family and Children's Service, 45
Faraday, Michael, 88
Fees, physicians', 302, 305
Fermi, Enrico, 411
Field, Marshall, 16
Filtration, 330, 331
Fitzgerald, Dr. Rufus H., 149, 279
Flexner, Simon, 9, 19, 85–86
Ford, Edsel, 16
Formalin-inactivated vaccines, 47, 85, 86, 108, 123–25, 129, 130, 135, 142, 145, 172, 184, 185, 199, 200, 209, 210, 218, 222, 247, 249, 331
Forrestal, James V., Jr., 16
Fort Custer, 48
Fort Dix, 94, 101, 141
Francis, Dr. Thomas, Jr., 174: Cutter incident, 312, 316, 317, 319, 328, 336; Immunization Committee, 125, 128; influenza research, 35, 42, 44, 45, 46–49, 351; Michigan, University of, 45–46; New York University, 34–36, 37, 38, 39, 200; polio research, 107; Rockefeller Institute, 34–35; Salk and, 37, 38–39, 41, 42–43, 44, 50, 51, 53, 63, 277–78, 281, 282; Salk vaccine trial, 6, 171, 202–6, 218, 231, 238–61, 263, 266–67, 268, 270–72, 274–78, 283, 358, 361; viral theories, 47, 85, 128, 142, 195, 355, 356
Francis report, 205, 255, 256, 266, 267, 268–69, 271, 274–77
Franklin County, Ga., 388
Freeman, Ruth, 224
Friedman, Lorraine, 70–71, 217, 218, 289, 412
Frost, Ernest M., 168

Galileo, 340
Gallup poll, 268

Gamma globulin, 98, 100, 102, 103, 104, 105, 108–9, 131–32, 142, 151, 160, 242, 317
Gard, Dr. Sven, 248–49, 299
Gebhardt, Louis P., 63, 78, 329
Geiger, Jack, 273
General Federation of Women's Clubs, 228
Gibran, Kahlil, 173
Glasser, Melvin A., 226, 227–28, 233
Gobel, George, 290
Goodpasture, Ernest, 42, 43, 44
Green, Dr. Robert G., 59–60
Greenbrier Hotel, 187, 188, 190
Hampden County, Mass., 388
Gregg, Dr. Alan, 149, 273–74, 283, 395
Gudakunst, Dr. Don W., 26, 42, 43, 44, 56, 63

Haag, Dr. Harvey B., 293
Haas, Dr. Victor, 309, 312, 313
Habel, Dr. Karl, 309, 313, 314
Hammon, Dr. William McDowell, 63, 101, 102, 103, 104, 105, 108, 109, 125, 132, 135, 142, 175, 246, 282, 312, 317, 319, 335, 336, 366
Hampden County, Mass., 388
Hardeeville, S. C., 73
Harkness, Edward, 24
Harriman, Averell, 16
Harris County Medical Society, 348
Harvard University, 63
Hatcher, Dr. Harland W., 258
Hayes, Helen, 84
Heidelberger, 249
Heine, Jakob, 8
Health, Education and Welfare, Department of, 208, 302, 303, 305, 311, 325, 383, 391
Hepatitis, 148, 149, 356
"Herd" effect, 50, 351–52, 377

Hershey, Pa., 108, 109, 110–11, 142, 144, 147
Hickey, Margaret A., 149, 240
Hill, Bradford, 203
Hippocrates, 191–92
Hirst, George K., 47
Hitler, Adolf, 32
Hobby, Oveta Culp, 282, 293, 294, 302, 303, 304, 306, 311, 316
Hoke, Dr. Michael, 14, 18
Hook, Arnold, 164
Hooper Foundation, 102
Horsfall, Frank, 188
Horstmann, Dorothy M., 59, 132, 133, 363
Hospital facilities for polio, 11, 18
Houston, Tex., 104
Howe, Howard A., 59, 108, 109, 111, 112, 125, 129, 142, 143, 144, 171
Hudson County, N. J., 388
Hungary, 341, 378
Hunter Award, Oscar B., 293
Hyperreactivity of vaccine, 183, 247, 280–81

Illinois Department of Public Health, 312
Illinois Medical Society, 302
Immunization Committee, see National Foundation for Infantile Paralysis
Influenza, 56, 85, 214, 252: Francis, 35, 42, 44, 45, 46–49, 351; Salk, 38–39, 51, 61, 69, 94, 98, 101, 141, 164, 166, 167, 172
Institute for Experimental Medicine, Pittsburgh, 396
Insurance for laboratory workers, 75–76
International Congress on Microbiology, 202
International News Service, 273

Jackson, Andrew, 12, 16
James, William, 72
Jenner, Edward, 175, 214, 249
Jewish Child Care Association of New York, 40
Jews, 42, 213
Johns Hopkins University, 63, 79, 85, 100, 108, 145, 171, 202, 236
Johnson Samuel, 150
Junior Chamber of Commerce, 350

Kansas, University of, 63
Kansas City epidemic, 353
Karaganda, 363
Karolinska Institutet, 299
Kaye, Danny, 290
Kazakhstan, 363
Kefauver, Estes, 327
Kelvin, Lord, 88
Kennedy Administration, 372
Kerr, Randy, 237
Kessel, John F., 63, 64, 78, 110, 111
Kidney disease, 210, 234, 250
Kirkpatrick, William F., 139
Knight, Goodwin, 286
Kodlin, Dr. Dankward, 213
Kolmer, Dr. John A., 22–23, 58, 63, 69, 154, 197
Koprowski, Dr. Hilary, 97, 99, 109–11, 132, 143, 249, 354–55, 357, 358, 364–65
Korns, Dr. Robert F., 218
Kramer, Dr. Sidney, 131
Krieger, Jane, 291, 322, 335
Kuhn, Thomas, 88
Kumm, Henry, 278, 400

Laboratory of Biologics Control, 184, 207, 209, 211, 221, 222, 234, 242, 251, 254, 309, 311, 314, 316, 318, 319, 320, 328, 329, 333
Ladies' Home Journal, The, 149, 240
Landsteiner, Karl, 9, 19

Langmuir, Dr. Alexander D., 309, 310, 312, 316, 318, 319, 366
Lansing strain, 80, 111, 114, 129
Larson, Dr. Carl, 334
Larson, Dr. Leonard W., 373
Lasker Award, 298, 411
Lasker Foundation, Albert and Mary, 329
Latin America, 359
Lauffer, Dr. Max A., 54, 55, 62, 80
Laurence, William L., 263, 272–73
Lavin, George, 36, 37
Lawrence, David, 54, 56, 64, 288
Le Hand, Marguerite, 14
Leader, George M., 290
Leake, Dr. James P., 23, 197
Lederle Laboratories, 63, 97, 109, 354, 357, 364: Cox vaccine, 365, 367; Sabin vaccine, 367
Legion of Honor, 398
Leningrad Academy of Medical Sciences, 359
Lennette, Dr. Edward H., 317
Lennox, Edwin, 411
Leukemia, 380
Levinson, Sidney O., 199
Lewis, L. James, 70, 279, 288
Lewis, P. A., 9
Li, C. P., 248
Life (magazine), 142, 166, 215, 216, 219
Lindsay, Donna, see Salk, Donna Lindsay
Litchfield, Edward H., 396
Literary Digest, 22
Look (magazine), 166
Louisiana epidemic, 8
Loyalty Day parade, 289-90
Loynd, Harry J., 165
Lyon, 8

MacArthur, Mary, 84
Mahoney strain, 107, 180, 195, 196, 320, 329, 336

Maisel, Albert Q., 166
Manhattan Project, 411
March of Dimes, 16–18, 64–65, 91–92, 146, 147, 156, 157, 168, 177, 229, 231, 268, 292, 293, 337, 373
Maricopa County Medical Society, 373
Martin, Joseph W., 305
Martin, Dr. Walter B., 246
Massachusetts Institute of Technology, 408
McCoy, Dr. George W., 21, 22
McEllroy, Dr. William S., 52–53, 54, 55, 56, 61, 62, 64, 95, 102, 279, 288
McEwen, Dr. Currier, 34
McGinnes, G. Foard, 196, 197, 198, 220, 221, 231, 278, 317, 318
McIntosh, Dr. Rustin, 149
McLean, I. W., Jr., 164
McMath, Robert E., 16
MEF–1 strain, 107, 195
Measles, 356, 400
Medal of Merit, 398
"Medicare," 372
Medium 199, 125
Mellon family, 54, 65
Melnick, Joseph L., 59, 113, 132, 279, 358, 366, 381
Mendel, Gregor, 88
Meriwether Inn, 12
Merriam, Carroll B., 16
Merrill, Dr. Malcolm, 313
Merthiolate, 210–11, 218, 241–42, 251, 254–55, 256, 261, 273, 274, 281
Meyer, Dr. Karl F., 102
Michael Reese Hospital, 197, 199
Michigan, 385
Michigan, University of, 5, 42, 49, 70, 203, 204, 206, 238, 255, 258–59, 260, 269, 270–73, 286, 351, 398
Michigan Clinical Institute, 219

Michigan Medical Society, 219, 232, 233
Midway Trading Company, 74–75
Milbank, Jeremiah, 16, 21, 24
Milk, 98, 100, 103
Milzer, Albert, 197, 199–200
Minnesota, University of, 49, 59
Molner, Dr. Joseph G., 352–53
Monod, Jacques, 411
Morgan, Isabel, 64, 85, 86, 96, 100, 108, 109
Morgan, Keith L., 13, 15, 18
Morse, Wayne, 327
Moscow Institute for Poliomyelitis Research, 359
Moscow Ivanovsky Institute, 362
Moses, Dr. Campbell, 83
Mount Sinai Hospital, 37, 40–41, 52, 290
Mountain, Isabel Morgan, see Morgan, Isabel
Movies, 287
Mumps, 400
Municipal Hospital, Pittsburgh, 54, 61, 62, 64, 66, 82–83, 107–8, 139, 395, 396
Murdock, Dr. Thomas P., 149, 171, 176, 236
Murray, Dwight H., 348
Murray, Dr. Roderick, 234, 309, 366
Murrow, Edward R., 166, 264, 265, 283, 284, 285, 289, 290
Mutual of Omaha Criss Award, see Criss Award
MV virus, 115

National Academy of Sciences, 2, 122, 257–58, 299–300, 336
National Advisory Committee on Poliomyelitis Vaccine, 304–5
National Association of Science Writers, 272
National Committee for the Birthday Ball, 13

National Congress of Parents and Teachers, 228
National Council of Catholic Women, 228
Nassau County, New York, 388
National Education Association, 374
National Foundation for Infantile Paralysis: fellowships, 43, 44, 45, 54; gamma globulin, 104, 105; Hershey meeting, 108; Immunization Committee, 125–29, 132–36, 176, 194, 195, 262; March of Dimes, 16–18, 64 65, 91, 146, 147, 156, 157, 169, 177, 229, 231, 268, 292, 293, 373; monkeys, 73, 75–76; program, 136, 226–27; publicity, 89–90; Salk vaccine, 91–93, 96–97, 100, 112, 121–22, 130, 132, 144, 148–52, 165, 166, 169, 170, 171, 173, 174, 175, 176, 179, 180, 181, 187, 188, 189, 194, 196, 197, 198, 199, 201, 202, 203, 204, 205, 206, 226–27, 243, 244, 255, 265, 292, 293; Vaccine Advisory Committee, 175–76, 183, 184, 186, 187, 193, 194, 201, 203–4, 224, 233, 234, 236, 245, 254–55, 261, 262, 278, 330, 357, 380, 381, 382, 383, 392; virus typing project, 71, 78, 101; Weaver, 56–62, 64, 68
National Institute for Allergy and Infectious Diseases, 309
National Institutes of Health: Cutter incident, 309, 311–12, 313, 314, 316, 320, 322, 326; Sabin vaccine, 366, 392; Salk vaccine, 24, 127, 176, 184, 207, 208, 209, 210, 211, 221, 222, 224–25, 232, 234, 235, 254, 255–56, 263, 304
National Research Council, 43, 44
Nebraska, 383
Negroes, 351
Nesbitt, 189

New Deal, 31
New Jersey, 308
New Orleans Graduate Medical Assembly, 219
New York Academy of Sciences, 355, 400
New York City, 10, 305
New York School of Social Work, 36
New York State Department of Public Health, 218
New York Times, The, 16, 263, 270–71, 272–73, 291, 322, 327, 333, 391
New York University, 23, 28, 290, 398
Newspaper Guild of Pittsburgh, 263
Newsweek, 260
Nobel prizes, 2, 50, 59, 60, 86, 299, 410
Northampton County, N. C., 388
Norton, Thomas W., 110

O'Connor, Daniel Basil, 65, 84, 228–29, 246, 400: gamma globulin, 104, 105, 134; Rivers and, 23–24, 25, 26, 27, 57, 134–35; Roosevelt and, 11–12, 17; Sabin vaccine, 341, 344, 350, 368, 369, 374, 383, 386, 387–88; Salk and, 4–5, 73, 91, 118–22, 141, 146–47, 148, 149, 152–53, 154–55, 156–58, 162, 170–206, 207–8, 215–16, 222–25, 227–28, 231–38, 242–44, 254, 255, 256–61, 262, 266–68, 273, 278, 287, 292, 294, 296, 301, 302, 306–7, 324, 328–30, 334–37, 344, 371, 396, 404, 407–9, 412
Office of Defense Mobilization, 104
Ohio Department of Health, 149
Okatie Farm, 73, 76
Olitsky, Dr. Peter, 22, 90, 91, 115
Oppenheimer, Robert, 404

Orgel, Dr. Leslie E., 412
Oslo, 8, 291
Ottawa County, Mich., Medical Society, 231
Otter Creek valley, 9

Pait, Charles F., 64
Park, Dr. William H., 20–21, 22, 24
Parke, Davis & Company, 164–65, 184, 185–86, 194, 197, 198, 199, 207, 208, 217, 218, 220, 221, 222, 225, 242, 304, 315, 321, 327
Parker, Dr. Raymond, 125
Parran, Dr. Thomas, 101, 288
Pasteur, Louis, 214, 249, 348
Pasteur Institute, 411
Patents, 2, 198, 283–84
Paul, Dr. John R., 109, 171, 299, 366: Cutter incident, 317, 319, 320, 335, 336; Immunization Committee, 125, 175, 195, 196, 261, 262; polio research, 59, 60, 63, 92, 93, 246
Pennsylvania, University of, 171, 236
Pennsylvania State Legislature, 291
Pennsylvania State Medical Society, 349–50
Person to Person, 290
Pharmaceutical firms, 164–65, 174, 184, 185–86, 197, 198, 199, 208, 210, 211, 216–17, 221–22, 223, 238, 242, 260, 263, 278, 304, 309–17, 325, 329–30, 341
Philadelphia Children's Hospital, 131
Physician-patient relationship, 155–56
Physics, 405
Picadome School, 240
Pima County Medical Society, 373
Pitman-Moore, 208, 217, 242
Pitt vaccine, see Salk vaccine

Pittsburgh, University of, 2, 52–53, 54–56, 61–62, 64–65, 73, 76, 101, 149, 157, 165, 215, 258, 279, 285, 286, 290
Pittsburgh vaccination program, 349–50, 389, 390
Pittsburgh Press, The, 83, 165, 166–67, 215, 218, 276, 389
Pittsburgh Sun Telegraph, 164
Pius XII, 148, 149
Placebos in field trials, 191–92, 194
Planck, Max, 3, 88
Pneumococcus, 35
Pocatello, Idaho, 315–16
Polk State School, 141, 151, 279
Polio and Its Problems, 16
Polio Pioneers, 237, 268, 301
Poliomyelitis, 8–11, 18, 19–20, 24–26, 59–60, 61, 63–64, 131–34: delayed effects, 400–1; incidence, 343, 347, 351–54, 363, 364, 369, 370; incubation period, 362, 363; types, 8–9, 61, 63–65, 67, 68–71, 78–82, 106–7, 117, 159, 180, 195, 199, 211, 217, 241, 248, 254, 262, 274, 275, 276, 283, 320, 329, 336, 354, 355, 377, 380, 381–83, 385, 387, 392
Poliomyelitis Surveillance Unit, 315
Popper, Erwin, 9
Porterfield, Dr. John D., 149
Potter County, Pa., 388
Pray, Francis, 166, 169
Presidential Citation, 398
President's Birthday Ball Commission for Infantile Paralysis, 18, 19, 20, 21, 23
Press, 15, 163, 164, 165–66, 216: field trial results, 269, 270–73, 275–76, 279
Preston, David R., 270, 292
Price, Dr. David E., 149, 171, 176, 236, 309, 310
Priest, J. Percy, 336
Prisoners as subjects, 148, 149

Provo, Utah, 104, 132, 145–46
Public Health Service, *see* United States Public Health Service, individual states
Publicity, 15, 138, 163, 164, 165–66, 172, 216, 219, 229–31, 239, 258, 269–73, 275-76, 279

Queen Mary (ship), 118

Rabies, 93, 109, 178, 214
Ratner, Dr. Herbert, 370, 371
Reader's Digest, 260
Resistance by Scientists to Scientific Discovery, 88
Respiratory infections, 400
Reversion, 380
Rhodes, Andrew J., 125, 171
Rivers, Dr. Thomas M.: Cutter incident, 330, 336; field trials, 141, 146, 149–50, 152, 153, 155, 156, 166, 167, 170, 171, 178, 202, 207, 208, 210, 254, 255, 269, 271, 273; Immunization Committee, 125, 126, 128, 133–35; Koprowski and, 97, 99, 110, 111; O'Connor and, 23–24, 27, 57, 105, 174, 218; Rockefeller Institute, 23, 41–42, 86, Sabin and, 144, 181, 246, 248, 357, 358, 368, 369; Salk and, 277, 280, 281, 299; tissue culture, 90–91, 112; Vaccine Advisory Committee, 175, 176, 183, 186, 197, 200–1, 245, 262, 278; viral theories, 69, 92–93, 96, 97, 99, 100, 141, 142, 196
Robbins, Frederick C., 60, 86, 299
Rockefeller Foundation, 35, 37, 149, 273, 406
Rockefeller Institute, 9, 18, 22, 23, 34, 35, 36, 41, 86, 90, 149, 171, 218, 233, 245, 330
Rome, University of, 202
Roosevelt, Franklin D., 5, 11–12, 13, 14, 15, 16, 17, 27, 65, 411

Roosevelt University, 398
Rotundo, Robert, 288
Rouse, Dr. Milford O., 349
Royalties, 198

Sabin, Albert, 42, 63, 110, 299:
Immunization Committee, 125,
128–29, 176, 195, 196, 200, 261,
262; papers and speeches, 75, 219,
248; polio typing project, 79, 81,
101; Salk vaccine and, 6, 145,
151, 156, 171, 175, 176, 179–80,
181, 231, 232, 250–51, 257, 262,
282, 317, 318, 320, 335, 336, 354,
364, 365; Second polio congress,
113, 114, 115–17; Third polio conference, 246; Vaccine Advisory
Committee, 176, 261; viral theories, 90–93, 142–43, 254; viremia,
131, 132, 133, 135–36
Sabin vaccine, 143–44, 219, 262,
333, 337, 340–43, 354–64, 365,
366–76, 377, 379, 380–87, 388–
91
St. Helena, 8
St. Mary's County, Md., 388
Salk, (Mr.), 289–90, 291
Salk, Darrell, 66, 170, 206, 295,
296
Salk, Dolly, 28–29, 31, 36, 52, 289–
90, 291
Salk, Donna Lindsay, 36–37, 40, 45,
66, 130, 170, 267, 286, 287, 288,
290, 293, 295, 296, 322
Salk, Dr. Jonas Edward, 87–88, 93,
97, 123–30, 135, 137–40, 163–66,
231, 251, 254, 255, 264–67, 355,
364, 367–68: childhood and education, 23, 28–36, 37–38; Hammon and, 102–4; honors, 285–
99, 395, 398; influenza studies,
45–50, 94–95, 351; marriage and
family, 36–37, 45, 66, 398;
O'Connor and, 4–5, 73, 91, 118–

22, 141, 146–47, 148, 149, 152–
53, 154–55, 156–58, 162, 170–
206, 207–8, 215–16, 222–25,
227–28, 231-38, 242–44, 256–60,
262, 266–68, 273, 279, 287, 292,
294, 296, 301, 302, 306–7, 324,
328–30, 334–37, 344, 370, 397,
404, 407–8, 412; papers and
speeches, 50–51, 151, 154–62,
166, 219–20, 232, 246–48, 251–
54, 267, 277–81, 332, 400, 405,
408–10; personality, 1–7, 30–31,
32–33, 39–40, 66–69, 82, 83–85,
89, 107, 113, 117, 130–31, 138,
190, 204, 212, 213, 264, 267,
296–99, 396–97, 399, 409, 413;
Pittsburgh, University of, and,
42–44, 51–53, 54–56, 61–71, 73–
82, 85, 94, 98–99, 100–1, 117;
recent work, 393, 399, 400–410,
411–13; Sabin vaccine and, 343–
44, 368–69, 374–79; Stockholm
Congress, 113–18; tissue culture,
95–96, 106, 108, 112–13, 198
Salk, Jonathan, 170, 289, 290, 295,
296
Salk, Peter, 66, 170, 206, 288, 295,
296
Salk Hall, 396
Salk Institute for Biological Studies,
120, 215, 254, 344, 390, 403–4,
406–7, 410–13
Salk vaccine, 1–3, 5–7, 24, 214–15,
264–65: cost, 305–6, 307, 360;
Cutter incident, 309–39; distribution, 301–9, 344–51, 359–64,
367–68, 389–90; effectiveness,
219–20, 247–49, 250, 253,
264, 351–53, 369–70, 377; field
trial, 170–206, 207–37, 238–46,
255–66, 268–77, 280–81, 282–84,
337, 385; formula, 207–8, 210–
11; production, 197–99, 208–10,
216–17, 220–22, 242–43, 247,
249, 330–32, 353; vs. Sabin, 340,

341, 358, 364, 367, 368–71, 372, 375–76, 382, 387, 388; safety, 208–10, 223, 231–32, 244–46, 249–50, 255
Sanitation and polio, 9
Sara Mellon Scaife Foundation, 65
Sarkett, James, 107, 289
Saukett strain, 107, 195
Scandinavia, 368
Schaefer, Morris, 248
Scheele, Dr. Leonard A., 237, 281, 282, 346: Cutter incident, 310, 311, 312, 313, 315, 316, 319, 320, 322, 324–26, 328, 329, 330, 333, 335
Scholarships, Salk, 291
Schwenkter, Francis, 202
Science (magazine), 86, 88
Science and Human Values, 410
Scientific Advisory Committee, 188
"Scientist Speaks for Himself, The," 156–57
Scripps-Howard newspapers, 266, 294
Searching Wind, The, 18
Sebrell, Dr. William H., Jr. 222, 225, 237, 320, 328
Second International Poliomyelitis Congress, 113, 407
Secrecy of government, 223, 311, 318, 380, 384
See It Now, 264, 283, 286
Semmelwiess, Ignace, 250
Shannon, James A., 222, 223–24, 225, 309, 312, 318, 320–21, 324, 330, 333, 336
Sharp & Dohme, 242
Shaughnessy, Howard, J., 199, 312, 317, 319, 335
Shearer, John B., 11
Shingles, 400
Shope, Dr. Richard E., 149, 330
Shwartzman, Gregory, 41
Siems, Werner, 389
Sioux City, 104

Sloan Foundation, Alfred P., 406
Smadel, Dr. Joseph E., 38–39, 40, 69, 125, 126, 145, 149, 153, 154, 170, 171, 176, 207–8, 211, 236, 282, 299, 312, 317, 319, 328, 330, 333, 336
Smallpox, 175, 178, 253, 254, 356
Smith, Alfred E., 11
Smith, Austin, 155
Smith, Dr. Homer, 43, 44
Smorodintsev, Anatoli A., 359, 360, 361, 362, 364
Social Security Administration, 302, 372
Society for Experimental Biology and Medicine, 38
Society of American Bacteriologists, 410
Southern California, University of, 63
Soviet Academy of Medical Sciences, 393
Spang Foundation, 95
Special Committee to Consider Problems Related to Poliomyelitis Vaccine, 318
Special Oral Poliomyelitis Vaccine Advisory Committee, 379
Spring, Dr. William C., Jr., 372
Squirrel Hill, Pa., 288
Stambaugh, Harry F., 137, 278, 279
Stanly County, N. C., 388
Stebbins, Ernest L., 171, 176, 236
Stegen, Edward F., 219, 230–31, 397
Stettinius, Edward, Jr., 16
Stickle, Gabriel, 243
Stimpert, Dr. F. D., 164, 184, 218
Stockholm, 8
Stockholm, 113, 114
Stokes, Joseph, Jr., 131
Suffolk County Medical Society, 387
Sullivan, Dr. Robert F., 388–89
Sweden, 378

Syphilis, 400, 401
Szilard, Leo, 404, 411

Talbott, Dr. John H., 370
Talmadge, Eugene, 15
Taylor, A. R., 164
Teething, 8
Television, 257, 258, 269
Terry, Dr. Luther L., 379, 382, 386, 391–92
Tetanus, 214, 380
Texas Medical Association, 349
Theiler, Dr. Max, 149, 214, 249, 299
Theiler's disease, 234
Thermodynamics, Second Law of, 88
Third International Poliomyelitis Conference, 246–51, 332
Time (magazine), 155, 216, 260
Tissue-culture, 112, 200, 250, 402: Enders, 60, 86–94, 96, 105–6, 114–15, 116, 128, 135, 161, 185, 188, 198, 264, 299; Sabin, 142, 358; Salk, 95, 101, 108, 112, 123, 127, 130
Titration of viruses, 185, 214
Topping, Dr. Norman H., 127, 128, 149, 171, 176, 235, 236
Toronto, University of, 125
Townsend Harris High School, 30
Trask, Dr. James D., 59, 60
Trapp, William, 313, 314
Troan, John, 83–84, 165–66, 215, 218, 267, 276, 289, 350, 370
Trujillo, Rafael, 291
Tuberculosis, 9, 218
Tully, Andrew, 294
Turner, Dr. Thomas B., 79, 80, 125, 145, 149, 171, 176, 236
Typhoid, 9, 214
Typhus, 69

Ultraviolet inactivation, 199–200
Union County, N. J., 388

Union of Soviet Socialist Republics, 358–60, 361–64, 381, 392–93
United States Children's Bureau, 226
United States Public Health Service, 62, 101, 248: Cutter incident, 309–13, 315, 318–26, 328, 329, 332–35, 337; Sabin vaccine, 341–42, 354, 360, 366, 367, 368–69, 380, 381, 382, 383, 384, 385, 386, 387, 389, 390–92; Salk vaccine, 149, 171, 194, 208, 209, 231–32, 237, 345, 347, 368–69, 376; see also National Institutes of Health
Utah, University of, 63, 329

Vaccine Advisory Committee: Sabin vaccine, 357, 380, 381, 382, 383, 392; Salk vaccine, 175–76, 183, 186, 187, 193, 194, 200, 203, 224, 233, 234, 236, 245, 254–55, 261, 262, 278–79, 330
Vaccines, 9, 25, 39, 102, 149, 177–78, 214, 359: influenza, 45, 46–50, 141, 161, 164, 166, 167, 172; killed vs. live, 6, 22, 33–34, 35, 47, 49, 85–86, 87, 90–92, 96, 108, 110, 111, 112, 123–58, 172, 175, 179, 180, 184–85, 196, 198–200, 209, 210, 218, 222, 246–49, 251–53, 299, 312, 331, 337, 355–57, 375–80, 385; multiple, 393, 399–400; smallpox, 174, 177, 214; see also Cox vaccine, Sabin vaccine, Salk vaccine
Van Riper, Dr. Hart, 125, 149, 170, 180, 181, 182, 188, 199, 202, 203, 205, 206, 232, 245–46, 257, 266, 269–70, 273, 278, 302, 329, 338
Vanderbilt University, 42
Veterinary medicine, 47
Viral protein, 355
Viremia, 131–35
Virus Hunters, 272, 276

Virus Research Laboratory, Pittsburgh, 278–79, 280
Voight, Robert B., 243
Von Helmholtz, 88
Voroshilova, Marina K., 361, 362

Wagner, Robert F., 286, 291
Walker, Mrs. T. C., 240–41
Wallingford strain, 111
Walter Reed Hospital, 69, 236
Ward, Elsie, 70, 95, 106, 212, 402
Ward, Robert, 123, 132
Warm Springs, Ga., 12–13, 14–15, 18
Warsaw, University of, 109
Watson, David T., 137
Watson, J. D., 411
Watson, Thomas J., 16
Watson Home for Crippled Children, 137–40, 141, 151, 170, 211, 262, 278, 279, 289
Wayne County, Miss., 388
Wayne University, 56
Weaver, Harry M., 56–64, 67, 68, 69, 73–77, 79, 84–86, 92–94, 97, 98, 99, 100, 101, 104, 108, 118, 121, 125, 126, 128, 132, 133, 135, 136–37, 141, 142, 143, 145, 146–48, 155, 164, 168, 170–72, 176–77, 179, 181–82, 184, 187, 189, 191, 193, 194, 202, 269, 278
Weaver, Warren, 406–7, 409, 411
Wegemer, Don, 288
Weller, Thomas H., 60, 86, 299
Wenner, Herbert A., 63, 78, 171
West Feliciana, 8
Westchester County Department of Laboratories and Research, 108
Western Reserve University, 52

Westinghouse Electric Corporation, 55
Wexford, Pa., 66, 185
White House Conference on Children and Youth, 226
Whitelaw, Elaine, 42, 84
Whooping cough, 178, 214
Wilkins, M. H. F., 411
Williams, Greer, 272, 276
Wilson, Earl, 156
Winchell, Walter, 231, 233
Wistar Institute, 365
Woodruff, Robert W., 16
Woolley, Clarence M., 16
Workman, Dr. William G., 207, 208–9, 220, 221, 222, 225, 234, 254, 255, 281–82, 291: Cutter incident, 309–10, 314, 316, 327, 330, 334
Worksop, England, 8
World Health Organization, 361, 363
Wright, Jessie, 137, 279
Wrigley, Tom, 17
Wydro, John J., 168
Wyeth Laboratories, 208, 217, 242
Wyllie, Cleland, 272

X-rays, 88

Yale University, 63, 363
Yellow fever, 109, 149, 214, 253, 356
Youngner, Dr. Julius S., 70, 106, 123, 185, 212, 214, 279
Yurochko, Francis, 217, 218

Zhdanov, Dr. V. M., 393
Zinsser, Hans, 88